MW00989738

JAN 16 2019

D. R. Toi
223 Southlake Pl.
Newport News, VA 23602-8323

K. E. TSIOLKOVSKY

Selected

Works

Compiled by V. N. SOKOLSKY
General editor Acad. A. A. BLAGONRAVOV
Translated from the Russian by G. YANKOVSKY

University Press of the Pacific
Honolulu, Hawaii

Selected Works of Konstantin E. Tsiolkovsky

by
Konstantin E. Tsiolkovsky

ISBN: 1-4102-1825-2

Reprinted from the 1968 edition

University Press of the Pacific
Honolulu, Hawaii
http://www.universitypressofthepacific.com

Contents

FROM THE EDITORS

The present period is one of a magnificent flowering of science and technology when the inquisitive mind of man is penetrating ever deeper into the phenomena of nature, moving into the depths of the microworld and far out into the expanses of the universe. The tools for conquering nature are becoming more powerful and more intricate, as also are the facilities that utilize the laws of nature and its material resources for the needs of society. During recent years the prestige of Soviet science has risen immeasurably in the eyes of the whole world as Soviet scientists and engineers accomplished extraordinary feats in the exploration of outer space, the first impetus for which was given by the writings of the great K. E. Tsiolkovsky.

The works of Tsiolkovsky contain in embryo nearly all the scientific-technical attainments of the Soviet Union in the exploration of space. With amazing accuracy he determined the path, stage by stage, of the development of engineering facilities for the solution of this problem. It is quite natural therefore that with each new development in this field we recall Tsiolkovsky as the scientist who foresaw in one way or another the outcome of these events.

Tsiolkovsky lived the arduous life of an investigating scientist, the basic content of which is best expressed by his own words: "My whole life consisted of work—everything outside that was inaccessible."

Tsiolkovsky's scientific legacy is tremendous both in content and significance. Just a glance through the bibliography of his works gives an idea of the extreme diversity of his scientific interests, the versatility of his investigative thought. Alongside his basic studies on rocket dynamics and the problem of conquest of the air, we find Tsiolkovsky elaborating problems of a geophysical and astronomical character; he investigated purely physical problems, such as the properties of matter, energy, and the structure of the atom. A number of his papers are devoted to power engineering. He also worked on problems of geology, geochemistry, and biology; he was extremely interested in the origin of life and evidence of it elsewhere in the universe. He likewise touched on problems of philosophy.

Yet this diversity of effort cannot be interpreted as a scattering of scientific thought. Tsiolkovsky's works are united by a single purpose—concern for the welfare of humanity, and a single idea— extension of the power of man over nature and over space for the accomplishment of this purpose.

To describe Tsiolkovsky the scientist, let us use his own words: "The prime motive of my life is to do something useful for people, not to live my life purposelessly, but to advance humanity even the slightest bit. That is why I have interested myself in things that did not give me bread or strength. But I hope that my studies will, perhaps soon but perhaps only in the distant future, yield society mountains of grain and limitless power."

The only true science, said Tsiolkovsky, is that which is at the service of society. However, this did not mean that he reduced science to the solution solely of the current demands of human society, although he wrote in 1923 in "The Significance of the Basic Sciences Concerning Matter": "... science... has an extraordinary, even tangible, so to speak, import, like that of our daily bread." At the same time, in that very article he took up long-range problems such as the study of the atomic nucleus. He pointed out that the study of atoms will lead not only to a transformation of substances but also to the utilization of enormous energy resources of nature. That was the standpoint from which Tsiolkovsky appraised the essence of technological progress—the standpoint of elevating the welfare of society. As early as 1915, he wrote in "The Future of the Earth and Man": "... man, science and technology will develop simultaneously. Each one will contribute to transforming the face of the earth. Let us begin with technical progress. First, great refinements will be attained in what is presently manufactured. The productivity of the worker will be increased hundreds of times with the aid of machines. Labour in all branches will become perfectly safe, noninjurious to the health, even pleasant and interesting. The working day will be reduced to 4-6 hours. The rest of the time will be given over to free, nonobligatory work, creativeness, recreation, science, dreaming..."

Many of Tsiolkovsky's writings give a vivid picture of his outstanding trait as a man of science—his profound scientific intuition and his ability to see far into the future of science. Looking ahead he wrote: "The mines will multiply and deepen and will yield much heat and many new substances and materials with valuable properties.... . Materials with all kinds of properties will be discovered. Cutting materials harder than diamond— a tool alloy for working hard substances. Materials will be found that will be light and unusually strong, refractory, nonoxidable or neutral, and very light gases with a variety of properties, ... elastic substances, excellent heat-conducting materials, and the reverse: extremely radioactive, transparent and yet extraordinarily strong materials. Ways will be found to obtain unusually high and unusually low temperatures and this will be utilized for the working of raw materials and for other purposes."

This was written at a time when the prerequisites for many of the aforementioned items were still lacking. Today, most of these predictions have come to full fruition, to say nothing of the achievements in the exploration of space during recent years.

Thus, many of Tsiolkovsky's ideas, which at the time of writing appeared fairly groundless though a brilliant enticing fantasy, were actually based on profound scientific principles. Tsiolkovsky was endowed with a fertile imagination that sparkled both in his scientific works and in his science-fiction writings, but as a rule it was not divorced from firm scientific ground. This was scientific fantasy of which Lenin said: "... it is wrong to think that only poets need imagination. That is a silly prejudice! It is needed even in mathematics; it would have been impossible to discover the differential and integral calculus without imagination. Imagination is a very valuable asset."* It was precisely this valuable asset that spurred Tsiolkovsky to take up problems which to most of his contemporaries appeared unrealistic and very distant from technical realization. From youth, Tsiolkovsky's thoughts were directed at solving the problem of conquering cosmic space. This is evident from his recollections, notes and drawings done in his youthful years of 1878-1879 and, finally, from the paper "Free Space" which he wrote in 1883. For the first time, this manuscript presented, in general form, ideas concerning the conditions arising in space in the absence of the force of gravity, the principles of reactive motion, the possibility of controlling motion in cosmic space, and methods of stabilizing a body moving in an absolute void.

The concluding sentence of this paper is remarkable. He states that the conquest of outer space is an attainable goal and that for mankind it lies not so far in the future. We can only regret that Tsiolkovsky did not live to see later events which brilliantly confirmed the perspicacity of his scientific thought.

* V. I. Lenin, Works, Vol. 33, p. 318.

Tsiolkovsky was clearly aware of the complicated path along which the accomplishment of this task lay. It was evident to him that before getting out beyond the earth's atmosphere it would be necessary to solve the problem of mastering the atmosphere itself, and he turned his attention to the problem of aerial flight. He worked out the design of an all-metal dirigible and devoted a great deal of energy to accomplishing this project, but he never gave up the idea of heavier-than-air flying machines. However, the most significant part of Tsiolkovsky's scientific legacy at present are his works on rocketry. It is precisely in this sphere that his talent as a scientist and his highly original gifts stand out so brilliantly.

The outstanding scientist and thinker Tsiolkovsky had a very peculiar style of work. One can't help recalling and repeating the colourful description that Academician A. E. Fersman gave to people like Tsiolkovsky at a meeting commemorating the fifth anniversary of his death: "... throughout the history of scientific thought there have always been—and always will be—fighters for that which is new. By sheer intuition, from among the thousands of threads of surrounding nature, life and science, they grasp the linking ones. Frequently they are unable to substantiate their conclusions, of which nevertheless they are convinced and in which they have faith; with bold fantasy they overstep long periods of reasoning and discussion, raising and suggesting the ultimate conclusions without the intermediate calculations. They summarize the past and the present and execute audacious leaps into the future... . They cannot be accepted by the official science, for, often, in a thrust of passionate enthusiasm, they go too far or even take the wrong path... . And yet these fighters for the new have led the world throughout human history and have cut pathways of new creative thought." The only correction to be made here with respect to Tsiolkovsky is that he was recognized by official science, though somewhat belatedly. Such was the strength of his pioneering creativity.

In his works, Tsiolkovsky dealt mainly with trends in science that appeared to him to be fundamentally new. And when we find ideas or conclusions that are not really new, his novel approach to them is indicative of a thinking search on the part of the author, who, due to adverse conditions, was not always able to follow the literature on that question. The strength needed for audacious flights of thought into the future was drawn from his profound faith in the limitless advance of science, in the boundless extent of man's mastery over nature, in the unlimited abilities of human reason to transform nature in accord with the needs of society.

Characteristic of Tsiolkovsky was his ardent desire to investigate every problem in its multiple interconnections. For example, when studying the problem of the conquest of the air, he examined it both technically and economically. When engaged in "the investigation of world spaces" he did not confine himself to engineering calculations, but made a deep study of the life-support conditions of manned flight, investigated changes of the physiological functions of the human body under these conditions, and set up centrifugal facilities to examine the effects of accelerations on the living organism.

Tsiolkovsky stood firm and persistent in upholding his scientific views. But this persistence had nothing whatsoever in common with intolerance to criticism. Quite the contrary, he realized that the absence of criticism leads to stagnation in science: "... if we cease to express freely new ideas, then science will cease to move forward" was what he wrote in "The Reversibility of Phenomena in General".

Like a truly great scientist, Tsiolkovsky in the main adhered to the dialectical materialistic world view, which perhaps at times manifested itself spontaneously in his most profound thoughts concerning many of the scientific problems he was engaged in.

The materialist conception is evident in his views on the boundlessness of human knowledge, the inevitability of life outside our planet in the depths of space, where, he believed, specific conditions of evolution might lead to special forms of life unlike terrestrial forms. In his own original way he came close to the dialectical conception of the evolution of matter in the process of the struggle of contradictory properties or, as he put it, of "the mutually opposite processes of destruction and creation".

The present edition contains the principal works of Tsiolkovsky dealing with rocketry and the theory of interplanetary communications, including also "The High-speed Train", in which he describes the concept of a high-speed nonwheel transport facility—a vehicle on an air cushion.

The papers are arranged in chronological order and are based on the texts of works published during Tsiolkovsky's lifetime or left by him in manuscript form. The terminology of the author has been retained as far as possible, as also his system of numbering formulas and sections of the text and all the peculiarities of his highly original style.

Certain obscure places or dubious sheets and also terms he used that differ from presently accepted ones are explained in footnotes.

In the notes and commentaries we have taken into account remarks made by the editors of earlier editions of Tsiolkovsky's works: F. A. Tsander, M. K. Tikhonravov, and A. A. Kosmodemyansky.

Academician A. A. Blagonravov and Candidate of Sciences V. N. Sokolsky selected the works and compiled and edited the volume. The introduction was written by Academician A. A. Blagonravov. The text was prepared by associates of the Institute of the History of Natural Science and Technology of the USSR Academy of Sciences: I. V. Balandina, V. I. Belolipetsky, and Yu. I. Novokshonov under the guidance of S. A. Sokolova, Candidate of Sciences. The index was prepared by G. Yankovsky.

ON THE PRACTICAL SIGNIFICANCE OF THE SCIENTIFIC AND ENGINEERING PROPOSITIONS OF TSIOLKOVSKY IN ROCKETRY*

S. P. Korolyov

Today rocketry is one of the leading branches of modern science and technology. The time is long since past when the word "rocket" was linked with the "fiery arrows" of ancient China and India or with the rocket projectiles of the Englishman W. Congreve and the Russian general K. I. Konstantinov.

During the years of World War II, the Soviet Guards mortar units armed with solid-fuel rocket missiles defended our Fatherland and repeatedly devastated hordes of fascist invaders.

After the war, jet aircraft of various types came into common use. The TU-104 jet liner took to the airways. New marvelous types of high-speed jet aircraft were developed; considerable speeds and high ceilings were reached, and the so-called sound barrier was left behind. New types of aircraft, military planes for example, are as a rule jet-propelled.

At present, high-speed aviation stands at a critical period of transition from the air-breathing engine to the rocket. Soviet pilots were the first in history to fly aircraft driven by liquid-fuel rocket engines.

The USSR Academy of Sciences has been carrying out extensive studies of the upper atmosphere and epi-atmospheric space by means of vertical rocket shots. The rocket vehicles carry complex research apparatus and test animals that are brought safely back to earth. Soviet rockets reach very high altitudes above the earth's surface that have never before been reached by anyone.

The Soviet Union has successfully tested superlong-range intercontinental multi-stage ballistic missiles. The results obtained indicate that it is possible to launch rockets into any region of the globe.

---

* Based on a lecture given by S. P. Korolyov on 17 September 1957, on the centennial of Tsiolkovsky's birth.

13

During the present International Geophysical Year, many tens of rockets will be launched for scientific purposes based on a wide range of programmes to a variety of altitudes and in different regions of the Soviet Union, including areas of the Far North, as well as in the Antarctic.

In the very near future, the first trial launchings of artificial earth satellites will be attempted in the USSR and the USA. The aims will be scientific.

Soviet scientists are working on many new problems of rocketry, such as that of sending rockets to the moon, to circumnavigate the moon, the problem of manned rocket flight, and problems of deep penetration into and exploration of outer space.

Such, in brief survey, is the picture of outstanding achievements in the field of scientific and technical progress associated with the development of rocket technology in the Soviet Union during the past 15 to 20 years.

We are witnessing the accomplishment of the predictions of Konstantin Eduardovich Tsiolkovsky about rocket flight and missions into interplanetary space that he expressed over 60 years ago.

In one of his letters Tsiolkovsky wrote (in 1911) with great force and conviction: "Mankind will not remain on the earth forever, but in the pursuit of light and space will at first timidly penetrate beyond the limits of the atmosphere, and then will conquer all the space around the sun."

The most remarkable, audacious and novel of all Tsiolkovsky's creative thinking are his ideas and studies in rocket technology. Here, he has no predecessors and is far ahead of the scientists of all other countries and his own times.

Tsiolkovsky was a self-educated scientist and experimenter who by unremitting effort was able, alone, to rise to unprecedented heights of science and scientific foresight. He was an inventor who affirmed the priority of our Fatherland in a series of outstanding inventions and technical innovations in aeronautics, aviation, and particularly in rocket technology, which is today so topical.

As a researcher, he boldly cut fresh pathways into the scientific unknown and, like the true scientist that he was, he provided his discoveries with brilliant scientific substantiation. He was also an ardent patriot, a tireless worker and a flaming enthusiast of science, to which he was completely dedicated and to which he gave his whole life.

In 1873, at the age of 16, Tsiolkovsky came to Moscow. It was during the Moscow period of his life that the general trend of future strivings, technical ideas and research that he was to follow to the end of his days came into clear focus.

These were ideas about whether or not it would be possible to utilize certain properties of matter to set a given type of vehicle into motion. Tsiolkovsky at that time was engaged in gravity and ways of overcoming it.

He was already beginning to grope for the idea of manned flight beyond the limits of terrestrial gravitation, or, as he put it later on, "enchanting dreams" were awakening. The first conceptions were untenable, the first attempts at invention were a failure, but this did not diminish Tsiolkovsky's efforts.

Many years passed filled with persistent work, tormenting doubts and reflections; he was completely alone, without any support, even without any sympathy; he was quite obviously discouraged and even derided by the local officials and the bureaucratic technical and engineering bigwigs of tsarist Russia as the eccentric near-deaf schoolteacher and "crazy inventor".

In 1883, in his work "Free Space", which is actually a kind of scientific diary, Tsiolkovsky examined the most elementary phenomena of mechanical motion in space in the absence of gravitational forces and the resistance of any medium.

In considering modes of communicating motion to a body in free space, Tsiolkovsky arrived at his most fundamental and important conclusion that the simplest thing is to impart motion to a stationary body (or to alter existing motion) by the ejection of mass; that is, by the reaction of particles ejected from the given body. Here is what Tsiolkovsky wrote in "Free Space":

"28 March 1883. Morning.

"... Suppose we have a barrel filled with a highly compressed gas. If we open one of its minute stopcocks, the gas will stream out of the barrel in a continuous jet, and the elasticity of the gas (it is this elasticity that pushes the gaseous particles into space) will likewise continually repel the barrel.

"The result will be a continual change in the motion of the barrel.... By means of a sufficient number of stopcocks (six) it is possible to control the exit of gas so that the motion of the barrel or of an empty sphere will entirely depend on the will of the stopcock operator, which is to say that the barrel will execute any desired curve and in accord with any law of velocity whatsoever.

"Change of motion of the barrel is possible only so long as there is still some gas in it.

"... Generally speaking, curvilinear uniform motion or rectilinear nonuniform motion is associated, in free space, with a continuous loss of matter (support)."

Thus, from the very beginning of his scientific activities Tsiolkovsky was fully aware of the principle of reactive motion.

In his article "Free Space" he does not give quantitative results, all conclusions being based on qualitative inferences from the law of conservation of momentum for closed mechanical systems, but the desirability of utilizing the reaction effect of exhaust jets for moving in free space was formulated in a definite and clear-cut fashion.

In 1896 Tsiolkovsky was finally convinced that the rocket is the only technical means for getting out into epi-atmospheric space. In 1903 he published his "Investigation of World Spaces by Reactive Vehicles". This classical work is justly considered the first scientific paper in the world devoted to problems of the theory of motion and to a whole range of cardinal engineering propositions in rocketry.

Tsiolkovsky saw a great future for rocket technology, but at the same time he clearly realized the difficulties that lay ahead. Here is the way he put it: "... for investigating the atmosphere I propose a reactive device, that is a kind of rocket, but one of enormous dimensions and specially designed. The idea is not new, but calculations referring to it have yielded such remarkable results that it is impossible to keep silent about them.

"This study of mine does not by far examine all aspects of the matter and does not at all resolve it from the practical viewpoint (relative to its feasibility); but in the far distant nebulous future one perceives such intriguing and significant promises as hardly anyone today dreams of."

In supplementary studies published in 1911-1912 and 1914 and later and in numerous papers, articles, projects and manuscripts that Tsiolkovsky worked on up to the very end of his life, he considered a broad range of problems of a theoretical, investigative and computational nature, and also numerous applied problems of engineering, design and technology.

In elaborating the theory and in studying the laws of motion of rockets, Tsiolkovsky is extremely consistent. At first he solves the elementary problem on the assumption that there is no gravity and no air resistance acting on the rocket in flight. This problem is today called *Tsiolkovsky's First Problem.*

He introduced the assumption of constant relative velocity of particle ejection for definite ejection substances. This assumption is called *Tsiolkovsky's hypothesis.*

He wrote the basic equation of rocket motion in a medium without the effects of external forces. This is known as *Tsiolkovsky's formula.* In this equation the ratio of the weight of the propellant to the ultimate weight of the empty rocket is called *Tsiolkovsky's number.* He also wrote a number of theorems that bear his name.

A complicating factor in the analysis of rocket motion is the appreciable variation in the mass of the rocket vehicle during flight. This condition does not permit using the formulas of classical mechanics. Undoubted credit goes to Tsiolkovsky, in the development of rocket theory, for solving a number of applied problems in a new field of classical mechanics—the mechanics of bodies of varyable mass—which he did independently and irrespective of other similar studies.

Examining the motion of a rocket in a medium in the absence of external forces, Tsiolkovsky made a careful study of the effect of gravity and air resistance on the flight of the rocket. A salient feature in this approach was his stubborn fight against the force of gravity, which he considered a chain holding humanity to the surface of the planet. To the sphere of action of gravitational forces he gave the name armour of gravitation.

In nearly all his works, Tsiolkovsky repeatedly reverts to the problem of fighting gravity. He made investigations and performed calculations to determine the fuel supplies necessary for overcoming this gravitational armour and to find the optimal conditions under which energy expenditure at take-off would be a minimum.

Also prominently investigated were: the problem of the effects of air-resistance forces on rocket flight, the problem of fuel supplies and optimal flight conditions required to break through the earth's atmosphere. Tsiolkovsky called the sphere of action of air resistance the armour of the atmosphere.

In his theoretical studies Tsiolkovsky came to a number of cardinal conclusions that are still in use today in rocket technology.

Moreover, the expansion of practical work and refinements in rocket technology again and again and more precisely corroborate many of the conclusions and suppositions that were expressed by Tsiolkovsky a very long time ago.

His studies demonstrated that the velocity and, hence, the range of a rocket increase with increasing relative supply of explosives (propellant) carried by the rocket. With sufficient supplies of propellant it is possible to attain any final velocity of motion and any desirable distance.

The velocity at burn-out (at the end of acceleration) increases with the relative velocity of the ejected particles. The rocket velocity at the end of acceleration likewise increases with an increase in the ratio of the initial weight of the rocket to its weight at burn-out.

From Tsiolkovsky's formula there follows a very important practical conclusion: higher rocket velocities are attained more effectively by increasing the relative velocities of the ejected particles (that is, by refining the power plant) than by increasing the relative fuel supply carried by the rocket; in other words, by improving the design of the rocket.

Tsiolkovsky was the first to define the rate of utilization, or the efficiency of a rocket. He pointed out that rocket engines have an advantage only at high velocities of motion. He arrived at negative conclusions when examining the use of liquid-fuel rockets for flights in the dense layers of the atmosphere.

Tsiolkovsky carried out investigations and calculations dealing with take-off and determination of optimal conditions for take-off: he considered vertical and inclined take-off and take-off from a given initial altitude.

He was the first to perform calculations dealing with choice of optimal angle of rocket ascension, making allowance for losses due to gravitational forces and air resistance in a medium of variable density and taking into account changes in the engine performance with altitude. He also made many other calculations and investigations.

A feature of Tsiolkovsky's research method was the profundity of practical elaboration of every problem he investigated. In tsarist Russia, Tsiolkovsky had limited opportunities for experimenting, he did not have at his disposal properly equipped laboratories or test stands, or designing bureaus and industrial facilities. He had no assistants. He worked in extreme solitude and independently.

But he did not simply theorize; on the contrary, with exceptional perspicacity and profundity he built up around his theoretical conclusions (which at times were extraordinary) such solid and detailed practical suggestions that a great number of them have found application and are still extensively used in all countries engaged in rocketry.

Among the more interesting problems are the following. Tsiolkovsky was often engaged in studies of energy problems, choice of propellants and engine design. He formulated the basic demands with respect to propellants and proposals regarding choice of propellants relative to maximum energy production per unit mass, to maximum density and to a number of other characteristics. Tsiolkovsky chose a liquid fuel: liquid oxygen, liquid hydrogen, petroleum and its derivatives.

He proposed a special explosion pipe in the shape of a flared cone and a combustion chamber into which the propellant was pumped; combustion processes in the engine were visualized as being automatically controlled, the operating regime being varied with the trajectory conditions of rocket flight.

To set up optimal combustion conditions, it was suggested that lattices with skew openings be installed at the entrance to the explosion pipe. Tsiolkovsky believed that the number, dimensions and incline of the openings should be determined by experiment.

Of particular concern were problems of cooling the explosion pipe, where extremely high temperatures were expected. The suggestion was made to cool the pipe by the propellant components or by some kind of liquid metal circulating in a special jacket.

Tsiolkovsky made a very detailed study of the possibilities of protecting the explosion pipe from high temperatures; he considered various materials for the pipe and proposed shielding it with refractory and heat-resisting materials.

He determined the power requirements of pump operation for a range of combustion pressures and feed systems and investigated the processes of feed, atomization, ignition, and combustion of fuel.

In the works of Tsiolkovsky, one can find mention of the probable use of atomic energy, the sun's radiant energy, and the energy of cosmic radiations for rocket propulsion.

However, he was quick to add that his calculations did not yield the desired results and that although all kinds of discoveries are possible and dreams might unexpectedly come true, he wished, in his works, to stand on practical ground as far as possible.

Tsiolkovsky expressed an interesting idea about controlling rocket flight by using the energy of jets of exhaust gases. He proposed a device for turning the flared end of the explosion pipe or gas rudders in the form of blades placed in the gas stream.

Tsiolkovsky foresaw that manual control of rocket flight would not only be difficult but even impossible in actuality. This made it necessary to have automatic devices and gyroscopic instruments on board to supply the needed control signals. Orientation in space could be handled by an automatic guiding system based on magnetic properties or locked on the sun or some star.

At the same time, provisions were made for aerial rudders of direction, altitude, and something like ailerons for operation during rocket flight in sufficiently dense layers of the atmosphere.

Tsiolkovsky worked on a wide range of interesting problems of rocket design: shape, internal arrangement, distribution of masses inside the rocket and possible schemes for a variety of strong and hermetically sealed joints, making allowance for operating conditions in flight.

He proposed utilizing internal pressure in the rocket for enhancing its strength and he examined the problem of maintaining and regulating pressure gradients within optimal limits, which, in turn, he related to the problem of reducing the dead weight of the rocket at burn-out. Tsiolkovsky investigated the possible conditions of heating the rocket vehicle during passage through the dense layers of the atmosphere and proposed a variety of schemes for cooling and thermal shielding.

When working on a single-stage rocket, Tsiolkovsky kept hoping to reach flight velocities capable of overcoming the earth's gravity and ensuring manned rocket flight into outer space. This desire permeates all of Tsiolkovsky's works. His early projects for composite, multi-stage rockets and rocket trains represent a remarkable, truly stupendous achievement.

Here is what Tsiolkovsky wrote in "Cosmic Rocket Trains" in 1929:

"By rocket train I mean a combination of several identical reactive vehicles moving first along a roadway, then in the air, then in empty space beyond the atmosphere, and finally between the planets or suns.

"But only one part of this train reaches celestial space, the other parts, since they lack the necessary speed, return to the earth.

"To reach cosmic velocity, a single rocket has to have a large supply of fuel... . This complicates the construction of reactive vehicles.

"Now a train permits attaining high cosmic velocities or makes it possible to reduce the supply of components of explosion to relatively small amounts."

Tsiolkovsky investigated the basic technical data, flight performance characteristics and design parameters of a number of different versions of composite multi-stage rockets.

It is difficult to overestimate the significance of Tsiolkovsky's proposal for composite multi-stage rockets and rocket trains. Actually, it opened the way into outer space.

The above-mentioned spheres of Tsiolkovsky's work, which include great quantities of technical details, proposals and ideas, are organically interwoven with his theoretical ideas and justifications. At the present time very much of this is utilized as something quite familiar and is largely taken for granted.

Isn't it quite obvious today that the rocket is the vehicle of space flight, that liquid oxygen is one of the propellants and, for example, gas vanes are needed for flight control? Yet all these were proposed by Tsiolkovsky 60 years ago when even a heavier-than-air flying machine was not yet in existence and rockets were simply pyrotechnic toys.

Today, the Soviet people are ceremoniously celebrating the 100th anniversary of the birth of Konstantin Eduardovich Tsiolkovsky, outstanding scientific worker in the field of rocket technology and astronautics. Soviet scientists remember and treasure his ideas and his works and are creatively developing and continuing them.

The most interesting and intriguing part of Tsiolkovsky's writings was undoubtedly his studies on the problem of interplanetary travel. It would be more correct to say that nearly all of Tsiolkovsky's work had a single direction and were associated with problems of interplanetary flight.

Even his studies of reactive vehicles for flights in the atmosphere Tsiolkovsky regarded solely as a stepping stone to flights into outer space. He predicted that following the era of propeller airplanes would come a period of jet stratoplanes and, finally, rocket trains of the future and artificial earth satellites in the form of manned interplanetary stations.

With the appearance and elaboration of the concept of composite multi-stage rockets and rocket trains, the problem of space flights utilizing known chemical sources of energy became a sufficiently realistic technological problem.

Tsiolkovsky carried out extensive research and calculations concerning problems of interplanetary rocket flight beyond the limits of terrestrial gravitation, its subsequent motion in free space and the possibility of return to the earth. He determined the optimal conditions of such flights in a wide range of variables for different initial data.

Tsiolkovsky was the first to investigate flight paths and characteristics of different orbital trajectories of space rockets on take-off from the earth and from the surfaces of planets and asteroids.

He also examined the probable conditions of life in the rocket of future interplanetary travellers. To protect human beings from the effects of acceleration at take-off and during deceleration of the rocket, he proposed special suits and immersion in liquid baths having a density close to that of the human body.

Foreseeing that extended missions in a medium without gravitation may prove difficult for the human organism, Tsiolkovsky proposed generating an artificial field of gravitation for flight on interplanetary rockets or on an artificial satellite of the earth.

Tsiolkovsky once again took up the idea of utilizing the radiant energy of the sun for supplementing the power resources of an interplanetary rocket and for using this energy on an artificial interplanetary station, particularly if it is a manned station on an extended mission.

The problem of available power sources was always foremost in Tsiolkovsky's mind when working on return-to-earth problems or in connection with landings on a planet with subsequent take-off and descent to the earth.

Tsiolkovsky suggested a most interesting approach to the problem of landing the rocket on the earth without expenditure of fuel. The rocket would enter the atmosphere of the earth, decelerating as it moved in orbit round the globe during a time sufficient to shed the enormous re-entry velocities and all the while retaining permissible regimes of heating and G-loading during deceleration. This idea was further developed by Kondratyuk, one of Tsiolkovsky's followers and pupils.

Tsiolkovsky paid special attention to the problem of setting up interplanetary stations. In solving this stupendous problem he envisaged not only the tremendous fundamental simplification for the launching of space rockets, which, in his view, could use such a station as a base, and not only an outstanding scientific achievement, but the possibility of realizing his earliest dream of the actual conquest of circumsolar space by man.

Tsiolkovsky pictured an interplanetary station as a composite of several rockets that link up after orbiting; the station would be a well-equipped spacious room filled with the light of the sun and devoid of the binding fetters of terrestrial gravity.

Provisions would be made for small supplies of fuel to be burnt when it became necessary to change the orbit of the interplanetary station. Further, communications between the earth and the station could, Tsiolkovsky thought, be maintained by special rockets.

The take-off of space rockets from the region of the interplanetary station would be greatly simplified (and the same would go for landing on return voyages), for it would be possible for a rocket to take on fuel from the supply of the interplanetary station.

Tsiolkovsky proposed a thermal scheme for maintaining differentiated temperatures in the living quarters of the interplanetary station through the use of solar heat.

This is what he wrote on the subject: "The opaque part of the living quarters is black on the outside. A short distance away is a second part with brilliant scales on both sides. Its components can rotate and become normal to the surface like the needles of a hedgehog. Then the temperature will go down. But when the armour covers the black surface, the highest degree of warmth is attained. The same scales may also be on the transparent part of the living quarters. Then it is possible to obtain a lower temperature. Depending on the designation of the ether chambers, their design may be greatly diversified.

"... At first there will be the simpler types of homes suitable both for human beings and for plants. They will be filled with oxygen having a density one fifth that of the atmosphere with small quantities of carbon dioxide, nitrogen and water vapour. There will also be a bit of fertile humid soil. Illuminated by the sunlight and containing seeds, it can yield nutritiously rich roots and tubers and other plants. The people would respire spoiling the air, and eat the vegetables, and the plants would purify the air and produce edibles."

"In order to exist during an indefinitely long time without our atmosphere and our planet, we will have to take advantage of the strength of the sun's rays. Just as the earth's atmosphere is purified by plants with the aid of the sun, so our artificial atmosphere can be regenerated in the same way... Just as on the earth's surface there is an endless mechanical and chemical cycle of matter, so in our little world there will be one too... ."

Calculations show "that one square metre of greenhouse facing the sun's light is already sufficient for the feeding of one person. But what is there to prevent taking along an extensive surface in packed-up form, i.e., in a small volume! When our vehicle has settled into circular motion round the earth or the sun, we assemble our hermetically sealed cylindrical boxes with various plant seeds and suitable soil and extend them from the rocket."

That is how the necessary living conditions can be maintained on an interplanetary station during an extended period of time.

But gravity! Is it a necessary condition for vegetative life? Very probably not, because, as experience shows, changes in the direction and force of gravity by means of centrifugal forces do not destroy the process of vegetative life.

Tsiolkovsky did not doubt the possibility of human life in outer space if the proper conditions are maintained.

Rockets were familiar things and the launchings of pyrotechnic rockets had been observed long before Tsiolkovsky. But it was Tsiolkovsky who proposed a reactive vehicle like a rocket as a new thing and the sole engineering facility for attaining unheard-of velocities and altitudes and for flights into the boundless vasts of outer space. Therein lies the great talent of Tsiolkovsky, his exceptional originality.

Tsiolkovsky extended the limits of human knowledge and his idea of rocket flight into outer space is only today being grasped in all its immensity.

For many long years, actually for most of his life, Tsiolkovsky lived and worked in the exceedingly difficult conditions of tsarist Russia surrounded by a solid wall of ignorance and indifference.

He wrote: "The prime motive of my life is to do something useful for people, not to live my life purposelessly, but to advance humanity even the slightest bit. That is why I have interested myself in things that did not give me bread or strength. But I hope that my studies will, perhaps soon but perhaps in the distant future, yield society mountains of grain and limitless power."

The Great October Socialist Revolution was the power-giving force that inspired the sixty-year-old Tsiolkovsky to fresh creative endeavours and opened up unparalleled opportunities. His name and his works became known and dear to the Soviet people. Though already aged and ill, Konstantin Tsiolkovsky took up his work again with great enthusiasm.

He lived to the time when his most cherished dreams about rockets and the conquest of stellar spaces by man ceased to be a utopian dream and turned into the prime scientific and engineering problem of our times.

Tsiolkovsky bequeathed his works on aviation, rocket flight and interplanetary communications to the Bolshevik Party and the Soviet state, the true leaders of cultural progress.

Today we can say that the scientific legacy of Tsiolkovsky transferred to the Bolshevik Party and the Soviet state is not lying idle and is not taken dogmatically, but is being creatively developed and successfully continued by Soviet scientists.

It is apparently impossible at the present time to assess in full measure the overall significance of the scientific ideas and engineering propositions of Konstantin Tsiolkovsky, particularly in the field of penetration into outer space.

Time, on occasion, inexorably erases the outlines of the past, but the ideas and works of Tsiolkovsky will more and more attract attention as rocket technology proceeds in its development.

Konstantin Eduardovich Tsiolkovsky was a man that lived far in advance of his times as befits a true and great scientist.

Tsiolkovsky's Works

(From the Manuscript

"Free Space")

(1883)

28 *March 1883*, *Morning*

✳ CURVILINEAR MOTION WITH THE AID OF A GAS OR
LIQUID OR EVEN A SOLID SUPPORT

When a body has an infinite multitude of supports from which
it is constantly pushing away, that body is constantly changing
its motion so that its path may be in the form of a curved line.
Also, the velocity of the body varies constantly in the process
and may be accelerative or decelerative.

Suppose we have a barrel filled with a highly compressed gas.
If we open one of its minute stopcocks, the gas will stream out
of the barrel in a continuous jet, and the elasticity of the gas
(it is this elasticity that pushes the gaseous particles into space)
will likewise continually repel the barrel.

The result will be a continual change in the motion of the
barrel.

If, for example, the barrel is stationary and the repulsion of
the gas occurs along a line connecting the free centre of inertia
of the body with the opening of the stopcock or if the barrel is
in rectilinear motion coincident with the direction of the repelling
gas, then the barrel will, due to the action of the gas, acquire
a rectilinear accelerated or decelerated motion. But if the barrel
is in motion not coincident with the direction of the ejected particles of gas, then its motion will be parabolic on the assumption
that the gas is repelled with a constant force and in a constant

quantity. By means of a sufficient number of stopcocks (six) it is possible to control the exit of gas so that the motion of the barrel or of an empty sphere will entirely depend on the will of the stopcock operator, which is to say that the barrel will execute any desired curve and in accord with any law of velocity whatsoever. It may, for example, uniformly describe a circle, although there will be no central attracting force. At any rate, the general free centre of the body and of the ejected gas molecules will always retain its original motion or its original state of rest. Change of motion of the barrel is possible only so long as there is still some gas in it. But since it is losing gas all the time and under average conditions the loss is proportional to the time, so the motion too may be arbitrary for only a limited time: a minute, an hour, a day, after which it becomes rectilinear and uniform. Generally speaking, curvilinear uniform motion or rectilinear nonuniform motion is associated, in free space, with a continuous loss of matter (support). Likewise, broken-line motion is associated with a periodic loss of matter.

29 March, Morning

Incidentally, if the main body and the support are connected by long thin threads, then although the motion of the bodies will be more or less restricted (depending on the length of the threads), still the supports and the main body can again be connected to form a whole.

In the process, the free centres of the bodies will come to rest and will be in the original position; or all of them will have the uniform and rectilinear motion that they had prior to their interaction.

Theorem. Any body (any plastic—at first stationary—body), the large or small solid parts of which can attract or repulse, can take any shape and go in any direction.

30 March, Morning

❋ ON PARALLEL MOTION

Up till now I have been speaking only about parallel motion, that is, such, for example, as that which the earth's axis has in the course of the year, about motion in free space such that all points of a body are in absolutely identical motion. This means that their trajectories are equal and their velocities at each instant of time are identical both in magnitude and direction. If, for instance, some point describes an ellipse, then all other points describe absolutely identical ellipses; and though the velocities of the points may at different times be different, they are identical at one and the same instant.

But besides this parallel motion, the points (even though the shape of the solid remains invariable) may in free space describe different paths and have different velocities even at one and the same instant. This is rotational and cycloidal motion. I will use the latter term to describe rotational and parallel motions combined. For example, I will call the motion of planets cycloidal motion. Of course, cycloidal motions may be very diversified: rectilinear cycloidal motion, circular, and so on and so forth.

✳ ROTATIONAL MOTION. STABLE ROTATION

Let us take two points of a body and fix them stationary. If the body is now set into motion by some force, this motion will be rotational. The straight line passing through these fixed points is called the axis; it is likewise stationary.

All points lying outside this axis describe circles. The farther the points are away from the axis, the greater their velocities and, hence, the greater the paths traversed. Points lying at an equal distance from the axis describe equal circles and, for a given instant of time, have the same velocity.

Rotational motion is called uniform if points equidistant from the axis are in uniform motion, that is, when these points traverse equal distances in equal times or when the body turns through one and the same number of degrees in equal intervals of time. In free space, rotational motion may also be executed about an unattached axis freely suspended in space. The simplest thing is to call this axis a free axis. It is about just such rotational motion of a solid body round a free axis that I shall now speak.

Not every straight line drawn through a body is a free axis, i.e., a free body cannot rotate about just any unattached straight line. It is a familiar fact that the rotation of flywheels in machines is sometimes attended by a shaking of the axle and the machine itself. This happens when the actual axle of the flywheel does not coincide with its free axis. Shaking of the flywheel means that it strives to rotate about its free axis, of which it has been deprived by force.

A free axis must pass through the free centre of the body, or through its centre of gravity.

Every body has at least three free axes that are mutually perpendicular. But there may be only three, yet there may be more than three. There may be an infinite number; thus, in a sphere, any diameter is a free axis. It is easy to imagine a body that would have a given number of free axes, but not less than three. A free axis sometimes lies outside the material of the given body, then it may be called imaginary. For example, such axes are found in a ring or in a hollow tub without a bottom.

Later on I will describe free axes and the rotation of (soft) bodies which are variable in shape (plastic); I will also describe axes of a system of unattached bodies.

If in free space a body, unattached and unsupported in any way, has acquired rotational motion about a free axis, then this motion, being only uniform, could never cease by itself without the intervention of forces. On the contrary, if the solid body did not have rotational motion, then it would never acquire it by itself.

1 April 1883, Morning

✳ A WAY TO IMPART STABLE ROTATION TO A BODY
BY MEANS OF A FIXED SUPPORT

Rotational motion about an unattached axis may be imparted to a body in different ways.

It is possible, for example, if there is a stationary support, to fix any two points lying on the free axis of the given body and then make an arbitrary force impart motion to the body about these points.

If, when the action of the force ceases, the two sharp points that held the axis stationary are carefully removed, then the given body will acquire a uniform rotational motion about the free stationary axis that is not attached in any way.

This method is suitable when the free axis is real, that is, when several points of the free axis lie in the material of the body. But it is also possible to impart rotational motion to a body, even without first attaching the free axis.

Imagine a straight line perpendicular to the free axis; imagine two points on it equidistant from the axis; draw a plane through the straight line and the axis.

Now imagine that equal and opposite forces normal to this plane are acting on the two chosen points.

When the action of the forces ceases, the body will acquire a uniform rotational motion about the free unattached axis. This method is used in the case of bodies that do not have a real axis.

In a word, then, stable rotation may also be imparted to a body by a couple (special term).

2 April

✳ UNSTABLE ROTATION

Incidentally, even if we compel a body to rotate about a nonfree material axis, but one which passes through the centre of gravity, then in that case, too, the body, when released, will perform several oscillations and will begin to rotate about the free unattached and stationary axis. However, in this case, the work of rotation diminishes and the lost part is converted into partial forces (heat...). Any other rotational motion without the influence of constantly acting forces is impossible in free space.

This rotation about a nonfree axis may be called unstable, because sooner or later it turns into stable motion.

✳ IMPARTING STABLE ROTATIONAL MOTION BY MEANS OF A MOBILE SUPPORT

Imagine two separate stationary bodies in no way connected, and let one of them in some way (but only by means of the other body which plays the part of a support) acquire rotational motion; then the other body will begin to rotate in the opposite sense. Free axes can take up arbitrary (desired) positions but must be parallel, otherwise the rotation is unstable and must by itself turn into stable rotation, the lost part of the work being converted into heat; but if a device prevents the bodies from taking up a position parallel to the axes, then the bodies will very gradually come to a halt and will heat up. Only with the aid of a fixed axis can one impart nonparallel motion to bodies.

Now the velocities of the bodies may be equal or different.

By velocity of rotational motion of a solid I mean the velocity of the points of the body that lie at unit distance from the axis. It is the same as angular velocity. The ratio of these velocities depends on the shapes and masses of the given bodies. The greater the mass of a body and the farther its particles are from the axis, the greater the difficulty of putting it into motion and the lower the angular velocity that it acquires. And the converse is true.

✻ THE INERTIA OF ROTATION

The sum of the moments of inertia, or simply the moment of inertia, is the name given to the force which, acting at unit distance from the axis, is capable of imparting to points of a solid body, which points are located at unit distance from the axis, a velocity equal to unity at the end of one second of action.

The ratio of angular velocities is equal to the inverse ratio of the moments of inertia:

$$\frac{\omega_2}{\omega_1} = \frac{\text{Moment of inertia of the first body}}{\text{Moment of inertia of the second body}}$$

I said that the moment of inertia depends on the location of the mass, and so, though the mass of the support may be slight, the moment of its inertia or the resistance to rotational motion may be arbitrarily great so that in the limit it may even be considered a stationary mass. In parallel (rectilinear) motion the resistance (inertia of rectilinear parallel motion) depends only on the mass to which it is proportional and in no way on the shape of the substance. In rotational motion the inertia depends on the location of the mass relative to the axis.

3 April 1883, Morning

✻ A METHOD OF IMPARTING STABLE ROTATION BY MEANS OF A MOBILE SUPPORT

Here is how we can imagine a method of imparting stable rotational motion to two stationary bodies. The axes are parallel; forces are operative in some kind of plane that is perpendicular to these axes. Four points of application of two equal and parallel forces are at an equal distance from the line connecting the axes and lying in the same plane. There are two forces: one tends to bring together its points of application; the other (equal to the first) strives to separate its points of application. Obviously, in such conditions a couple will be acting on each body; this couple will strive to impart stable rotational motion to each. The motions of the bodies are opposite, like the motions of two meshed gear wheels of a machine. Stable rotational motion is also imparted to the bodies in exactly the same way when the axes are parallel.

✳ THE ROTATION OF A HUMAN BEING

With the aid of a toy top that children set in motion by means of a spring or a string, a person can put himself into rotational motion in free space. In doing so, one should hold the box containing the spring so that the free axis of the top lies on a line with one of the free axes of the human body. If we now let the spring open up, it will impart rotation not only to the top but also to the man. Depending on the position of the axis of the top, the man can be made to turn round the longitudinal axis of his body or about one of the two transverse axes.

If the mass of the top is 200 times less than that of the man, then its moment of inertia will be 10,000 times less than that of the man, and the angular velocity of the top will be 10,000 times more than the angular velocity of the man. The converse is also true. So if the top makes one hundred rotations in a second, the man will execute in one second only $100/10,000 = 1/100$ of a rotation, which means that one rotation will be performed in 100 seconds or 1 and 2/3 minutes.

This is apparently a rather slow rotation, but it is much faster than the rotation of the earth, which is completed once in 1,440 minutes.

It is also possible, using your hand, to impart rotation to a support and thus to one's own originally stationary body; however, this is difficult to do in such a way that in the process one avoids imparting to the bodies a translational motion in addition to the rotational motion.

✳ THE SENSATION OF ROTATION

In the case of slow rotation, like in the previous instance, the centrifugal force arising from this rotation is so insignificant as compared with the force of the muscles that it may be considered nonexistent. Yet in the case of faster rotation it is not only perceptible but may even be injurious, may even tear a person apart. Very slow rotation is readily noticeable by the apparent reverse rotation of surrounding stationary bodies.

The human eye will be quite convinced that it is not his own rotation but the opposite rotation of the surrounding black starry sphere about points lying on one straight line with his eye.

He will believe like people did in antiquity and in the Middle Ages: they could not accept the fact that the earth was in rotation, but saw only the rotation of the crystal blue vault of the sky. This continued up to the time of Galileo, who almost came to be burnt at the stake for his contradiction.

4 April, Morning

✴ THE ROTATION OF A BUILDING OR A VEHICLE

Imagine a stationary building and various, also stationary, objects within it. Inside the building is a wheel, the free axis of which coincides with one of the free axes of the building taken as a whole together with the objects inside it.

Let the wheel be put into rapid or slow rotation by muscular or other force applied within the building; then people in the building will immediately notice the rotation of the building by the apparent movement of the stars that will be calmly floating past the windows in even alternation. Only two stars appear to be stationary: through these two stars (polar stars) passes a straight line that is parallel to the axis of rotation of the building and forms the diameter of the black sphere.

If the rate of rotation of the wheel is increased, then the rotational velocity of the building will also increase; if the velocity of the wheel is reduced by a factor of ten, then the velocity of the building will diminish 10 times.

If the wheel is stopped, the building will come to a halt; if the wheel is rotated in reverse, the building will go the other way too. For a specific position of the axis of rotation of the wheel, the position of the axis of rotation of the building will remain unchanged; but there is nothing to prevent us from turning the building round its axis any desired number of degrees. We assume that the moment of inertia of the wheel is 360 times less than that of the building; then if the wheel executes one full rotation and comes to a halt, the building during this time will complete 1/360 of a rotation and will also come to a halt. When the wheel makes 90 turns, the building will make 90/360 turns, or will turn through 90 degrees.

The building may house more than one wheel.

One wheel may be used to turn the building about one of its free axes; another wheel may be used to turn it round another axis. When describing a vehicle for travelling in free space,

I shall demonstrate that the building may be made to take up any position through the sole agency of internal forces and without loss of matter, but without movement of the free centre.

Given a certain amount of agility, two persons who are stationary to begin with can by means of their muscles impart to each other opposite rotational motions. Rotation will of course be performed round the free and parallel axes. At certain times during the rotation, they will be looking at each other, then in opposite directions, then in the same direction. If one stops or slows down, the other will too, and conversely.

8 April

※ ACCELERATION, DECELERATION AND HALTING OF ROTATIONAL MOTION

If a body together with its support has already had one and the same angular velocity about one and the same free axis of rotation, then this motion may be enhanced, reduced, stopped or reversed by means of the support.

When the speed of motion of the support is increased, the motion of the vehicle is decelerative; and the slowing down proceeds until the vehicle stops; when the velocity of rotation of the support is increased further, the motion of the vehicle is reversed and the speed of this motion increases as long as the speed of the support is increased.

When the rotational speed of the support is reduced, the vehicle or other body speeds up its rotation and continues to accelerate until the support stops; but even when the rotation of the support has reversed, the vehicle continues to accelerate in step with the acceleration of the reversed rotation of the support. Generally speaking, there is a law: the sum of the products of the moments of inertia of the bodies by their angular velocities (or their work of rotation) prior to and following their interaction is one and the same. Reverse velocity is taken to be negative and the product of the moment of inertia by the negative or reverse velocity is also negative.

The same law is also operative for an arbitrary number of interacting rotating bodies. This law of rotation is analogous to the law of parallel motions, which reads: the quantity of motion of a system is a constant, i.e., the sum of the products of the masses by the velocities does not change.

Generally speaking, the quantity of motion in the world is equal to zero or is a constant quantity. The living force of the world is a variable quantity.

✷ DESCRIPTION OF A VEHICLE. STABILITY OF A VEHICLE. STABLE CYCLOIDAL MOTION (RECTILINEAR). UNSTABLE (CIRCULAR) MOTION

The vehicle for travelling in free space that I will now describe will serve for transportation of man and various objects in an absolute void without tracks, that is, without a stationary support or directed pathway.

✷ THE ABSOLUTE VOID AND FREE SPACE

Imagine an iron or steel sphere capable of withstanding the pressure of the air within it (see Fig. on page 37).

The sphere has a large number of circular openings on all sides: left, right, front, rear.

These openings, which serve as windows, are hermetically sealed with thick transparent glass strong and elastic enough to withstand an air pressure of, say, one hundred kilograms per square decimeter.

This elasticity is close to that of the atmosphere at the earth's surface (103.4). The vehicle taken as a whole including the animate and inanimate bodies inside has (like any simple or complex body) at least three mutually perpendicular axes passing through its free centre.

One of the axes (Π, Π_1) we will call polar, the other (M, M_1) meridional, and the third (Θ, Θ_1) equatorial.

Through the three axes we can pass three planes.

We call equatorial the plane that passes through the latter two axes (meridional and equatorial); its intersection with the sphere yields the equator.

The plane passing through the polar and meridional axes we call the meridional plane; its intersection with the sphere is a meridian.

To turn the meridional plane of the vehicle without altering the position of the equatorial plane, there is a material axis coinciding with the polar plane and capable of rotating together with the discs or wheels (one wheel if desired) mounted concentrically on its ends.

Two devices are mounted on the ends of the meridional axle (in the plane of the equator). One (M), something like a cannon,

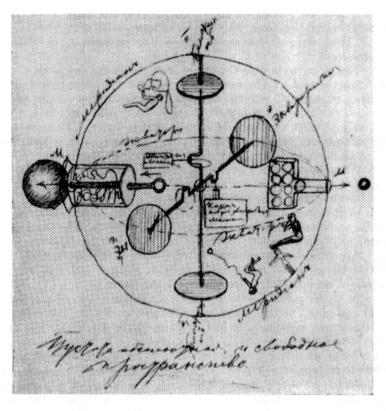

Author's drawing in the manuscript "Free Space", p. 104

serves to eject a cannon-ball in the direction of the meridional axle.

The other device has the same purpose and is in the shape of a large pipe with a corresponding cannon-ball of considerable size and density.

The ball is ejected not with the aid of powder or other explosive, as in the case of the first one, but by a smaller force, for example, a spring or the hand; the ball has attached to it a long thread that does not allow it to move off to infinity, whereas every ball ejected from the first cannon is lost to the travellers completely if it is not caught by other travellers and returned.

The cannon serves to move the whole vehicle in a straight line over indefinitely long distances; the second device serves to transport the travellers over short distances such as permitted by the length of the thread which is used to bring the shell to its original position in the same way as the vehicle itself is.

These devices (cannons) allow for movement only in one direction.

The polar axle and the discs permit the sphere to turn about this axle and at the same time to turn the meridian and both devices, which nevertheless remain in the plane of the equator.

With the force of my hand or of some other machine I make the axle with the discs turn; this makes the sphere turn, but in the opposite direction and only so long as the polar axle moves by the force of the hand, by a machine or by inertia.

When the cannon has passed along the equator the desired number of degrees, I instantaneously stop the axle, and the sphere with cannon and meridian comes to a halt.

Now the only thing left is to fire, and the sphere containing the travellers will fly out in the desired direction in the limitless plane of the equator.

For turning the equator (of the sphere) or the cannon in the meridional plane, there is an axle with discs just like the polar axle, but coinciding with the equatorial axle.

With the aid of the polar axle, the cannon acquires any position in the plane of the equator; with the aid of the equatorial axle, it acquires any position in the plane of the meridian. The former axle turns the meridian of the sphere, the latter, its equator,

Quite obviously, using these two axles the cannon may be made to occupy any position in space and, hence, the sphere may be made to move in any direction. The motions of the cannon are similar to those of the tube of a theodolite. Just as the tube of this instrument may be directed at any star, so the cannon may be made to take up any desired direction and send the sphere with its travellers to any star.

✳ ATTAINING STABILITY OF A VEHICLE FOR TRAVEL IN THE ABSOLUTE VOID OF FREE SPACE

If the mass of a sphere is not great compared with the mass of the people within it, all movements of the latter give rise to movements of the sphere. The motions are just as irregular as are the movements of the objects inside. For this reason, an undesired turning of the sphere will give rise to needless turning of the cannon. This undesired turning may be arbitrarily reduced.

The point is that the faster a disc turns, the more difficult it is to alter in some way (through the action of a force) its axis of rotation or the plane of rotation.

All forces not acting towards the centre of the body tend to impart rotation to it. Now if the body is in very rapid rotation, then such forces will not, roughly speaking, alter the axis of rotation, but will impart to it, perhaps, a parallel motion.

Imagine that inside the travelling sphere there are two rapidly rotating discs whose axes or planes are mutually perpendicular (or only inclined).

Then the irregular (non-central) actions of the forces on the sphere, in the material of which the axes and discs are rotating, will impart, approximately, only parallel motion, and not rotational motion, to both the sphere and the axles. Thus, by means of a special pair of discs we attain stability of the sphere that is the greater, the faster the discs rotate. With the aid of a stationary support it is possible to impart a rapid motion to the discs without turning the sphere. Incidentally, the very same effect may also be achieved by means of a stationary support. In that case, stability is achieved by means of two pairs of discs. In each pair, the axles either coincide or are parallel, while the discs themselves rotate in opposite directions.

If we imagine that in the centre of the sphere for travelling in the absolute void of free space the axles are divided in half and each half with its own disc is able to rotate independently of the other halves, then we have a vehicle that is not only capable of moving wherever the people inside desire, but is also capable of acquiring great or small stability.

Indeed, by orienting the cannon in a definite (desired) latitude and longitude, as has been described, and then stopping the discs, we can now impart to them opposite and equal angular velocities (if their moments of inertia are equal).

This will not change the direction of the cannon, but the cannon, together with the sphere, will acquire stability that is the greater, the faster the rotation of the discs, the speeds of which are of course arbitrary so long as the discs are not torn to pieces by the centrifugal force.

✳ STABLE CYCLOIDAL MOTION

A combination of rectilinear and rotational motion yields rectilinear cycloidal motion. The non-central action of a force on a free body always gives rise to such motion after the action of the force has ceased.

Here is a practical illustration of this motion. Let there be a car on the earth with a body inside that is in uniform rotation about an attached free axis of the body! Let us now assume that the car is in rectilinear uniform motion in some direction, then the rotating body in the car will have rectilinear cycloidal motion just like all its points, with the exception of the points on the axis, which will have rectilinear uniform motion. Relative to the car, the motion will of course be rotational, but relative to the tracks along which the car is moving, it will be cycloidal.

These same rectilinear cycloidal motions are performed in free space, only without cars and attached axles. If the plane of rotation of a body is parallel to the motion of the axis, then each point of the body will describe a cycloid situated in that plane. This is a plane cycloid; it is the motion of the wheel of a moving cart.

But if the plane of rotation is not parallel to the motion of the axial points, then each point of the body will describe a cycloid located on an elliptical cylinder or, if the plane is perpendicular to the direction of the rectilinear motion, then on a circular cylinder. In the latter case, the points describe familiar helical lines.

(Tsiolkovsky's First Description of His Wind Tunnel)

(1897)

First of all, may I kindly ask the esteemed members of the Commission not to report anything to anyone about my investigations and plans until they are completed and published.

All drawings that I will show are schematic and done by hand and are therefore not intended for publication.

In Fig. 1 *HP* is a propeller blowing machine (a kind of winnower). The trial device that I have constructed is 150 cm in height and 40 cm in width. The air stream that gradually expands and diminishes in strength exits from *P* and at the beginning (mouth) is about 40 cm in height and width. *P* stands for a series of horizontal plates, the purpose of which is to straighten the stream, which is not quite uniform at the bottom of the opening *P* (without them). In *H* we see an axle (the supports and bearings are not depicted) and a holding clamp (something like the Proni clamp). The clamp has a handle (black dot) that turns the blades (*JI*). The clamp has two screws with nuts. By tightening them more or less, we get varied amounts of friction between the iron axle and the two wooden bars of the clamp. By revolving the blades faster and faster, we finally reach a time when the clamp will slide along the axle and the velocity of the air current becomes a maximum and constant. In all experiments, the air pressure on the forms will be determined for this maximum velocity which corresponds to the magnitude of pressure and depends upon us. In each individual experiment, the velocity is determined from the pressure

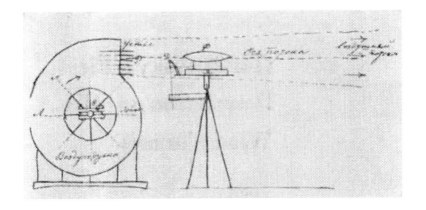

FIG. 1. *Diagram of installation for experiments with air resistance. (Inscriptions on the drawing: top, from left to right: flow exit, axis of flow, air flow; bottom, air blower.)*

of the air current on the plate in accordance with the coefficients of Caliete and Colardo (or Langley), knowing the barometric pressure and the temperature of the air.

Я is a rectangular tin box filled with water in which floats a similar box of smaller dimensions. Attached to the latter, on four supports (or in some other way), is the form to be tested, the pressure applied to it being what we want to determine. To the same stand (*Я*), on which the box with water is located, is attached a small support; on the latter, a pendulum made of a long fine iron wire is in free oscillation.

Attached to the wire is a thread that holds the floating form which tends to recede in the direction of the air current.

Because of this action, the wire is more or less strongly deflected from the vertical. The amount of deflection is experimentally determined by the tangent of the angle of deflection by means of a ruler divided into millimetres. The force of pressure of the current of air will be proportional to the number of divisions indicated by the wire. Preliminarily, by means of a special experiment, we determine the number of milligrams that correspond to a one-millimetre deflection of the wire. Thus, all deflections and the corresponding pressures of the air current may be expressed in milligrams.

The inner box is equipped with two light levers that make its motion almost strictly parallel to the direction of the air current (Fig. 2). During the experiment, the outer box is covered, the cover having narrow slits for the free motion of support columns that hold up the form.

I made the forms extremely light, out of paper. If the required form was that of a surface of revolution, I first made a careful drawing of the curve of the main longitudinal cross-section. Then a lathe was used to cut half the form, up to its largest cross-section (Fig. 3) (this was done for me in the local railway school). Then I took strips of wet paper, put them on the wooden half and wrapped the whole round with wide strips of cloth. When the paper had dried thoroughly, I removed the cloth and then, carefully, the paper, which took on the convex shape of elements of the wooden form. The only thing left was to paste together the pieces of paper on the form itself. After removal of the paper sheath, a paper hoop (band) is mounted on its wide opening (Fig. 3). If the form was very elongated, several hoops were pasted inside the paper surface. The other half of the form (sometimes not identical to the first) was prepared in the same manner. Both halves were neatly pasted together and the form was ready.

When preparing the experiments, it was necessary to see that the floating box and the attached forms were sufficiently mobile.

For this purpose, I placed the system of boxes on the table and noted what pressure on the form brought it into perceptible motion. Fig. 4 illustrates a device that produced extremely small pressures on the form. It consists of a bar A positioned more or

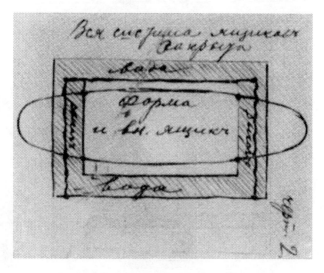

FIG. 2

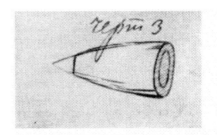

FIG. 3

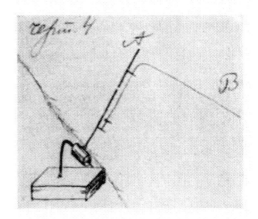

FIG. 4

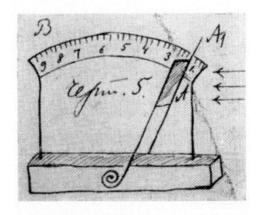

FIG. 5

FIG. 6

less close to the vertical and a fine wire bent into a 90° angle and in rotation about A. The lighter the wire B and the more vertical the axis A and the less we deflect B from the equilibrium position, the smaller the force of pressure of B on an encountered obstacle; using this device, it is easy to generate pressures of several milligrams. The form already begins to move perceptibly under a pressure of one milligram. And since in the experiments the pressure of the air current reaches 5 and more grams, the sensitivity of my device appeared to be quite sufficient.

Now it was necessary to investigate the artificial air current (Fig. 1).

It was necessary to know the velocity of the current of air at different distances from the mouth and from the middle horizontal axis. Fig. 5 depicts a device that indicates directly the rate of the air current. It consists of a plate A (on two spring feet) that deviates more or less from the equilibrium position depending on the speed of the wind. Vibrations of the plate indicate uneven flow, or gustiness. I obtained the divisions B in the following manner: first I calculated the pressures on plate A (from the Caliete-Colardo coefficient) for various wind speeds; then I produced these same pressures on plate A by means of a block and weights, noting on arc B the readings of a pointer A_1 and recording the appropriate speeds.

An apparatus like that shown in Fig. 2 (only of smaller size) may be used for the same purpose; a vertical plate (Fig. 6) is mounted in place of the form. The air current exerts pressure on B making B move and deflect plate A in proportion to the wind pressure. Scale C does not indicate exactly its speed or pressure but only its constancy or inequality in different places of the current.

On account of the water, the readings of this instrument are less susceptible to vibration.

The experimental arrangement is as shown in Fig. 1. The form is placed in the middle of the current not very close to the mouth and is aligned with the direction of flow so that there should not be a great difference between the air speeds at the ends of the form. The dimensions of the latter, particularly in the vertical direction, should be small compared with the width or cross-sectional area of the air current. In trial experiments the ratio of greatest cross-sectional area (80 sq cm) of the form under test to the area of normal flow cross-section (40×40 sq cm) was not in excess of 1/20. But it is desirable that this ratio should be much less. Theoretically the air current should be boundless. Incidentally, in experiments (applying various methods) I will have occasion to demonstrate how little the coefficient of resistance will change upon replacing a limited current by a boundless air current.

I begin an experiment with a small pressure on the screws (H in Fig. 1), which corresponds to small friction of the axle and low speed of the air current. All models (forms) are tested for the same position of nuts and for the same speed of the artificial wind. When the pressure on the last model has been determined and recorded, the model is replaced by a plate of known area placed normal to the air flow. From the pressure exerted on this plate, in connection with the readings of the barometer and thermometer, we determine the rate of the air flow. The centres of the forms and the plate must be located in the same point of the current. It is best to determine the pressure on the plate at the beginning and at the end of a series of experiments so as to be sure of constant air speeds throughout the experiment. We convert each of the numbers obtained into the coefficient of resistance of the appropriate form if we compare (by means of the divisions) the pressure exerted on the form with the pressure exerted on the area of its greatest cross-section (this is pre-calculated; and the earlier obtained pressure on the plate will also make it possible to determine the pressure on any area for the same rate of motion).

By making several turns of the nut of clamp H (Fig. 1) and thus increasing the speed of the artificial air current, we will obtain in exactly the same manner a number of other pressures, on the basis of which we learn a number of other coefficients for the same forms, but for a different speed, which, as has been indicated, is calculated from the Caliete-Colardo coefficient.

Performing another series of experiments with the same forms but with a new increase in friction and, hence, for a new speed, we get a third group of pressures and coefficients. Thus, performing observations with a score of forms and for ten different velocities, we get 200 numbers expressing the pressure on various forms at a variety of velocities. All that is left is to express in the form of a graph or by means of empirical equations the dependence between pressure and rate of air flow, and sometimes between pressure, rate of flow and variable form of the body. In any case, aside from deriving laws of resistance, the coefficients of resistance of different bodies that I obtained may be of some value as a fact or as checking material.

I intend to carry out experiments with the following forms under different velocities:

1. With bodies of different elongation obtained by rotating the arc of a circle about its chord.

This group of observations will include the spherical surface with its parts.

So far I have experimented with this kind of surface only for speeds of 1 metre per second and in a wind. The latter experiments are inconvenient and difficult, to say nothing of their inaccuracy (I am submitting to the Commission a printed description of these experiments in triplicate).

2. It would also be interesting to determine the pressure for an inclined position of the longitudinal axis of the same forms to the direction of air flow; but this would require excessive dimensions of the blowing machine.

3. With an ellipsoid of revolution of various elongation (Fig. 7).

4. With solids in the shape of flat cakes, fish, eggs (the article will contain drawings to illustrate their shapes or equations will be given).

5. With various kinds of cylindrical and conical surfaces (Fig. 8).

6. With polyhedra.

7. Some authors on resistance (Mr. Pomortsev) disregard the significance of the stern portion of the solid and neglect air friction (even for elongated solids). I shall do experiments that will illuminate this debatable point (Fig. 9).

6*. With a square plate placed normal to the direction of air flow but located at different distances from the horizontal plane (from the stand), Fig. 10.

7. With the same plate but inclined to the direction of the air flow. For this purpose, the box of water and the plate are located so that the direction of the plate coincides with the direction of the air flow; this occurs when the indicator (dynamometer, Fig. 1) reads zero. Then, the box together with the plate is turned (along a preliminarily drawn circle on the stand) through 5, 10,

* An error in the original numbering (Editors).

FIG. 7

FIG. 8

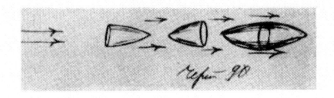

FIG. 9

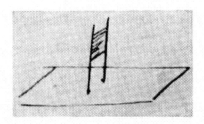

FIG. 10

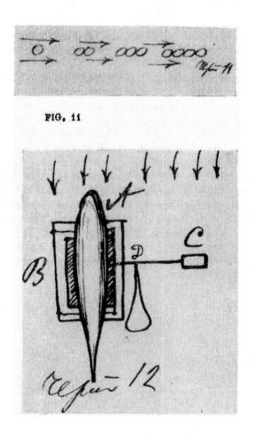

FIG. 11

FIG. 12

15, 20, etc., degrees in succession (a check of the formulae of Duchmin, Langley and Lord Reyleigh).

8. An experiment with an elongated rectangular plate located along the current of air slightly inclined to it. The elongation of the plate is varied. A law is derived that expresses the value of elongation, aside from the area.

9. An experiment with the same plate but with the long dimension normal to the air flow. The same law.

10. The pressure exerted on one or several identical bodies placed in the direction of the current of air in succession (Fig. 11). Applied, for example, to the problem of whether it is easier for one balloon or a group of balloons in series to fly (cleave the air). It may be noted that experiments with slightly elongated solids may be performed for one or two different speeds of air flow

because the coefficients of resistance of such bodies hardly at all depend on the speed of the air flow as long as it is at least one or two metres per second.

In order to demonstrate an experiment to a considerable number of persons, I propose the following interesting arrangement (Fig. 12): A is the form under test whose low resistance we wish to demonstrate to an audience; B is a box containing water as earlier described (Fig. 2); $Д$ is the point of support of lever BC; C is a plate, the air pressure on which strives to overturn form A. For example, by inserting plate C, whose area is 1/10 that of the cross-section, and then starting up the blowing machine (Fig. 1) with the clamp tightly screwed, we will see that as the speed of the air current is gradually increased, a time of equilibrium comes and plate C is overturned. Whence it is concluded that the coefficient of resistance diminishes with increasing speed of air flow, and, at the instant of equilibrium, is expressed by the number 1/10. I have already performed a trial experiment of this kind.

Investigation of World Spaces by Reactive Vehicles

(1903)

1. Small-size unmanned balloons with automatic observational instruments have risen only to an altitude not exceeding 20 versts.

Difficulties of going up by means of balloons increase extraordinarily fast with increasing altitude.

Suppose we want to send a balloon to an altitude of 27 km carrying a load of one kilogram. The air at 27 km has a density about 1/50 that of air under ordinary conditions (760 mm pressure and 0°C). This means that a balloon at such an altitude will have to occupy a volume 50 times greater than below. At sea level, it is inflated with at least 2 cubic metres of hydrogen, which at the designated altitude will occupy 100 m³. In this way the balloon will lift the load of 1 kg, that is, it will lift an automatic instrument, and the balloon itself will weigh 1 kg or thereabouts.

The surface area of its bag for a diameter of 5.8 m will come out to at least 103 m². Hence, each square metre of material including the attached net will have to weigh 10 g.

One square metre of writing paper weighs 100 g, while that of cigarette paper comes out to 50 g, so that even cigarette paper will be 5 times heavier than the material that should be used for our balloon. Such material cannot be used for a balloon because a bag made of it will tear and allow the gas to escape.[1]

---

[1] Modern synthetic materials have significantly extended the possibilities of obtaining fine strong fabrics (Editors).

Large-size balloons may have a thicker bag. Thus, a balloon of unprecedented diameter (58 m) will have a bag, one square metre of which weighs about 100 g, which is just a bit heavier than ordinary writing paper. It will lift a load of 1,000 kg, which is much too much for a self-recording instrument.

If for such enormous dimensions of the balloon we confine ourselves to a lifting force of 1 kg, then the bag can be made some two times heavier. Generally speaking, in that case the balloon may be extremely expensive, but still one cannot consider the construction of such a balloon an impossibility. At an altitude of 27 km its volume will come to 100,000 m³ with a surface area of the bag 10,300 m².

And yet what miserable results! An ascent to only some 25 versts.

What is there to say about sending instruments to a still greater height? The dimensions of the balloon will have to be considerably greater; but do not forget that as the dimensions of the balloon increase, the tearing forces acting on the bag will more and more dominate over the resistance of the material.

Naturally, it is quite inconceivable to lift instruments beyond the limits of the atmosphere by means of a balloon; from observations of falling stars it is clear that these limits do not extend beyond 200-300 km.

Theoretically, the height of the atmosphere has even been determined at 54 km, taking as the basis of calculations the fall of air temperature 5°C for every kilometre of ascent, which is quite close to actuality, at least for the accessible layers of the atmosphere.

Height of atmos-phere, km	°C	Air density	Height of atmos-phere, km	°C	Air density
0	0	1	30	−150	1 : 116
6	−30	1 : 2	36	−180	1 : 584
12	−60	1 : 4.32	42	−210	1 : 3,900
18	−90	1 : 10.6	48	−240	1 : 28,000
24	−120	1 : 30.5	54.5	−272	0

The foregoing is a table of altitudes, temperatures and densities of the air that I have compiled on this basis.[2] From this table one

[2] Modern data on the structure of the earth's atmosphere differ appreciably from those given in the table. It has been established (on the average) that up to 11 km altitude the temperature falls 6.5°C per km. In the stratosphere from 11 to 25-30 km it is constant at −56.5°C. Above 80 km the temperature increases, reaching +1200-1300°C at 200 km altitude (Editors).

can readily see how fast the difficulties of ascent increase with increasing altitude.

The divisor in the last column is what expresses this difficulty in balloon construction.

2. Let us now pass to another idea of ascent—by means of cannon-balls.

In practice, the initial speed of a cannon-ball does not exceed 1,200 m/sec. Such a ball launched vertically will rise to a height of 73 km if the ascent is made in airless space (a vacuum).[3] In air, naturally, the ascent will be considerably less, depending on the shape and mass of the ball.

Given a good shape, the ball would ascend to quite appreciable heights, but it is impossible to place observational instruments inside the ball, for they would be broken to pieces either upon the return to earth or in the barrel of the cannon itself.

The danger during motion of the ball in the barrel is less, but even so it is great as regards the integrity of the apparatus. For the sake of simplicity, let us assume that the gas pressure on the ball is uniform, as a result of which its acceleration per second will be W m/sec. Then all objects in the ball will have the same acceleration, in view of the fact that they are compelled to participate in the same motion. The result will be that a relative, apparent, gravity[4] will develop inside the ball equal to W/g, where g is the acceleration of the earth's gravity at the surface of the earth.

The length of the cannon, L, is expressed by the formula

$$L = \frac{V^2}{2(W-g)},$$

where V is the velocity acquired by the cannon-ball as it leaves the muzzle.

From the formula it is seen that W, and hence the increment in relative gravity of the ball, decreases with increasing length of the cannon for constant V; i.e., the longer the cannon, the safer are the instruments during ejection of the cannon-ball. But even for a very (impracticably) long cannon, the apparent gravity in the ball, when the latter is accelerated in the barrel of the cannon, is so great that the delicately built apparatus will hardly be able to withstand it without being damaged. All the more so it is impossible to send something living in the ball if the need should arise.

3. Now let us suppose that a cannon has been built 300 metres in height. Say it is positioned along the Eiffel Tower, which,

---

[3] The acceleration of gravity, g, is also considered constant (Editors).
[4] The g-force, or overloading (Editors).

as we know, has that height, and let the ball receive (by means of uniform gas pressure) a velocity, upon exit from the muzzle, that is sufficient to lift the ball beyond the limits of the atmosphere, for example, to an altitude of 300 km from the earth's surface. Then we compute the required velocity, V, from the formula $V = \sqrt{2gh}$,[5] where h is the altitude of ascent (we get about 2,450 m/sec). From the two latter formulae, substituting for V, we find

$$\frac{W}{g} = \frac{h}{L} + 1,$$

where W/g expresses the relative (or apparent) gravity in the ball. From the formula we find that it is equal to 1,001.

Consequently, the weight of all instruments in the ball will have to increase some 1,000 times; i.e., an object weighing one pound will experience, due to the apparent gravity, a pressure of 1,000 pounds, or 25 poods. Hardly any physical instrument could withstand such a pressure.

So as not to mislead anyone by the word "relative, or apparent, gravity", I can say that what I have in mind here is a force that is dependent on the accelerating motion of a body (the ball, for example); it also appears in the case of uniform motion of a body if that motion is curvilinear, and then it is called centrifugal force. Generally speaking, it always appears on a body or in a body if that body alone is acted upon by some mechanical force that upsets the inertial motion of the body.

Relative gravity exists as long as the force generating it lasts: as soon as the latter ceases, relative gravity disappears without a trace. When I call that force gravity, it is solely because its temporary action is completely identical with the action of the force of gravitation. Just as every material point of a body is subject to gravitation, so relative gravity is generated in every particle of a body contained in the ball; this is due to the fact that the apparent gravity depends on inertia, to which all the material parts of a body are identically subjected.

To return, the instruments inside the ball will be 1,001 times heavier. Even if it were possible under this terrible, though transient (0.24 sec), build-up of relative gravity to keep the instruments intact, there will be many other obstacles to the employment of cannons as devices for launching objects into celestial space.

First of all, there is the difficulty of constructing them even in the future; further, the tremendous initial velocity of the ball;

---

[5] In the derivation of this formula, air resistance is neglected (Editors).

indeed, in the lower dense layers of the atmosphere the velocity of the ball will fall off in large measure due to air resistance; now the loss of speed will greatly reduce the altitude reached by the ball; then too it is difficult to attain a uniform pressure of gases on the ball during its motion in the barrel, as a result of which there will be a much greater increase in gravity than we have calculated (1,001); finally, a safe return of the ball to earth is more than doubtful.

✳ THE ROCKET AS A REACTIVE DEVICE

4. Incidentally, the tremendous increase in gravity alone is quite sufficient for us to leave all thought of using cannons for our purpose.

In place of them, or balloons, for investigating the atmosphere I propose a reactive device, that is a kind of rocket, but one of enormous dimensions and specially designed. The idea is not new, but calculations referring to it have yielded such remarkable results that it is impossible to keep silent about them.

This study of mine does not by far examine all aspects of the matter and does not at all resolve it from the practical viewpoint (relative to its feasibility); but in the far distant nebulous future one perceives such intriguing and significant promises as hardly anyone today dreams of.

Let us picture such a vehicle (Fig. 1)[6]: an elongated metallic chamber (which is the form with the least resistance), equipped with lighting, supplied with oxygen, and with substances which absorb carbon dioxide, repugnant odours and other animal excretions, and designed for carrying not only diverse physical instruments, but also an intelligent being in control of the chamber (we shall take up the problem in its broadest aspects). The chamber has a large supply of substances which, upon being mixed, straightway form an explosive mass. These substances, which explode properly and rather uniformly in a definite place, will flow in the form of hot gases through pipes that flare out at the ends like a megaphone or a musical instrument. These pipes are situated lengthwise along the walls of the chamber. At one end (the narrow one) of the pipe the explosives are mixed together: here condensed, flaming gases are formed. At the other, broader, end the gases expand and cool and then race out through the flared pipes with a tremendous relative velocity.

_____
[6] In the 1903 edition the drawings are not included. They are given here on the basis of archive materials (Editors).

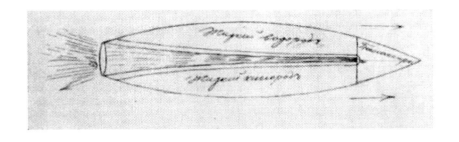

Fig. 1 *Diagram of a rocket. Liquid hydrogen and liquid oxygen are separated by a partition. The gases mix and explode at* A, *cold highly rarefied vapour (explosion products) exits at* B. *The pipe* AB *is surrounded by a jacket with circulating liquid metal. In the forward part of the rocket is a room for passengers*

Quite naturally, such a vehicle will, like a rocket, under certain conditions soar upwards.

Automatic instruments are needed to control the motion of the rocket (which is what we will occasionally call our device) and the force of explosion in accord with a predetermined scheme.

If the resultant force of explosion does not pass exactly through the centre of inertia of the vehicle, then the vehicle will rotate and, hence, will be to no purpose. Yet it is impossible to attain a mathematically precise coincidence here because just as the centre of inertia cannot but fluctuate due to the movements of the substances contained in the vehicle, so also the direction of the resultant force of gas pressure in the cannon cannot have a mathematically invariable direction. In the air it is still possible to direct the vehicle by means of a rudder, like a bird, but what can one do in airless space where the ether will hardly represent a perceptible support?

The point is that if the resultant is close enough to the centre of inertia of the vehicle, then its rotation will be rather slow. But as soon as it has begun to rotate, we move some mass inside the vehicle until the movement of the centre of inertia thus generated compels the vehicle to deviate in the opposite direction. Thus, by watching the vehicle and moving a small mass inside it, we can make the vehicle move to one side or the other, while the general direction of the action of explosives and motion of the vehicle will not be changed.

It may be that manual control of vehicle motion will not only be difficult but even impossible, practically speaking. In that case we will have to resort to automatic control.

The reasons for this, after what has been said, are clear.

The attraction of the earth cannot be that basic force of control because in the ball there will be only a relative gravity with an acceleration W, the direction of which will coincide with the relative direction of the exiting explosive substances or will be directly opposite to the direction of the resultant of their pressure. And since the direction varies as the ball and cannon are turned, this gravity is not suitable as a regulator of the control device.

It may be possible, for this purpose, to employ a compass needle or the force of the sun's rays concentrated by means of a biconvex lens. Every time the ball and cannon turn, the tiny bright image of the sun alters its relative position in the ball, and this can cause expansion of the gas, or initiate pressure, electric current, or movement of mass to restore a definite direction of the cannon; and in the process, the bright spot will fall on a neutral, so to say, unsensitive spot of the mechanism.

There must be two automatically mobile masses.

A small chamber with two discs rapidly rotating in different planes can serve as the basis for a device regulating cannon-ball direction. The chamber is suspended so that its position, or more precisely speaking, its direction, does not depend on the direction of the cannon. When the cannon turns, the chamber, by virtue of inertia (disregarding friction), will retain its earlier absolute direction (relative to the stars); this property is manifested to the highest degree during the rapid rotation of chamber discs.

When the cannon turns, fine springs attached to the chamber alter their relative position inside the cannon, and this can serve to generate a current and move the regulating masses.

Finally, turning the flared end of the pipe can also serve as a means of maintaining a definite direction of the vehicle.[7]

※ THE ADVANTAGES OF THE ROCKET

5. Before presenting the theory of the rocket or a similar reactive device, I shall try to interest the reader in the merits of the rocket over the cannon and cannon-ball.

---

[7] Here, Tsiolkovsky later added: "The simplest thing for rocket control is a double rudder placed outside, near the exit end of the pipe. It is possible to avoid rotation of the rocket about the longitudinal axis by turning a plate located in the gases and positioned in the direction of their motion."

Turning the chamber of the reactive engine to obtain controlling forces and moments (like gas rudders) is widely employed in modern rocket designs (Editors).

(a) Compared with a gigantic cannon, our apparatus is as light as a feather; (b) it is relatively cheap and comparatively easy to accomplish; (c) since the pressure of explosives is rather uniform, it brings about a uniformly accelerated motion of the rocket, which develops relative gravity; we can control the magnitude of this temporary gravity at will; i.e., by regulating the force of the explosion we can make it arbitrarily smaller or greater than the ordinary gravity of the earth. If for the sake of simplicity we assume that the force of explosion, while falling off little by little, remains proportional to the mass of the vehicle combined with the mass of the remaining unexploded explosives, then the acceleration of the vehicle and, hence, the magnitude of the relative gravity will be constant. Thus, when speaking of apparent gravity, a rocket can safely carry not only measuring instruments but also people, whereas in a cannon-ball the relative gravity increases 1,001 times even for an enormous cannon the size of the Eiffel Tower.

(d) Another significant advantage of the rocket is that its velocity increases in the desired progression and in the desired direction; it may be constant and may diminish uniformly, and this makes for safe descent onto a planet. It is all a matter of a good regulating device for explosion. (e) At the start of ascent, while the atmosphere is dense and air resistance is enormous at high speed, the rocket moves relatively slowly and for this reason suffers but little from the resistance of the medium and does not heat up greatly.

Quite naturally, the velocity of the rocket builds up only slowly; but then, as the rocket attains higher altitudes and the atmosphere becomes rarefied, it can artificially build up faster; finally, in the vacuum of outer space the rate of increase may be enhanced still more. In this way we will expend only a minimum of work on overcoming the resistance of the air.

※ THE ROCKET IN A MEDIUM FREE OF GRAVITY
AND ATMOSPHERE

6. Let us first consider the action of an explosion in a medium free of gravity and surrounding matter, that is, an atmosphere. We shall only undertake to analyze the resistance of an atmosphere to the motion of the vehicle but not to the motion of the vapours ejected at high speeds. The effect of the atmosphere on an explosion is not exactly clear: on the one hand, it is favourable because the exhausted substances have some support in the surrounding material medium, which support they entrain in their motion

and thus contribute to increasing the speed of the rocket; but on the other hand, this same atmosphere, due to its density and elasticity, inhibits expansion of the gases beyond a certain limit, as a result of which the explosives do not acquire the speed that they could when exploding in a void. This latter effect is unfavourable because the increment in rocket velocity is proportional to the speed of the ejected explosion products.

7. Let us denote the mass of the vehicle and everything it contains, with the exception of the supply of explosives, by M_1; the total mass of explosives by M_2; finally, the variable mass of explosives that remain unexploded in the vehicle at a given instant of time by M.

Thus the total mass of the rocket at the start of explosion will be $M_1 + M_2$; within a short time it will be expressed by the variable quantity $M_1 + M$; finally, at the termination of explosion, it will be equal to the constant M_1.

For a rocket to attain maximum speed, it is necessary that the products of explosion be ejected in the same direction relative to the stars. And to achieve this the rocket should not rotate; to prevent rotation, it is necessary that the resultant of the explosive forces passing through the centre of their pressure should at the same time pass through the centre of inertia of the entire assemblage of flying masses.

We have already examined to some extent how this is to be attained in practice.

And so, assuming this optimum ejection of gases in a single direction, we get the following differential equation on the basis of the law of constancy of momentum:

$$dV (M_1 + M) = V_1 dM. \tag{8}$$

9. Here dM is an infinitely small mass of explosive ejected from the flared end of the cannon with a velocity V_1 that is constant relative to the rocket.

10. I want to say that the relative velocity (V_1) of ejected elements, under the same conditions of explosion, is the same during the whole time of explosion (on the basis of the law of relative motions); dV is the increment in velocity (V) of rocket motion together with the remaining intact explosive materials; this increment (dV) is obtained due to the ejection of element dM with velocity V_1. The latter will be determined in its proper place.

11. Separating the variables in equation (8) and integrating, we get

$$\frac{1}{V_1} \int dV = - \int \frac{dM}{M_1 + M} + C, \tag{12}$$

or

$$\frac{V}{V_1} = -\ln(M_1 + M) + C. \tag{13}$$

Here, C is a constant. When $M = M_2$, i.e., prior to explosion, $V = 0$; on this basis we find

$$C = \ln(M_1 + M_2); \tag{14}$$

consequently,

$$\frac{V}{V_1} = \ln\left(\frac{M_1 + M_2}{M_1 + M}\right). \tag{15}$$

The signs of the two sides of the equation [will be] reversed because the velocities V and V_1 are opposite in direction.

The greatest velocity of the vehicle is attained when $M = 0$, i.e., when the entire supply M_2 is exploded; then, assuming in the preceding equation $M = 0$, we get

$$\frac{V}{V_1} = \ln\left(1 + \frac{M_2}{M_1}\right).^8 \tag{16}$$

17. Whence we see that the velocity (V) of the vehicle increases without bound with increasing quantity (M_2) of explosives. Thus, with different supplies of explosive materials, in the case of different voyages, we obtain highly diversified terminal velocities. From equation (16) it is also evident that the speed of a rocket upon expenditure of a definite supply of explosives does not depend on the speed or nonuniformity of explosion as long as the particles of ejected material move with the same speed (V_1) relative to the cannon-ball.

However, the velocity (V) of the rocket increases more and more slowly with increasing supply (M_2), though without bound. It increases approximately like the logarithm of the increase in quantity of explosive supplies (M_2) (if M_2 is great compared with M_1, i.e., if the mass of explosives is several times that of the vehicle).

18. Further calculations will be interesting when we have determined V_1, or the relative and terminal velocity of the exploded element.

Since the gas or vapour leaving the flared end of the cannon is extremely rarefied and cools (given a sufficiently long pipe) even becoming solid (turning into dust that rushes out at a terrible speed), it may be taken that the entire energy of combustion or chemical union in the case of an explosion turns into the motion

[8] This is now called Tsiolkovsky's formula (Editors).

60

of the combustion products or into kinetic energy. Indeed, picture a definite quantity of gas expanding in empty space without any instruments: it will expand in all directions and therefore will cool off until it turns into drops of liquid or into a fog.

The fog is converted into tiny crystals, but this time not because of expansion but due to evaporation and radiation into world space.

As it expands, the gas will release all of its apparent and part of its latent energy, which will ultimately turn into the rapid motion of crystals in all directions since the gas has been expanding freely in all directions. Now if it is compelled to expand in a reservoir with a pipe, the pipe will channel the motion of the gas molecules in a definite direction; we can utilize this for our purposes, that is, to propel the rocket.

It would seem that the energy of motion of the molecules is converted into kinetic motion as long as the substance retains its gaseous or vaporous state. But this is not exactly so. Indeed, a part of the substance can convert into the liquid state; but then, in the process, energy is released (the latent heat of vaporization), which is transferred to the remaining vaporous part of the matter and will for a time retard its conversion into the liquid state. We encounter a similar phenomenon in a steam engine cylinder when the steam works by its own expansion, any exit from the boiler into the cylinder being closed. Then, no matter what the temperature of the steam, part of it will be converted into fog, i.e., into the liquid state, while the other part will retain its vaporous state and work by borrowing the latent heat of the steam that has condensed into liquid.

Thus, molecular energy will be turned into kinetic energy at least as far as the liquid state. When the entire mass has turned into drops, conversion into kinetic energy will almost cease because at low temperature the vapours of liquid and solid bodies have an exceedingly small elasticity and it is difficult to make use of them, as this would require enormous pipes.

However, a certain insignificant part of the above energy will be lost to us, i.e., it will not turn into kinetic energy because of friction against the pipe and radiation of heat by its hot parts. Incidentally, a pipe made of red copper may be surrounded by a jacket containing a circulating liquid metal; the metal will transfer heat from the extremely hot part at one end of the pipe to its other part, which is cooled because of the considerable rarefaction of vapour. Thus, even this loss due to radiation and thermal conduction may be utilized or made very insignificant. In view of the brief time of explosion, which lasts from 2 to 5 minutes in extreme cases, the loss due to radiation is slight even without any devices; now the circulation of liquid metal in a jacket surrounding the pipes is necessary for another purpose: to keep the pipes at one and the same low temperature, i.e., to retain the strength of the pipes. Despite this, it is possible that a part of the pipe will melt, become oxidized and carried away with the gases and vapour. To avoid this, the inner part of the pipe will perhaps be lined with a special refractory material, carbon, lime (CaO) or something else. Though in the process some of the carbon will burn up, the strength of the metal cannon will not suffer through the slight increase in temperature.

Now the gaseous product of carbon combustion, carbon dioxide, will only help to lift the rocket. Perhaps a kind of crucible material will be employed, some kind of mixture of substances. At any rate, it is not I who will solve this problem, like so many others that refer to our reactive devices.

In many cases I am compelled only to guess and conjecture. I am not deceived in any way and I know full well that I do not only fail to resolve the problem in its entirety but that there remains a hundred times more to do than I have already done. My purpose is to kindle interest in it and point out the great significance that it will have in the future and the possibility of its solution....

To reduce the extent of the pipeline section while retaining the overall length of the pipes, we can form them into spirals or coils and surround them (in order to maintain a moderate and uniform temperature) with a rapidly circulating liquid that is a good conductor of heat.

At the present time, it is not particularly difficult to convert hydrogen and oxygen into liquids. These liquids must be separated by a partition. Their temperatures are extremely low; it is therefore practicable to use them to surround either jackets with circulating metal or the cannons themselves directly.

Experiment will show how best to do this. But the latter case is not suitable for copper pipes because at very low temperatures copper becomes brittle and probably loses its viscosity. Certain metals, on the contrary, become stronger upon cooling; those are the metals that must then be employed, say iron. I don't remember exactly, but certain experiments dealing with resistance, of iron in liquid air, it seems, have indicated that the viscosity at this low temperature increases almost tens of times. I am not positive about this, but these experiments, as applied to the matter at hand, merit the greatest attention. (Why not cool ordinary cannons in this fashion before firing them, particularly since liquid air is now such a common thing.)

In a certain proportion, liquid oxygen and liquid hydrogen pumped from their reservoirs into the narrow intake of the pipe to combine little by little can yield an excellent explosive material. The water vapour obtained upon the chemical combination of these liquids will, at a terribly high temperature, expand and move towards the end or mouth of the pipe until it cools to form a liquid in the form of an extremely fine fog streaming through the pipe to its flared exit.

The hydrogen and oxygen in liquid form will first (before entering the cannon) pass through a special jacket along the surface of the cannon, cooling it and heating up themselves; only then will they enter the cannon and explode; thus, the thermal energy carried away from the cannon by thermal conduction and radiation will again return and convert into the energy of the translational motion of vapour or fog.

19. When gaseous hydrogen and oxygen combine to form 1 kg of water, they develop 3,825 calories. One calorie signifies the amount of heat needed to raise the temperature of 1 kg of water 1°C.

This quantity will be slightly less in our case because the oxygen and hydrogen are in the liquid and not gaseous state, to which the number of calories given refers. Indeed, first, liquids have to be heated and then converted into the gaseous state, and all this requires the expenditure of a certain amount of energy. Due to the fact that this energy is small compared with chemical energy, we shall leave our number undiminished.

Taking the mechanical equivalent of heat at 427 kg-m, we will find that 3,825 calories correspond to 1,621,800 kg-m of work; this is sufficient to lift the explosion products, i.e., 1 kg of material, to a height of 1,622 km from the surface of the globe, on the assumption that the force of gravity is constant. This work converted into motion corresponds to the work of one kilogram of mass moving with a velocity of 5,700 m/sec. I do not know of any group of bodies which when combined chemically would yield per unit mass of resultant product such an enormous quantity of energy. Moreover, certain other substances do not, when combined, produce volatile products, which does not suit our case at all.

Thus, silicon burning in oxygen ($Si + O_2 = SiO_2$) releases a tremendous quantity of heat, namely 3,654 calories per unit mass of resultant product (SiO_2), but unfortunately with the formation of bodies of low volatility.

Having taken liquid oxygen and hydrogen for the material most suited for the explosion, I gave a number expressing their mutual chemical energy per unit mass of resultant product (H_2O) somewhat greater than the true number, since the substances that combine in the rocket must be in the liquid state and not in the gaseous state and they must also have a very low temperature.

I believe it is well worth comforting the reader here with the information that in the future we can count not only on this energy (3,825 cal) but even on incomparably greater quantities, when ways will perhaps be found to put our still insufficiently elaborated thoughts into practice. Indeed, when considering the quantity of energy released in chemical processes of diverse substances, we note (on the whole but not without exception, of course) that the quantity of energy per unit mass of the combining products depends (in most cases) on the atomic weights of the simple bodies being combined: the lower the atomic weights of the bodies, the more heat is released upon their combination. Thus, the formation of sulphur dioxide (SO_2) generates only 1,250 calories, the formation of cupric oxide (CuO) yields only 546 calories; yet in the formation of carbon dioxide (CO_2) coal yields 2,204 calories per unit mass. As we have seen, hydrogen and oxygen generate still more (3,825). To assess these findings as applied to the idea that I have expressed, note the atomic weights of the indicated elements: hydrogen 1, oxygen 16, carbon 12, sulphur 32, silicon 28, and copper 63.

There are of course many exceptions to this rule, but on the whole it is valid. Indeed, if we imagine a series of points, the abscissae of which express the sum (or the product) of the atomic weights of the combining simple bodies, and the ordinates the corresponding energy of chemical combination, then, by drawing a smooth curve through the points (as close as possible to them), we will see a constant reduction in the ordinates with increasing abscissae, which is proof of our view.

Therefore, if at some time it turns out that the so-called simple bodies are composite and can be decomposed into new elements, then the atomic weights of the latter should be less than those of the simple bodies we know. Then from the foregoing, the newly discovered elements, upon combining, should release an incomparably greater amount of energy than the bodies that are now conditionally termed simple and that have comparatively high atomic weights.

Ions have long been spoken of in the sense that it is believed that the conditional elements decompose into these ions under the action of the sun's light.

The very existence of the ether with its almost limitless elasticity and enormous velocity of its atoms indicates a limitlessly small atomic weight for these atoms and an unlimited energy in the case of their chemical combination.

20. However all that may be, as of now, for V_1 (see 15, 16, and 19) we cannot take more than 5,700 m/sec. But in time, who knows but that this figure may not be increased several times over.

Taking 5,700 m/sec, from formula (16) we can compute not only the ratio of the velocities $\frac{V}{V_1}$, but also the absolute magnitude of the ultimate (greatest) velocity (V) of the vehicle depending on the ratio M_2/M_1.

21. From formula (16) it is evident that the mass of the rocket with all its passengers and all its devices (M_1) may be arbitrarily great, and the velocity (V) of the vehicle will not lose anything as long as the supply of explosive materials (M_2) increases in proportion to the increase in mass (M_1) of the rocket. To summarize, then: vehicles of any size with any number of travellers may acquire a velocity of any desired magnitude. Incidentally, increasing rocket velocity is attended, as we have seen, by an incomparably more rapid build-up in the mass (M_2) of the explosive materials. For this reason, though increasing the mass of the vehicle being lifted into celestial space is easy and possible, just as difficult will it be to increase its velocity.

22. From equation (16) we get the following table:

TABLE 22

M_2/M_1	V/V_1	Velocity (V), m/sec	M_2/M_1	V/V_1	Velocity (V), m/sec
0.1	0.095	543	7	2.079	11,800
0.2	0.182	1,037	8	2.197	12,500
0.3	0.262	1,493	9	2.303	13,100
0.4	0.336	1,915	10	2.398	13,650
0.5	0.405	2,308	19	2.996	17,100
1	0.693	3,920	20	3.044	17,330
2	1.098	6,260	30	3.434	19,560
3	1.386	7,880	50	3.932	22,400
4	1.609	9,170	100	4.615	26,280
5	1.792	10,100	193	5.268	30,038
6	1.946	11,100	Infinite	Infinite	Infinite

23. From this table we see that the velocities obtained by reaction are not at all small. For instance, for a mass of explosives 193 times the mass (M_1) of the vehicle [rocket], the velocity at burn-out and expenditure of the supply (M_2) is equal to the velocity of the earth in its orbit round the sun. Do not think that the

storage of an enormous mass of explosives requires a tremendous quantity of strong material for the vessels that hold the explosive components. Indeed, in the liquid state, hydrogen and oxygen exhibit high pressure only when the vessels holding them are closed, i.e., when the gases themselves are heated by the comparatively warm bodies surrounding them. But in our case, these liquefied gases must have free access to the pipe (aside from their constant influx there in the liquid form) where they combine chemically and explode. The constant and rapid flow of gases, which corresponds to the evaporation of liquids, cools these liquids to the point where, with their vapours, they hardly at all exert any pressure on the surrounding walls. Hence, storing explosive components does not require a large mass of material for the vessels.

24. When the supply of explosives is equal to the mass of the rocket ($M_2/M_1 = 1$), the velocity of the rocket will be almost twice that required for a stone or cannon-ball launched by "selenites" from the surface of our moon to leave it forever and become a satellite of the earth, or a second moon.

This velocity (3,920 m/sec) is almost sufficient for eternal recession of bodies launched from the surface of Mars or Mercury.

If the ratio of masses M_2/M_1 is 3, the vehicle speed resulting from the expenditure of the entire supply will be just slightly less than that needed for it to revolve round the earth like a satellite[9] beyond the limits of the atmosphere.

For a ratio M_2/M_1 equal to 6, the rocket velocity will almost be sufficient to escape from the earth and become an eternal independent planet moving round the sun. Greater quantities of explosive material will make it possible to reach the belt of asteroids or even heavy planets.

25. From the table it is seen that even for a small supply of explosives, the ultimate velocity of a vehicle will be sufficient for practical purposes. For instance, for a supply that is only 0.1 the weight of the rocket, the velocity will be 543 m/sec, which is sufficient for sending a rocket to a height of 15 km. From the table we also see that for a small supply the velocity at the end of explosion is approximately proportional to the mass of the supply (M_2); consequently, in this case the altitude reached is proportional to the square of the mass (M_2) of the supply. Thus, for a supply that is one half of the mass of the rocket ($M_2/M_1 = 0.5$), the latter will fly out far beyond the limits of the atmosphere.

---

[9] The flight theory of an artificial earth satellite was considered by Tsiolkovsky in the second part of this work, see p. 107—114 (Editors).

26. It is interesting to determine what portion of the total work of explosive material (i.e., of their chemical energy) is transferred to the rocket.

The work of the explosives is expressed by $(V_1^2 : 2g) \cdot M_2$, where g is the acceleration of the earth's gravity; the mechanical work of a rocket having velocity V will be expressed in the same units: $(V^2 : 2g) \cdot M_1$,[10] or on the basis of formula (16)

$$\frac{V^2}{2g} \cdot M_1 = \frac{V_1^2}{2g} \cdot M_1 \left\{ \ln \left(1 + \frac{M_2}{M_1} \right) \right\}^2 .$$

Now, dividing the work of the rocket by the work of the explosive material, we get

$$\frac{M_1}{M_2} \left\{ \ln \left(1 + \frac{M_2}{M_1} \right) \right\}^2 .$$

From this formula we calculate the following table of utilization[11] of rocket energy of explosive materials.

TABLE 26

$\frac{M_2}{M_1}$	Utilization	$\frac{M_2}{M_1}$	Utilization	$\frac{M_2}{M_1}$	Utilization
0.1	0.090	3	0.64	10	0.58
0.2	0.165	4	0.65	19	0.47
0.3	0.223	5	0.64	20	0.46
0.4	0.282	6	0.63	30	0.39
0.5	0.328	7	0.62	50	0.31
1	0.480	8	0.60	100	0.21
2	0.600	9	0.59	193	0.144
				Infinite	Zero

From the formula and table it is seen that for very small quantities of explosive material, the utilization is equal to the ratio M_2/M_1;[12] that is to say, the smaller the relative quantity of explosives, the smaller the utilization. Further, as the relative quantity of explosives increases, the utilization increases, and for approximately a quadrupled quantity (compared with the mass of the rocket) it reaches a maximum (0.65). Subsequent

[10] As may be seen from the formulae given, in this case M_1 and M_2 are to be understood not as the masses of the rocket and exhaust but their weights (Editors).

[11] By utilization, Tsiolkovsky meant the efficiency of the rocket (Editors).

[12] Indeed, $\ln (1 + x) = x - \frac{x^2}{2} + \frac{x^3}{3} - \frac{x^4}{4} \cdots$. Hence, approximately,

$$\frac{M_1}{M_2} \left\{ \ln \left(1 + \frac{M_2}{M_1} \right) \right\}^2 = \frac{M_1}{M_2} \cdot \frac{M_2^2}{M_1^2} = \frac{M_2}{M_1} \quad \text{(Author)}.$$

increases in explosives constantly, though slowly, reduce their usefulness; and for an infinite quantity, the usefulness is zero, just as in the case of an infinitesimal quantity. From the table we also see that for values of the ratio M_2/M_1 from 2 to 10 the utilization comes out to more than one half; this means that in that case over one half of the potential energy of the explosive material is transferred to the rocket in the form of kinetic energy.

✳ THE ROCKET ACTED UPON BY GRAVITY.
VERTICAL ASCENT

27. We have determined the velocity acquired by a rocket in empty space and in the absence of the force of gravitation, depending on the mass of the rocket, the mass of the explosives and the energy of their chemical combination. Let us now examine the effect of a constant gravitational force on the vertical motion of a vehicle.

We have seen that in the absence of gravity, the rocket acquires enormous velocities and a considerable amount of the energy of explosion is utilized. This will also hold for a gravitational medium if the explosion is instantaneous. But such an explosion does not suit us because the jolt will be so terrible that neither vehicle, nor things, nor human beings inside would be able to withstand it. Obviously, what we need is a slow explosion; but in the case of a slow explosion the useful effect is reduced and may even become zero.

Indeed, let the explosion be so weak that the acceleration of the rocket due to it will be equal to the acceleration of the earth (g). Then, during the whole time of explosion, the vehicle will hover in the air, stationary and without support.

Of course, the vehicle will not acquire any speed whatsoever and the utilization of the explosive materials, despite their quantity, will be equal to zero. It is thus extremely important to investigate analytically the effect of gravitation on a vehicle.

When a rocket is moving in a medium free from the force of gravity, the time (t) during which the entire supply of explosive substances explodes is

$$t = V/p, \tag{28}$$

where V is the velocity of the vehicle at the termination of explosion and p is a constant acceleration imparted to the rocket by explosive materials in one second.[13]

[13] It is assumed that the rocket mass varies in accordance with an exponential law, then the acceleration p, due to a reactive force, will be constant (Editors).

The force of explosion, that is, the quantity of materials used up in the explosion in unit time, is, in this most elementary case of a uniformly accelerated motion of the vehicle, not constant but is constantly diminishing in proportion to the diminution in mass of the vehicle with the remainder of unexploded materials.

29. Knowing p, or the acceleration in a medium without gravity, it is also possible to express the magnitude of the apparent gravity within the rocket during its accelerated motion, i.e., during the time of explosion.

Taking the force of gravity at the earth's surface as unity, we find the magnitude of the temporary gravity in the vehicle to be equal to p/g, where g is the terrestrial acceleration; this formula indicates the increase in pressure of all things inside the rocket on their supports as compared with the pressure of the same things lying on the table in our room under ordinary conditions. It is exceedingly important to know the magnitude of the relative gravity in the vehicle, for it governs the integrity or breakage of apparatus and the health of the people taking off to study unknown spaces and their peculiar phenomena.

30. Under the influence of a constant or variable gravity of any force, the time during which one and the same supply of explosive material is expended will be the same as in the absence of gravitation; it will be expressed by the familiar formula (see 28) or by the following one:

$$t = \frac{V_2}{p - g}, \tag{31}$$

where V_2 is the velocity of a rocket at the termination of explosion in a gravitational medium having a constant acceleration of g. Here, it is of course assumed that p and g are parallel and opposite (see title of this chapter); $p - g$ expresses the apparent acceleration of the rocket (relative to the earth), which is the result of two opposite forces: the force of the explosion and the force of gravity.

32. The action of the latter does not at all affect the relative gravity in the vehicle and is expressed by formula (29) without any alteration: p/g. For example, if $p = 0$, i.e., if there is no explosion, then there is no temporary gravity, because $p/g = 0$. This means that if the explosion ceases and the vehicle is in motion in some direction solely due to its velocity and the force of gravitation of the sun, earth and other stars and planets, an observer inside the vehicle will himself, apparently, not have the slightest weight and with the aid of the most sensitive spring balance would not detect any weight in any of the things located on his person or in the rocket. The observer, falling or rising in

the rocket under the effect of inertia, even at the very surface of the earth, will not experience the slightest gravity until, quite naturally, the vehicle begins to encounter obstacles in the form, say, of the resistance of the atmosphere, water or solid ground.

33. If $p = g$, i.e., if the pressure of the exploding gases is equal to the gravity of the vehicle ($p/g = 1$), then the relative gravity will be equal to terrestrial gravity. In this case, and given initial immobility, the vehicle will remain stationary during the whole time of explosive action; but if prior to this the vehicle had some velocity (upwards, to the side, or downwards), that velocity will remain without any alteration until the entire supply of explosive material is exhausted: in this case the body (i.e., the rocket) is in equilibrium and is in motion only due to inertia in a medium free from gravity.

On the basis of formulae (28) and (31) we get

$$V = V_2 \left(\frac{p}{p-g} \right). \qquad (34)$$

Whence, knowing the velocity (V_2) the vehicle must have at the termination of explosion, we calculate V, with the aid of which, using formula (16), we also determine the required amount (M_2) of explosives.

From equations (16) and (34) we get

$$V_2 = V_1 \left(1 - \frac{g}{lp} \right) \cdot \ln \left(\frac{M_2}{M_1} + 1 \right). \qquad (35)$$

36. From this formula, as from the preceding one, it follows that the velocity acquired by a rocket is less under the effect of gravitation than without the latter (16). It (V_2) may be equal to zero, despite an abundance of explosives, if $p/g = 1$, i.e., if the acceleration imparted to the vehicle by the explosive material is equal to the acceleration of terrestrial gravity, or if the pressure of gases is equal and opposite to the action of gravitation (see 34 and 35).

In this case the rocket will stand motionless for some minutes without rising in the least; when the supply is exhausted, it will fall like a stone.

37. The greater p relative to g, the greater the velocity V_2 that the vehicle acquires for a given quantity M_2 of explosive substances (35).

Therefore, wishing to rise higher, we must make p as large as possible, i.e., we must produce a stronger explosion. However, in the process, we first require a stronger and more massive vehicle; second, stronger objects and devices in the vehicle because (by 32) the relative gravity in it will be extremely great and it will be particularly dangerous to a living observer if such ventures to take off in the rocket.

At any rate, on the basis of formula (35), in the limit we have

$$V_2 = V_1 \cdot \ln \left(\frac{M_2}{M_1} + 1 \right),$$ (38)

i.e., if p is infinitely great or the explosion is instantaneous, the velocity V_2 of the rocket in a gravitational medium will be the same as in a medium without gravity.

According to formula (30), the duration of explosion does not depend on the force of gravitation, but solely on the quantity of explosive material (M_2/M_1) and the rapidity of its explosion (p).

39. It would be interesting to determine this quantity. In formula (28) we put $V = 11,100$ m/sec (see Table 22) and $p = g = 9.8$ m/sec²; then $t = 1,133$ sec.

This means that in a medium free from gravity, a rocket would fly with uniformly accelerated motion less than 19 minutes, and this with a sixfold quantity of explosives relative to the mass of the vehicle (see Table 22).

And if the explosion took place at the surface of our planet, the vehicle would remain motionless during the full 19 minutes.

40. If $M_2/M_1 = 1$, then from the table $V = 3,920$ m/sec; hence, $t = 400$ sec, or 6 and 2/3 minutes.

For $M_2/M_1 = 0.1$, $V = 543$ m/sec, and $t = 55.4$ sec, or less than one minute. In this latter case, at the earth's surface, the vehicle would stand motionless for $55^1/_2$ sec.

Whence we see that explosion at the surface of a planet or generally in a medium that is not free from gravity may be quite resultless if it takes place with insufficient strength, even though over a long period of time: indeed, the vehicle remains in its place and does not have any translational velocity if it did not acquire it earlier; otherwise it will execute a certain movement with uniform velocity. If the movement is upwards, the vehicle will perform some work. In the case of an original horizontal velocity the movement will be in the horizontal direction; there will be no work,[14] but then the vehicle may serve the same purpose as a locomotive, steam ship or controlled balloon. But it serves these purposes of transportation only during several minutes, as long as the explosion is in progress; yet even in this small time it can cover a considerable space.

The time the vehicle stands in a gravitational medium is inversely proportional to g, i.e., to the force of the gravitation.

___

[14] If one disregards the work of atmospheric resistance (Editors).

Thus, on the moon the vehicle would be motionless without a support (for $M_2/M_1 = 6$) during two hours.

41. In formula (35) for a medium with gravity, we put $p/g = 10$; $M_2/M_1 = 6$; then we calculate $V_2 = 9,990$ m/sec. According to the foregoing, the relative gravity will be 10, i.e., a man weighing 70 kg will, during the entire time of explosion (about 2 minutes) experience a weight 10 times greater than on the earth, and on spring scales he would weigh 700 kg. A traveller can withstand such gravity without harm only by taking certain cautions: by immersing himself in a special liquid under specific conditions.

On the basis of formula (28) we also calculate the duration of explosion or the time of action of this enhanced gravity; we get 113 sec, which is less than 2 min. This is very little and it appears at first glance quite amazing that during such a negligible interval of time a vehicle can acquire a velocity that is just a little less than that required for escaping from the earth and moving round the sun like a new planet.

We have found $V_2 = 9,990$ m/sec, which is a velocity just slightly less than V acquired in a medium free from the force of gravitation under the very same conditions of explosion (see Table 22). But since during the explosion the vehicle rises to a certain altitude, the idea comes to mind that the total work of the explosive substances did not diminish at all as compared with their work in the medium without gravity. We shall now examine this question.

44. Acceleration of a vehicle in a gravitational medium is expressed by $p_1 = p - g$.

Over a distance from the earth's surface that does not exceed a few hundred versts we take g to be constant, and this will not lead to a large error; even the error will be favourable, that is, the true numbers will be more favourable for flight than those we calculated.

The altitude (h) of ascent of the vehicle during time (t) of the action of the explosion will be

$$h = \frac{1}{2}\, p_1 \cdot t^2 = \frac{p-g}{2} \cdot t^2, \tag{45}$$

eliminating t in accordance with equation (31), we get

$$h = \frac{V_2^2}{2\,(p-g)}, \tag{46}$$

where V_2 is the velocity the vehicle acquires in a gravitational medium after the whole supply of explosives has been used up.

Now eliminating V_2 from (34) and (46), we get

$$h = \frac{p-g}{2p^2} \cdot V^2 = \frac{V^2}{2p} \cdot \left(1 - \frac{g}{p}\right), \qquad (47)$$

where V is the velocity acquired by the rocket in a medium free from gravitation. The useful work of the explosive substances in such a medium will be expressed[15] by

$$T = \frac{V^2}{2g}. \qquad (48)$$

Now the work T_1 in a gravitational medium will be expressed as dependent on the altitude of ascent of the vehicle and its velocity at termination of explosion, namely:

$$T_1 = h + \frac{V_2^2}{2g}. \qquad (49)$$

The ratio of this work to the preceding (ideal) work is

$$\frac{T_1}{T} = \frac{2hg + V_2^2}{V^2}, \qquad (50)$$

Eliminating h and V by means of (46) and (34), we find

$$\frac{T_1}{T} = 1 - \frac{g}{p}, \qquad (51)$$

i.e., in a gravitational medium the work obtained from a definite quantity of explosive substances (M_2) is less than in a medium free of gravity; this difference $\left(\frac{g}{p}\right)$ is the less, the faster the gases explode or the greater p is. For example, in the case of (41) the loss comes to only 1/10, and the utilization (51) is 0.9. When $p = g$, or when the vehicle hovers in the air without even having a constant speed, the loss will be complete (1) and the utilization will be zero. Similarly, the utilization will be zero if the vehicle has a constant horizontal velocity.

52. In paragraph 41 we calculated $V_2 = 9,990$ m/sec. Let us apply formula (46) to the case of (41); we find $h = 565$ km; this means that during the explosion the vehicle will go far beyond the limits of the atmosphere and will in addition acquire a translational velocity of 9,990 m/sec.

Note that this velocity is 1,110 m/sec less than in a medium free of the force of gravitation. This difference is what makes up the 1/10 velocity in a medium without gravity (see Table 22).

---

[15] Formulae (48) and (49) are written on the assumption that the weight of the rocket is unity. Since in (50) and (51) the ratio $\frac{T_1}{T}$ is determined, this assumption is inessential (Editors).

Whence it is seen that the loss of velocity obeys the same law as the loss of work (see 51); this, by the way, follows rigorously from formula (34), after the transformation of which we get

$$V_2 = V\left(1 - \frac{g}{p}\right) \quad \text{or} \quad V - V_2 = V \cdot \frac{g}{p}.$$

We find from (51) that

$$T = T_1 \cdot \left(\frac{p}{p-g}\right), \tag{56}$$

where T_1 is the work obtained by the vehicle from the explosive substances in a gravitational medium with a force equal to g.

So that the vehicle can perform the necessary work as it rises in altitude, overcomes the resistance of the atmosphere and acquires the desired velocity, it is necessary that the sum of all these work items should equal T_1.

After determining all of them (work) by means of formula (56), we calculate T.

Knowing T, we calculate V as well, i.e., the velocity in a medium without gravity, using the formula

$$T = M_1 \cdot \frac{V^2}{2g}.$$

Knowing V now we can calculate the required mass (M_2) of explosive substances from the formula (16).

Thus, by means of the foregoing we find

$$M_2 = M_1 \{e^{\sqrt{\frac{T_1 \cdot p}{T_2(p-g)}}} - 1\}. \tag{57}$$

In the calculations, we put T_2 in place of $M_1 \cdot \frac{V_1^2}{2g}$ for the sake of brevity.

And so if we know the mass of the vehicle (M_1) with all its contents (with the exception of the explosive material M_2), the mechanical work (T_2) of the explosives for their mass equal to the mass of the vehicle (M_1), the work T_1 that must be performed by the vehicle in its vertical ascent, the force of the explosion (p) and the force of gravity (g), we can also find the quantity of explosive substances (M_2) needed for lifting the mass (M_1) of the vehicle.

In the formula, the ratio T_1/T_2 will not change if M_1 is cancelled out, so that T_1 and T_2 may be taken as the mechanical work, T_1, performed by a unit mass of the vehicle and the mechanical work, T_2, of a unit of explosive substances.

We must, generally speaking, take g to mean the constant resistance equal to the sum of the forces of gravity and of the resistance of the medium. But the force of gravitation gradually diminishes with recession from the centre of the earth, as a result of which a greater quantity of mechanical work of the explosive substances is utilized. On the other hand, the resistance of the atmosphere, which, as we shall see, is extremely insignificant compared to the gravity of the vehicle, reduces utilization of the energy of the explosive substances.

After a little reflection we will see that the latter loss continues for a short time during the flight through the air and is more than compensated for by the gain obtained from reduced attraction at appreciable distances (500 km) where the action of explosive substances ceases.

Thus, we may boldly apply formula (57) to the vertical ascent of a vehicle, despite the complication stemming from changes in gravity and air resistance ($g = 9.8$ m/sec^2).

✳ A GRAVITATIONAL MEDIUM. VERTICAL RETURN TO THE EARTH

59. Let us first consider stopping in a medium free from gravity or an instantaneous stopping in a gravitational medium. For example, let the rocket acquire a speed of 10,000 m/sec (see Table 22) due to the force of explosion of a certain quantity (but not all) of gases. Now, to stop the rocket requires setting up the same speed but in the opposite direction. Obviously the quantity of explosive substances left over should, according to Table 22, be 5 times greater than the mass (M_1) of the vehicle. Thus, at the end of the first part of the explosion, the vehicle should have (in order to acquire a translational velocity) a supply of explosive material of mass $5M_1 = M_2$.

60. The entire mass together with the supply will come to $M_2 + M_1 = 5M_1 + M_1 = 6M_1$.

Likewise, the initial explosion should impart to this mass ($6M_1$) a speed of 10,000 m/sec, but this requires a fresh quantity of explosive material, which again must be 5 times (see Table 22) the mass of the vehicle plus the supply mass for stopping; that is, we have to increase it ($6M_1$) five times; we get $30M_1$, which together with the supply for stopping ($5M_1$) makes $35M_1$.

We denote by q $\left(q = \dfrac{M_2}{M_1}\right)$ [16] the number from Table 22 that indicates how many times the mass of the explosive material is greater than the mass of the vehicle; the foregoing reasoning

---

[16] The number $q = \dfrac{M_2}{M_1}$ is now called Tsiolkovsky's number (Editors).

that determines the mass of explosive substance $\left(\frac{M_3}{M_1}\right)$ needed for acquiring a speed and shedding it may be expressed as

$$\frac{M_3}{M_1} = q + (1+q) \cdot q = q(2+q),\qquad (61)$$

or, by adding and subtracting unity from the second part of the equation, we get

$$\frac{M_3}{M_1} = 1 + 2q + q^2 - 1 = (1+q)^2 - 1.\qquad (62)$$

Then, together with the mass of the rocket (M_1, or 1) we find: $\frac{M_3}{M_1} + 1 = (1+q)^2$. This expression is easy to remember. When q is very small, the quantity of explosive substance is approximately equal to $2q$ (because q^2 will be negligible); i.e., it is only twice that needed to acquire speed alone.

63. On the basis of the formulae obtained and Table 22 we can set up the following table.

In a Medium Without Gravity

V, n/sec	M_2/M_1	M_3/M_1	V, m/sec	M_2/M_1	M_3/M_1
543	0.1	0.21	11,800	7	63
1,037	0.2	0.44	12,500	8	80
1,493	0.3	0.69	13,100	9	99
1,915	0.4	0.96	13,650	10	120
2,308	0.5	1.25	17,100	19	399
3,920	1	3	17,330	20	440
6,260	2	8	19,560	30	960
7,880	3	15	22,400	50	2,600
9,170	4	24	26,280	100	10,200
10,100	5	35	30,038	193	37,248
11,100	6	48	Infinite	Infinite	Infinite

From this table we see how insurmountably great is the supply of explosive material needed if we want to acquire a large speed and then lose it.

From (62) and (16) we have

$$\frac{M_3}{M_1} + 1 = e^{\frac{-2V}{V_1}}, \quad \text{or} \quad \frac{M_3}{M_1} = e^{\frac{-2V}{V_1}} - 1.$$

It will be noted that the ratio $-\dfrac{2V}{V_1}$ is positive because the velocities of the vehicle and the gases are in opposite directions and, consequently, have different signs.

If in the latter formula we put V twice that in the first column of the table, we get a ratio M_3/M_1, which is the relative quantity of explosive material required to attain the velocities of the last table and then to destroy them.

64. If we are in a gravitational medium, then in the most elementary case of vertical motion the process of stopping and descent to earth will be as follows: when the rocket has reached a certain altitude due to the acquired velocity and has come to a stop, it begins to fall to earth. When in its ascent the vehicle reaches the point at which the action of the explosive substances ceases, it will again be subjected to the effect of the remainder of the explosives—in the same direction and the same order. Obviously, by the time their action comes to an end and the entire supply is exhausted, the rocket will come to a halt at the same point on the earth's surface from which the ascent was begun. The mode of ascent is strictly identical with the mode of descent: the whole difference lies in the fact that the velocities are inverse at each point of the path.

Stopping in a gravitational medium requires more work and more explosive substances than in a medium free of gravitation; for this reason, in formulae (61) and (62), q must be greater if the rocket is employed in a medium of gravity.

Denoting this greater ratio by q_1, we find, on the basis of the foregoing,

$$\frac{q}{q_1} = \frac{T_1}{T} = 1 - \frac{g}{p},$$

whence

$$q_1 = q \left(\frac{p}{p-g} \right). \tag{65}$$

Putting q_1 in place of q in equation (62), we obtain

$$\frac{M_4}{M_1} = (1 + q_1)^2 - 1 = \left(1 + \frac{pq}{p-g} \right)^2 - 1. \tag{66}$$

Here, M_4 denotes the quantity, or mass, of explosive substances needed to lift a rocket from a certain point and to return it to the same point to a full stop and to maintain it in flight in a gravitational medium.

67. On the basis of the last formula we can set up a table on the assumption that $\dfrac{p}{g} = 10$, i.e., that the pressure of the explosive material is 10 times that of the gravity of the rocket with the

remainder of explosive substances. In the table below V expresses the work proper, $\frac{V^2}{2g}$; now the velocity will be less because a part of this work was expended on lift in a medium of gravity.

For a Gravitational Medium

V, m/sec	M_2/M_1	M_4/M_1	V, m/sec	M_2/M_1	M_4/M_1
543	0.1	0.235	7,880	3	17.78
1,497	0.3	0.778	9,170	4	28.64
2,308	0.5	1.420	10,100	5	41.98
3,920	1.0	4.457	11,100	6	57.78
6,260	2	9.383	11,800	7	76.05

✳ A GRAVITATIONAL MEDIUM. INCLINED ASCENT

68. Although vertical motion of a rocket would seem to be the most advantageous since the atmosphere is traversed in the shortest time and the vehicle rises to a high altitude, on the one hand, the work of traversing the atmosphere is extremely insignificant compared with the total work of the explosive substances, and, on the other, in inclined motion one can set up a permanent observatory moving beyond the limits of the atmosphere about the earth, like the moon, for an indefinitely long time. Moreover, and this is the most important thing, an incomparably greater part of the energy of the explosion is utilized in inclined flight than in vertical motion.

69. Let us first consider a particular case, when the flight of the rocket is horizontal (Fig. 2). If we designate by R the magnitude of the resultant of horizontal acceleration of the rocket, by p the acceleration due to the action of the explosion and by g the acceleration of gravity, then we have

$$R = \sqrt{p^2 - g^2}. \tag{70}$$

The kinetic energy obtained by the vehicle in time t is (on the basis of the preceding formula)[17]

$$\frac{R}{2} \cdot t^2 \left(\frac{R}{g} \right) = \frac{R^2}{2g} \cdot t^2 = \frac{p^2 - g^2}{2g} \cdot t^2, \tag{71}$$

where t is the duration of explosion. This is the total useful work acquired by the rocket. Indeed, the rocket will not rise in the least if we take the direction of gravity as constant (which in practice is true only for a short trajectory of the vehicle).

78

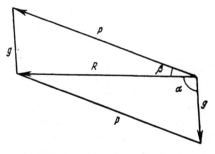

FIG. 2

Now the work performed by the explosive substances and transferred to the rocket in a medium free from gravity is equal to

$$\frac{p}{2} \cdot t^2 \cdot \left(\frac{p}{g}\right) = \frac{p^2}{2g} \cdot t^2. \qquad (72)[17]$$

Dividing the useful work (71) by the total work (72), we get the utilization for horizontal rocket flight:[18]

$$\left(\frac{p^2 - g^2}{2g} \cdot t^2\right) : \left(\frac{p^2}{2g} \cdot t^2\right) = 1 - \left(\frac{g}{p}\right)^2. \qquad (73)$$

As before, we still disregard the resistance of the air.

From the latter formula it is seen that the loss of work, as compared with work in a medium free from the force of gravitation, is expressed by $(g/p)^2$. Whence it follows that this loss is much less than in the case of vertical motion. For example, for $g/p = 1/10$ the loss is $1/100$, which is one per cent; yet in vertical motion it was expressed by g/p and equalled $1/10$, which is 10 per cent.

74. The following is a table where β is the angle of inclination of the force p to the horizon.

Horizontal Rocket Motion

$p : g$	Loss $\left[\left(\frac{g}{p}\right)^2\right]$	Sin β	β, deg	$p : g$	Loss $\left[\left(\frac{g}{p}\right)^2\right]$	Sin β	β, deg
1	1	1	90	5	1 : 25	1 : 5	11.5
2	1 : 4	1 : 2	30	10	1 : 100	1 : 10	5.7
3	1 : 9	1 : 3	19.5	100	1 : 10,000	1 : 100	0.57
4	1 : 16	1 : 4	14.5				

[17] In formulae (71) and (72) Tsiolkovsky computes the work of the resultant force and reactive force, both equal to unity (Editors).
[18] Formula (73) holds for any weight of the rocket (Editors).

79

✳ INCLINED ASCENT. WORK OF ASCENT WITH RESPECT TO WORK IN A MEDIUM WITHOUT GRAVITATION. LOSSES OF WORK

75. Let us now solve the problem in general, for any inclination of the resultant R. As I have already said, the horizontality of the trajectory or of the resultant is not advantageous because in such motion the path of the vehicle in the atmosphere is terribly increased, and this leads to an increase in the work of cleaving air.

And so we shall remember that α, or the angle of inclination of the resultant to the vertical, is greater than a right angle. We have[19]

$$R = \sqrt{p^2 + g^2 + 2pg \cdot \cos \gamma}, \tag{76}$$

where $\gamma = \alpha + \beta$ (the obtuse angle of the parallelogram in the drawing). Further,

$$\sin \alpha : \sin \beta : \sin \gamma = p : g : R \tag{77}$$

and

$$\cos \alpha = \frac{R^2 + g^2 - p^2}{2Rg}. \tag{78}$$

The kinetic work is expressed by formula (71), where R is determined from equation (76). The vertical acceleration of the resultant R is

$$R_1 = \sin(\alpha - 90°) \cdot R = -\cos \alpha \cdot R. \tag{79}$$

Hence, the work of lifting a vehicle will be

$$\frac{R_1}{2} \cdot t^2 = \frac{-\cos \alpha}{2} \cdot R t^2, \tag{80}$$

where t is the duration of explosion of the entire supply of explosive substances. The total work acquired by the vehicle in a gravitational medium is expressed [on the basis of (71) and (80)] by

$$[T_1] = \frac{R^2}{2g} \cdot t^2 + \frac{-\cos \alpha}{2} \cdot R t^2 = \frac{R t^2}{2} \left(\frac{R}{g} - \cos \alpha \right). \tag{81}$$

Here, unit work is taken to be the lifting of the vehicle per unit altitude in a medium with an acceleration of g. If $\alpha > 90°$, for example in the case of lifting the vehicle, then $-\cos \alpha$ is a positive quantity, and conversely.

Work in a medium free from gravity will be equal, according to (72), to $[T] = (p^2 : 2g) \cdot t^2$ (we should not forget that the duration of explosion, t, does not depend on the forces of gravitation).

---

[19] All the calculations involving (76) to (83) are made not for forces but for accelerations due to these forces (Editors).

Taking the ratio of these two pieces of work, we get the utilization of energy of the explosive substances as compared with their utilization in a medium devoid of gravity, namely:

$$\left[\frac{T_1}{T}\right] = \frac{Rt^2}{2}\left(\frac{R}{g} - \cos\alpha\right) : \frac{p^2}{2g}\cdot t^2 = \frac{R}{p}\left(\frac{R}{p} - \frac{g}{p}\cdot\cos\alpha\right). \quad (82)$$

Eliminating R by means of formula (76), we find

$$\left[\frac{T_1}{T}\right] = \left(1 + \frac{g^2}{p^2} + 2\cos\gamma\cdot\frac{g}{p}\right) - \cos\alpha\,\frac{g}{p}\cdot\sqrt{1 + \frac{g^2}{p^2} + 2\cos\gamma\cdot\frac{g}{p}}.$$

$$(83)$$

Formulae (51) and (73), for example, are only special cases of this one, as will readily be seen.

84. Let us straightway apply the formula that we have found. Assume that the rocket is rising at an angle of 14.5° to the horizon; the sine of this angle will be 0.25; this means that the resistance of the atmosphere increases 4 times compared with its resistance in vertical ascent of the vehicle; because, roughly speaking, its resistance is inversely proportional to the sine of the angle of inclination ($\alpha - 90°$) of the rocket trajectory to the horizon.

85. The angle $\alpha = 90 + 14^1/_2 = 104^1/_2°$; $\cos\alpha = -0.25$; knowing α, we can find β; indeed, from (77) we find: $\sin\beta = \sin\alpha\,(g:p)$; thus if $g/p = 0.1$, then $\sin\beta = 0.0968$, whence $\beta = 5^1/_2°$ and $\gamma = 110°$; $\cos\gamma = -0.342$.

Now, using formula (83) we compute the utilization as 0.966. The loss comes out to 0.034, or about 1/29, more precisely 3.4%.

This loss is three times less than in vertical motion. The result is not bad if we take into account that the resistance of the atmosphere even in inclined motion ($14^1/_2°$) is in no way more than one per cent of the work of sending the vehicle away from the earth.

86. For a number of reasons we give the following table. The first column indicates the inclination of motion to the horizon, the last column, the loss of work; β is the deviation in direction of pressure of explosive substances from the line of actual motion (see Fig. 2).

87. For very small angles of inclination ($\alpha - 90°$), formula (83) may be greatly simplified by replacing the trigonometric quantities by their arcs and making the appropriate simplifications. Then we get the following expression for loss of work:

$$x^2 + \delta x\left(1 - \frac{x^2}{2}\right) + \delta^2 x^2\left(x - \frac{\delta}{2}\right),$$

where δ denotes the angle of inclination of motion ($\alpha - 90°$) expressed by the length of its arc, the radius of which is equal to unity, and x is the ratio g/p.

Inclined Motion

Degrees				Utilization	Loss
α − 90	α	β	γ = α + β		
0	90	$5^2/_3$	$95^2/_3$	0.9900	1:100
2	92	$5^2/_3$	$97^2/_3$	0.9860	1:72
5	95	$5^2/_3$	$100^2/_3$	0.9800	1:53
10	100	$5^2/_3$	$105^2/_3$	0.9731	1:37
15	105	$5^1/_2$	$110^1/_2$	0.9651	1:29
20	110	$5^1/_3$	$115^1/_3$	0.9573	1:23.4
30	120	5	125	0.9426	1:17.4
40	130	$4^1/_3$	$134^1/_3$	0.9300	1:14.3
45	135	4	139	0.9246	1:13.3
90	180	0	180	0.9000	1:10

Suppressing infinitesimals of higher orders in the latter formula, we get for the loss

$$x^2 + \delta x = \left(\frac{g}{p}\right)^2 + \delta\frac{g}{p}.$$

We can put $\delta = 0.02N$, where 0.02 is the part of the circle roughly corresponding to one degree ($1^1/_7$), while N is the number of these new degrees. Thus, loss of work will be expressed approximately by

$$\frac{g^2}{p^2} + 0.02\frac{g}{p}\cdot N.$$

Using this formula, it is easy to set up the following table, putting $g/p = 0.1$:

N	0	0.5	1	2	3	4	5	6	10
Loss . .	$1/_{100}$	$1/_{91}$	$1/_{83}$	$1/_{70}$	$1/_{60}$	$1/_{55}$	$1/_{50}$	$1/_{45}$	$1/_{33}$

From this we see that even for large angles (up to 10°) the contradiction between this table and the preceding (more precise) one is slight.

We could examine much more: the work of gravitation, resistance of the atmosphere; we have not said anything at all yet about how a researcher can stay a long time (even indefinitely long) in a medium without oxygen; we did not mention the heating of the vehicle during its brief flight in the air, we didn't even give a general theoretical picture of the flight and the extremely interesting phenomena that attend it; we hardly at all pointed to the great promise that accomplishment of this task holds, so far we have only given hazy sketches; finally, we could trace out the cosmic curves of motion of a rocket in celestial space.

Investigation of World Spaces by Reactive Vehicles (1911—1912)

✳ THE REACTIVE VEHICLE "ROCKET" OF K. TSIOLKOVSKY

Introduction

For a long time, like everyone else, I viewed the rocket from the standpoint of amusements and small applications.

I do not remember exactly when the idea came to me to make calculations relative to the rocket.

It seems to me that the first seeds of the idea were cast by the famous fantasy writer Jules Verne; he awakened my mind in this direction. Then desires arose and they were followed by activities of the mind, which of course would have led to nothing had they not encountered the aid of science.

What is more, I have the feeling—probably erroneous—that the principal ideas and love for an eternal striving outwards to the sun, to a release from the chains of gravitation, were almost inborn in my case. At any rate, I have a perfect recollection that my favourite dream from the earliest years of childhood, even before books, was a nebulous consciousness of a medium without gravity, where motion in all directions would be perfectly free and where one would feel better than a bird in the air. Where these desires came from I cannot understand even to this day; there weren't any fairy tales of this nature, yet I dimly believed and felt and desired precisely this medium without the encumbrances of gravitation. An old page in my manuscripts with the final formulae relating to the reactive vehicle is dated 25 August 1898. Obviously, I had been engaged in this matter earlier. But it was not the paltry flight of a rocket that intrigued me, it was the precise calculations. In 1903 I made public my calculations and the conclusions from them. The present article is a development of that one. But since that publication is not widely known, I include here a resumé of it and even its most important formulae.

I never laid claim to a complete solution of the problem. At first we inevitably have an idea, fantasy, fairy tale, and then come scientific calculations; finally execution crowns the thought.

My work has to do with the middle phase of creativity.

More than anyone else I am aware of the chasm that separates an idea from its accomplishment, for during my whole life I not only did many calculations but also worked with my hands.

But there must be an idea: execution must be preceded by an idea, precise calculation by fantasy.

I shall be happy if my work induces others to further effort.

All know how unimaginably great, how infinite is the universe. Too, everyone knows that the entire solar system with its hundreds of planets is but a dot in the world.

If people penetrate into the solar system and take charge there like a woman in her home, will the secrets of the world open up? Not in the least! Just as examining a stone or shell does not open up the secrets of the ocean. Even if people conquered another sun, investigated the whole Milky Way, these thousands of millions of suns and these hundreds of thousands of millions of planets— even then we would say the same thing. These thousands of millions are also a dot, and neither would they lay bare the secrets of the world... . All our knowledge both present and future is as nothing compared with that which we will never know... .

How pitiful is man in his delusions! Was it so long ago that rising into the air was considered a sacrilegious encroachment and was punishable by death and that talk of the rotation of the earth was punished by burning at the stake.

Can it be that for eternal ages man is doomed to repeat his mistakes?!...

A Resumé of the Article of 1903

Working on the theory of a reactive device since 1896, we have come to the following conclusions.

The vehicle is outwardly of the shape of a wingless bird that easily cleaves the air. Most of the inside of the vehicle is occupied by two substances in the liquid state: hydrogen and oxygen. Both liquids are separated by a partition and are combined little

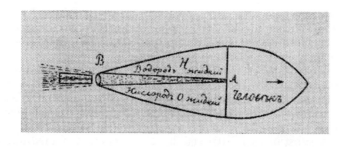

1—liquid hydrogen; 2—liquid oxygen
3—a man

FIG. 1. *Schematic drawing of Tsiolkovsky's reactive vehicle*

by little. The remaining portion of the chamber, of smaller capacity, is designed for housing the investigator and various facilities needed for supporting his life, for scientific observations and for controlling the "rocket" (that is the name we gave to our reactive vehicle) (Fig. 1).

Hydrogen and oxygen mix in the narrow part of a gradually flaring pipe, something like a musical instrument, and combine chemically to form water vapour at a terrifically high temperature. It has tremendous elasticity and streams out of the broad end of the pipe with a terrifying speed in the direction of the pipe or the longitudinal axis of the chamber. The directions of the pressure of steam and the flight of the vehicle are opposite.

In accelerated flight, the motion of the steam is opposite that of the rocket; the converse is true for decelerated motion. I am here speaking of the apparent motion of the steam relative to the rocket.

The explosion pipe which extends along the longitudinal axis of the rocket through its centre of inertia is cooled by the low temperature of the liquid oxygen and hydrogen surrounding the pipe or its jacket. These freely evaporating liquids are at temperatures of about 200-250°C below zero and prevent melting of the pipe due to the extremely high inside temperature. Since explosion lasts only a few minutes, the loss of cold liquids due to evaporation is not great.

Rotation of the rocket may be eliminated by various automatically operated instruments so that the direction of the longitudinal axis of the rocket and the direction of flight will be approximately the same: the path is a straight line.

The simplest way to control the direction of the rocket is by turning the flared end of the pipe or by turning a rudder behind it. When these are turned, the gases take a different direction, and the vehicle is turned or controlled.

The energy of the chemical combination of hydrogen and oxygen is tremendous. A considerable part of it, namely up to 0.65 (65%) is transferred to the rocket, that is to say it goes into the energy of its motion. The remaining part (35%) is used to produce the motion of the steam. Such a considerable part of energy of the explosive substances is utilized by the rocket in a medium free from gravitation; but in a medium of gravity, such utilization can occur only in the case of an instantaneous explosion, which is totally unsuitable for practical purposes. The slower the explosion and the longer it continues in a medium with gravity and the stronger the latter is, the lower the utilization of the energy of the explosive substances.

Now in a medium without gravity, utilization does not depend on the duration and order of explosion.

Because of the accelerating motion of the rocket, an apparent gravity develops inside the vehicle (as long as the rocket is undergoing acceleration), or a temporary gravity, which is the greater, the faster the explosion or the greater the pressure of vapour emerging from the pipe. As far as the effects inside the vehicle go, this relative gravity is in no way different from natural gravity. In an instantaneous explosion it is infinitely great and so the rocket and everything it contains must be completely destroyed and perish. That is why an instantaneous or extremely rapid explosion is not suitable.

When the temporary gravity produced during the explosion attains 10, which is 10 times that at the earth's surface, 0.9 (90%) of maximum energy utilization of the explosive substances in a medium without gravity is put to use, namely $0.65 \times 0.9 = 0.585$, which is over 58% of the total potential chemical energy contained in a mixture of hydrogen and oxygen.

In inclined rocket flight much greater quantities of stored energy are utilized. In the limit, when the flight is horizontal, utilization is greatest and reaches 0.99 (or 99%) in the case of a tenfold increase in temporary gravity inside the rocket. In rocket flight at an angle of $14^1/_2°$ to the horizon, the slight resistance of the atmosphere is only quadrupled compared to vertical flight, whereas for this inclination, utilization is 0.965. This makes up 0.627 (0.65×0.965) of the total chemical energy of explosive substances.

The maximum utilization (65%) both in a gravitational medium and in a medium without gravity is obtained only when the explo-

sive mixture is four times the weight of the vehicle with everything in it; otherwise utilization is less than 65%. For this ratio
of the quantity of explosive substances (4) to the weight of the
vehicle (1), the latter attains a speed of up to 9 km per second.
The vehicle can acquire an arbitrarily greater or arbitrarily
smaller velocity, but then less energy of the explosive material
is utilized. This percentage of utilization is the smaller, the greater the deviation of the relative quantity of explosive substances
from the number 4.

For a ratio of 1 to 18, over 48% of the energy is utilized.
The appropriate velocities in a medium without gravity range
from 3.9 to 16.9 km per second. This velocity is more than enough
to overcome the attraction of the sun and the earth and for the
rocket to wander out among the stars if launched in the direction
of the annual motion of the earth.

Indeed, calculations yield two principal launching velocities,
14 and 74 km/sec.[1] The latter figure refers to launching in the
direction counter to the earth's motion, the former, in the annual
direction of the earth. Thus, the act of breaking away from the
solar system is already accomplished for a twelvefold quantity
of explosive substances.

Theoretically speaking, a rocket can lift a mass of any desired
magnitude.

For example, if it is required to lift 200 kg, then to send it
away from the sun we must have at least 2,400 kg of explosives.

We note that oxygen may be cheaply extracted from the atmosphere by liquefying the air and subsequently evaporating away
the nitrogen. That is the way it is done nowadays. Hydrogen may
be obtained by liquefying illuminating gas. The first to be liquefied are the more complex products with higher molecular
weights, the hydrogen remaining in the gaseous state. Even marsh
gas may be left because with oxygen it also yields volatile compounds (water, carbon dioxide) which, consequently, are suitable
for a rocket. Thus, the industrial production of hydrogen and
oxygen may not be particularly expensive. Liquefying hydrogen
is (still) difficult, but with equal or even greater success we could
take liquid or liquefied hydrocarbons, such as ethylene, acetylene
and the like.

Storing gases in the liquid state does not require especially
strong vessels; they simply have to be slightly stronger than
vessels for water on the earth.

Likewise, the explosion pipe is extremely light when compared
with an ordinary cannon because in an artillery cannon the

---

[1] More exact values of velocities are given on p. 112 (Editors).

explosion is nearly instantaneous, and in a small fraction of a second a comparatively enormous quantity of substance is exploded. Now in our explosion pipe only a negligible fraction of the supply is exploded in the same small time interval; the supply is completely expended during several minutes (1 to 20 min).

If, for example, the entire vehicle with all its contents weighs 1,000 kg and the temporary gravity is increased tenfold, the pressure on the base of the pipe (that is, in its narrowest section) will amount to less than 10 tons. Assuming that the area of the base, or the area of the normal cross-section at the narrowest section, comes out to 100 cm^2, the pressure of the exploding gases at the base of the pipe will be less than 100 atmospheres. In other sections of the pipe, the pressure will decrease with increasing distance from the base and also as the pipe flares. It is now easy to calculate that the greatest wall thickness of a pipe made of steel need not exceed 5 mm.

Nothing definite can be said now about the material of the explosion pipe. We can only mention experiments which have demonstrated that iron retains great strength at the temperature of the liquefied gases surrounding the pipe. Of course, it is well known that iron melts like wax in the flame of detonating gas. But iron has a melting point of only 1,300°C.[2] There are substances which are more refractory; tungsten, for instance, has a melting temperature of 3,200°C. The same may be repeated concerning the explosive components: oxygen and hydrogen were taken only as an illustration.

In the calculations I took a tenfold temporary gravity in the rocket; but the magnitude of this gravity depends on us, and we can make it only slightly more than terrestrial gravity (1), particularly in the case of inclined or horizontal flight. For example, in the case of a vehicle in horizontal motion and with tripled relative gravity, utilization of explosive substances as compared with an instantaneous explosion comes out to 8/9 (or about 89%). Incidentally, there is a way to safeguard things and animals even under tremendous gravities; we shall deal with this somewhat later.

Let us imagine the utterly impossible: suppose we have a marvelous vertical or inclined track (gear-operated, for example) extending thousands or millions of versts with cars, machines and all manner of accessories needed for comfortable travelling beyond the atmosphere. In ascending on it to some altitude, we will do a certain definite amount of work. If in performing the

[2] More precisely, 1,539°C (Editors)

ascent we use some kind of engine, even the most sophisticated for the present state of technology, we will utilize no more than 10% of the chemical energy of the fuel that we take with us to that altitude.

As we have seen, to reach such an altitude without stairs and hoisting machines but with the aid of our vehicle, at least 50% of the chemical energy of the union of hydrogen and oxygen is utilized if the problem is approached properly. Thus, our imaginary vertical roadway consumes at least 5 times more fuel than a reactive vehicle. This conclusion is true only for ascents to altitudes not less than 700 versts, when a considerable portion of the energy of explosive substances is utilized.

The result may be quite miserable for a low relative gravity and a small ascent. For instance, for a temporary gravity equal to the earth's gravity (1) and vertical position of the explosion pipe, the result will be a twenty-minute hovering at the same altitude at the cost of a relatively enormous expenditure of explosives. For a somewhat greater acceleration of the rocket (the temporary gravity in it would be a little more than unity, or the earth's gravity), the total ascent would amount to a few arshins during about 20 minutes!!!

Those are the miserable reactive phenomena which we ordinarily observe on the earth. That is why they could not spur anyone to dreams and investigations. Only intelligence and science were able to show how stupendously, almost inconceivably these phenomena could be transformed.

The following are the most important formulae which all these conclusions are based on:

$$V = W \ln \left(1 + \frac{M_2}{M_1} \right). \tag{16}[3]$$

Here, ln stands for natural logarithm, V for the velocity of the vehicle or rocket at termination of the explosion of the mass (M_2) of explosive substances; M_1 is the mass of the vehicle with all its contents, except the explosive substances. The total mass is $M_1 + M_2$; W is the relative speed of a component of the cooled (by expansion) products of combustion leaving the muzzle of the explosion pipe. Relative to the rocket, this speed is independent of time and place. The formula refers to a medium without gravity. Utilization of the absolute energy of explosive substances by the rocket in a medium without gravity is expressed as

$$\frac{M_1}{M_2} \cdot \left\{ \ln \left(1 + \frac{M_2}{M_1} \right) \right\}^2. \tag{26}$$

[3] These formulae are given without derivation, their numbers are taken from the article "Investigation of World Spaces by Reactive Vehicles (1903)" (Editors).

89

When M_2/M_1 is small, utilization is equal to M_2/M_1. Then formula (16) is expressed as follows:

$$\frac{V}{W} = \frac{M_2}{M_1} ; \qquad t = \frac{V}{p} , \qquad (28)$$

where t is the duration of explosion in such a medium[4]; p is the constant acceleration of the vehicle due to the action of the explosion. The relative, or temporary, gravity that develops in the vehicle is expressed in terms of the ratio p/g, where g is the acceleration of the earth's gravity at the surface.

$$t = \frac{V_2}{p-g} , \qquad (31)[5]$$

where V_2 is the terminal velocity (when the explosion is over) of a rocket ascending vertically from the earth.

$$V = V_2 \left(\frac{p}{p-g} \right) ; \qquad (34)$$

$$V_2 = W \left(1 - \frac{g}{p} \right) \cdot \ln \left(1 + \frac{M_2}{M_1} \right) ; \qquad (35)$$

$$p_1 = p - g, \qquad (44)$$

where p_1 is the acceleration of the vehicle moving vertically in a gravitational medium.

The height (h) of ascent in this case is determined by the formula

$$h = \frac{1}{2} p_1 \cdot t^2 = \frac{p-g}{2} \cdot t^2. \qquad (45)$$

g is considered constant, since prior to full consumption of the explosive material the vehicle ascends to an altitude that is small compared with the radius of the earth.

$$h = \frac{V_2^2}{2(p-g)} ; \qquad (46)$$

$$h = \frac{V^2}{2p} \cdot \left(1 - \frac{g}{p} \right) ; \qquad (47)$$

$$\frac{T_1}{T} = 1 - \frac{g}{p} . \qquad (51)$$

[4] The medium here is understood to be without gravity (Editors).
[5] This formula is derived on the assumption that the body is acted upon by the force of gravity, the acceleration of gravity (g) being constant and directly opposite to the acceleration p, which is imparted to the rocket by the explosive materials (Editors).

Here T_1 is the useful work of the explosive substances in a gravitational medium and T is the same in a medium without gravity.

$$\frac{M_3}{M_1} = (1+q)^2 - 1; \tag{62}$$

$$q = \frac{M_2}{M_1}.$$

This formula indicates the relative quantity of explosives (M_3/M_1) required not only to attain velocity in a medium without gravity, but also to shed it by way of reverse explosion. If q is small, then $M_3/M_1 = 2q$.

The same, but for ascent in a gravitational medium and for a safe return descent:

$$\frac{M_4}{M_1} = \left(1 + \frac{pq}{p-g}\right)^2 - 1. \tag{66}$$

Again, if q or M_2/M_1 is small, then

$$\frac{M_4}{M_1} = 2q \cdot \left(\frac{p}{p-g}\right).$$

In horizontal motion of the rocket, the useful work is much greater than in vertical motion. Its ratio to the useful work in a medium without gravity is

$$1 - \left(\frac{g}{p}\right)^2. \tag{73}$$

Here the loss amounts to $(g/p)^2$, whereas in vertical motion the loss is g/p.

$$\left[\frac{T_1}{T}\right] = 1 + \left(\frac{g}{p}\right)^2 + 2\cos\gamma \cdot \frac{g}{p} - \cos\alpha \cdot \frac{g}{p} \sqrt{1 + \frac{g^2}{p^2} + 2\cos\gamma \cdot \frac{g}{p}}. \tag{83}$$

This expression determines the utilization in inclined ascent in a gravitational medium relative to the energy obtained by the rocket in a medium without gravity. Here, α is the angle between the direction of rocket flight and the downward vertical; β is the angle of the same rocket trajectory with the direction of explosion or with the direction of the explosion pipe[6]; α is greater than a right angle, β is less; $\gamma = \alpha + \beta$.

It is easy to show that the expression (83) yields both special cases, i.e., (51) and (73).

---

[6] β is the angle between the velocity of flight and the direction of the reactive force; see the article "Investigation of World Spaces by Reactive Vehicles", Fig. 2, p. 79 of this volume (Editors).

The preceding expression may be simplified if the inclination of the rocket path to the horizon does not exceed $10°$; then we obtain

$$\left[\frac{T_1}{T}\right] = 1 - \frac{g^2}{p^2} - 0.02 \cdot \frac{g}{p} N. \tag{87}$$

Here, N indicates (in degrees) the inclination of the rocket trajectory to the horizon.

The Work of Gravitation upon Recession from a Planet

By very simple integration we can obtain the following expression for the work T needed to send unit mass[7] from the surface of a planet of radius r_1 to a height h:

$$T = \frac{g_1}{g} \cdot r_1 \left(1 - \frac{r_1}{r_1 + h}\right).$$

Here, g_1 signifies the acceleration of gravity at the surface of the given planet; g is the acceleration of the earth's gravity at the surface of the earth.

In this formula, let us put h equal to infinity. Then we determine the maximum work upon recession of unit mass from the surface of the planet to infinity and get

$$T_1 = \frac{g_1}{g} \cdot r_1.$$

Noting that g_1/g is the gravity on the surface of the planet relative to the earth's gravity, we see that the work required for sending unit mass from the surface of the planet to an infinitely great distance is equal to the work of raising this mass from the surface to one planetary radius, if it is assumed that the force of gravity does not fall off with increasing distance from the surface of the planet.

Thus, though the distance to which the force of gravitation of any planet reaches out is limitless, the force may be pictured as a wall or sphere of negligible resistance surrounding the planet at a distance of one radius. Overcome this wall, plunge through this elusive, equally dense shell, and gravitation is conquered throughout its infinite extent.

From the last formula it is seen that the limiting work (T_1) is proportional to the force of gravity g_1 at the surface of the planet and to the magnitude of the planetary radius.

For planets of equal density, for example, having the density of the earth (5.5), the force of gravity at the surface is known to

---

[7] A consideration of subsequent formulae shows that they are derived for unit weight and not unit mass (Editors).

be proportional to the radius of the planet and is expressed by the ratio of the radius (r_1) of the planet to the radius of the earth (R). Consequently,

$$\frac{g_1}{g} = \frac{r_1}{R} \quad \text{and} \quad T_1 = \frac{r_1}{R} \cdot r_1 = \frac{r_1^2}{R}.$$

Hence, the limiting work (T_1) diminishes with extreme rapidity with decreasing radius (r_1) of the planet, namely, as its surface.

Thus, if this work for the earth $(r_1 = R)$ is equal to R, or 6,366,000 kg-m,[8] then for a planet with a diameter one tenth that of the earth it is equal to 63,660 kg-m (the kilogram is the unit of mass).

But from a certain point of view it is not very great even for the earth. Indeed, if we take the calorific value of petroleum at 10,000 calories, which is rather correct, the energy of its combustion will be expressed as mechanical work to the extent of 4,240,000 kg-m[9] per kilogram of combustible material.

It thus turns out that for an extreme recession of unit mass from the surface of our planet we require work contained potentially in one and a half mass units of petroleum.

Thus, as applied to a man weighing 70 kg we obtain 105 kg of petroleum.

The only thing lacking is an ability to make use of this powerful energy of chemical affinity.

It becomes clearer now why a quantity of explosive material eightfold the weight of the vehicle can help the vehicle to overcome the force of the earth's gravitation.

According to Langley, a square metre illuminated by normal rays of the sun yields 30 calories in one minute, or 12,720 kg-m.[10]

To obtain the full work required for the victory of 1 kg over the earth's gravity, one has to utilize a square metre illuminated by the sun's rays in the course of 501 minutes, or 8 hours and some.

All this is very little; but in a comparison of human strength and the force of attraction, the latter appears to be enormous.

For example, suppose a man climbs 20 cm up a well-built staircase every second.

Then the limiting work will be performed only in 500 days of arduous labour if we allow 6 hours for rest every day. If one horsepower is employed, we reduce the work by a factor of 5.

Ten horsepower would require only 10 days, and only a week in the case of uninterrupted work.

[8] A more precise value of work for the earth is 6,371,000 kg-m (Editors).
[9] A more precise value of the mechanical work is 4,270,000 kg-m (Editors).
[10] More precisely, 12,810 kg-m (Editors).

For the work performed by a flying aeroplane (70 horsepower), one day would suffice.

For most asteroids and for the moons of Mars, the work of completely overcoming gravity is amazingly small. The Martian moons are less than 10 km in diameter. If we assume a terrestrial density of $5^1/_2$ for them, the work T_1 will come to no more than 4 kg-m, which corresponds to climbing a birch tree two sagenes in height. If there were intelligent beings on our moon or on Mars, they would be able to overcome gravity much more easily than earth dwellers.

For the moon T_1 is 22 times less than for the earth. On large planetoids and the satellites of planets, victory over limitless space or, more precisely, over the space about the sun or planets would be extremely simple with the aid of the reactive devices I have described. For example, on Vesta, T_1 is 1,000 times smaller than on the earth. Vesta has a diameter of 375 versts. The diameter of Metis is only 100 versts, and T_1 is 15,000 times less.

But these are enormous asteroids; most asteroids are 5 to 10 times smaller. For them T_1 is millions of times less than for the earth.

From previous formulae we find for any planet

$$\frac{T}{T_1} = \frac{h}{h+r_1} = \frac{\dfrac{h}{r_1}}{1+\dfrac{h}{r_1}}.$$

Here, we expressed the work T of lifting to a height of h above the surface of a planet of radius r_1 relative to the total maximum work T_1. Using this formula we calculate

$$\frac{h}{r_1} = \frac{1}{10} \quad \frac{1}{5} \quad \frac{1}{4} \quad \frac{1}{3} \quad \frac{1}{2} \quad 1 \quad 2 \quad 3 \quad 9 \quad 99 \quad \text{infinity,}$$

$$\frac{T}{T_1} = \frac{1}{11} \quad \frac{1}{6} \quad \frac{1}{5} \quad \frac{1}{4} \quad \frac{1}{3} \quad \frac{1}{2} \quad \frac{2}{3} \quad \frac{3}{4} \quad \frac{9}{10} \quad \frac{99}{100} \quad 1.$$

The first row indicates ascent in planetary radii; the second, the corresponding work, taking the work of complete overcoming of gravity as unity. For example, to move out from the surface of a planet only one radius requires half the total work, to move out to infinity, we only need twice (1).

The Speed a Body Must Have to Leave a Planet

Since we have frequently given speeds acquired by a rocket due to the action of explosive substances, it will be interesting to know what they have to be to overcome the resistance of gravitation.

94

Again, we will not give the trivial calculations that yield these velocities and will confine ourselves to the conclusions.

The velocity V_1 needed to lift a rocket to a height of h and then to impart a velocity V is equal to

$$V_1 = \sqrt{V^2 + \frac{2g_1 r_1 h}{r_1 + h}} \; .$$

Here, if we put $V = 0$, i.e., if the body moves upwards until stopped by the force of gravity, we find

$$V_1 = \sqrt{\frac{2g_1 r_1 h}{r_1 + h}} \; .$$

When h is infinitely great, that is, when the ascent is limitless, and the terminal velocity is zero, the velocity at the surface of the planet needed to achieve this will be expressed as

$$V_1 = \sqrt{2g_1 r_1}.$$

From this formula we calculate for the earth: $V_1 = 11,170$ m/sec, or 5 times faster than the fastest cannon-ball emerging from the muzzle.

For our moon, $V_1 = 2,373$ m/sec, which is close to the speed of the cannon-ball and to the speed of hydrogen molecules. For the minor planet Agata, which is 6 versts in diameter and has a density no greater than that of the earth (5.5), V_1 is less than 5.7 m/sec; just about the same speed V_1 is found for the satellites of Mars as well. On these bodies of the solar system, one has only to take a good run to be able to get away from their gravitational pull for all time and become an independent planet.

For planets of the same density as the earth, we get

$$V_1 = r_1 \sqrt{\frac{2g}{R}} \, ,$$

where g and R refer to the earth. From the formula it is seen that the limiting launching velocity (V_1) is in this case proportional to the radius r_1 of the given planet.

Thus, for the largest planetoid, Vesta, whose diameter is close to 400 km, we find that $V_1 = 324$ m/sec.

This means that even a rifle bullet would leave Vesta for ever and would become an aerolite circling the sun.

The last formula is convenient for rapid calculations of launching velocities on equally dense planets of different sizes. For instance, Metis, one of the larger asteroids, has a diameter about 4 times less than Vesta; and so the velocity will be just as many times less, or about 80 m/sec.

Eternal circling round the planet requires half the work and $\sqrt{2} = 1.41...$ times smaller velocity than for moving off to infinity.

Duration of Flight

We will not give the extremely complicated formulae that determine the duration of flight of the vehicle. All the more so since this problem is not new and has been solved. We will only repeat what is known.

We will take advantage of one conclusion that is extremely simple and useful for solving the most elementary type of problems concerning the time of motion of a rocket.

For duration t of fall onto a planet (or the sun) of an originally stationary body concentrated in one point (for the same mass), we find

$$t = \frac{r_2}{r_1} \sqrt{\frac{r_2}{2g_1}} \left\{ \sqrt{\frac{r_2}{r} - 1} + \arcsin \sqrt{\frac{r}{r_2}} \right\}.$$

Here, r_2 signifies the distance at which the body begins to fall; r is the magnitude of the fall; r_1 is the radius of the planet, and g_1 is the acceleration of gravity at this time at its surface.

The same formula of course also expresses the time of ascent from $r_2 - r$ to r_2 when the body loses all its velocity.

If we put $r = r_2$, i.e., if one determines the time of fall to the centre of a planet of concentrated mass, then from the last formula we get

$$t = \frac{\pi}{2} \cdot \frac{r_2}{r_1} \sqrt{\frac{r_2}{2g_1}}.$$

Under ordinary conditions this formula also gives, approximately, the duration of fall to the surface of the planet or the time a rocket takes to ascend from this surface to a full stop.

On the other hand, the time of a complete circuit of some body (say a vehicle) round a planet (or the sun) is

$$t_1 = 2\pi \frac{r_2}{r_1} \sqrt{\frac{r_2}{g_1}},$$

where r_1 is the radius of a planet with acceleration g_1 at the surface, and r_2 is the distance of the body from its centre.

Comparing both formulae, we find $t_1 : t = 4\sqrt{2} = 5.657$. Therefore, the ratio of the time of revolution of some satellite to the time of its central fall onto a planet concentrated in a single point is equal to 5.66.

And so to obtain the time during which some celestial body (say our rocket) falls onto the centre (or, roughly speaking, onto the surface) around which it is revolving, the time of sidereal revolution of this body must be divided by 5.66.

In this way we find that the moon would fall to the earth in 4.8 days, and the earth would fall on the sun in $64^{1}/_{4}$ days.

Conversely, a rocket launched from the earth and stopping at the moon distance would fly for 4.8 days, or about 5 days.

In the same way, a rocket launched from the sun and brought to a stop by the powerful force of solar gravitation and the insufficient velocity of the rocket at the sun-earth distance would have spent 64 days, or over 2 months, in flight.

✳ THE RESISTANCE OF THE ATMOSPHERE

Let us determine the work a rocket performs in cleaving the air in the case of ordinary rectilinear uniformly accelerated motion; we also have to take into account the variable density (d) of the atmosphere at different altitudes.

It is (see my article "Aerostat and Aeroplane", 1905)

$$d = d_1 \left\{ 1 - \frac{d_1 h}{2(A+1) \cdot f} \right\}^{2A+1}, \tag{1}$$

where

$$A = \frac{d_1 M T_1 C}{f}. \tag{2}$$

In these formulae, d_1 is the air density at sea level ($d_1 = 0.0013$); h is the altitude of the vehicle, or the altitude of the part of the atmosphere under consideration; f is the air pressure at sea level per unit area ($f = 10.33$ tons/m²); M is the mechanical equivalent of heat ($M = 424$ ton-m); T_1 is absolute zero, $T_1 = 271$;[11] C is the heat capacity of air at constant volume ($C = 0.169$); so that $A = 2.441$, and the first formula takes the form

$$d = d_1 \left(1 - \frac{h}{h_1} \right)^a; \tag{3}$$

where

$$a = 2A + 1 = 5.88, \tag{4}$$

and $h_1 = 54,540$ m and expresses the limiting theoretical altitude of the atmosphere on the accepted basis. Indeed, if in formula (1)

---

[11] This is an error: $T_1 = 273°$ (Editors).

$d = 0$, then h will express the altitude of the atmosphere; but then from (1) we obtain

$$h = \frac{2\,(A+1)\,f}{d_1} \ . \tag{5}$$

Denoting this altitude by h_1, we get formula (3).

Although the altitude of $54\frac{1}{2}$ km is extraordinarily small, observations of falling stars show without doubt that the atmosphere above 54 km is so rarefied that its resistance may readily be neglected. Indeed, if we calculate the density of the air layer at this altitude, assuming constant temperature (like at sea level) and consequently a boundlessness of the atmosphere, even then we will have $d/d_1 = 0.001$, which means that at this altitude the air is rarefied 1,000 times and, hence, above 54 km there is no more than a thousandth (0.001) of the mass of the entire atmosphere.

But due to the fall in temperature, this remaining mass is incomparably smaller.

The differential of the work of resistance T is expressed by

$$dT = Fdh, \tag{6}$$

where F denotes air resistance to the moving vehicle. It is equal to

$$F = \frac{kSdV^2}{2g\cdot U} \ . \tag{7}$$

Here, k is a coefficient equal to 1.4 according to Langley; S is the area of maximum cross-section of the vehicle; d is the air density at the place the rocket is located at that instant; d is of course a variable quantity because air density falls off rapidly with increasing altitude of the place; V is the velocity of the vehicle; g is the acceleration of the earth's gravity at the surface of the planet ($g = 9.8$); U is the utilization, or usefulness of the shape of the rocket, which is a number that indicates by what factor the resistance is reduced (thanks to the bird-like shape of the vehicle) compared to the resistance of the area of its maximum cross-section; U is also a variable quantity, which, as numerous experiments have shown, increases with increasing velocity V of the moving body; incidentally, it also increases with its dimensions.

Incidentally, U will be taken to be constant since its dependence on the velocity V is a very debatable question.

Further, since the air resistance compared to the pressure of explosives on the rocket is slight (about 1% or less), the velocity V of the vehicle may be taken equal to

$$V = \sqrt{2\,(p-g)\,h}, \tag{8}$$

where $(p - g)$ is the true acceleration of the vehicle in one second. This means that adding velocity increases the work of atmospheric resistance and, hence, equalizes the error due to lowering the altitude of the atmosphere.

On the basis of the third equation and the last three formulae, we get

$$dT = b \left(1 - \frac{h}{h_1}\right)^a \cdot h \cdot dh, \qquad (9)$$

where

$$b = \frac{kd_1 S (p-g)}{Ug} \qquad (10)$$

and

$$a = 5.88. \qquad (4)$$

Integrating by parts and determining the constant, we find

$$T = b \left\{ \frac{h_1^2}{(a+1)(a+2)} \left[1 - \left(1 - \frac{h}{h_1}\right)^{a+2} \right] - \frac{h_1 h}{a+1} \left(1 + \frac{h}{h_1}\right)^{a+1} \right\}. \qquad (11)$$

Here, if we put $h = h_1$, we get the total work (T_1) of atmospheric resistance. Namely,

$$T_1 = \frac{bh_1^2}{(a+1)(a+2)}. \qquad (12)$$

Let us put $k = 1.4$; $d = 0.0013$; $S = 2m^2$; $\frac{p}{g} = 10$; $g = 9.8$ m/sec^2; $U = 100$; then $b = 0.0003276$; $a = 5.88$ and $h_1 = 54,540$ m. Now from (12) we calculate $T_1 = 17,975$ ton-metres.

The work of one ton of explosive substances, when obtaining one ton of water from hydrogen and oxygen, is equal to 1,600,000 ton-metres. If a vehicle with all accessories and travellers weighed 1 ton and the explosive supply was a sixfold quantity, or 6 tons, then the rocket would be carrying with it a potential energy of 9,600,000 ton-metres. Over half of this energy is converted into the mechanical work of rocket motion.

Thus, in this case the work of atmospheric resistance is only about 1/300 that of gravitation. The same may be obtained by comparing directly the work of atmospheric resistance (17,975) with the total work of gravitation (6,336,000). We find it to be about 1/353.

The following is a table (based on our assumptions) which shows the time in seconds from the start of vertical flight, the appropriate seconds velocity of the rocket in metres, the altitude of ascent in metres, the density of the surrounding air (the density at sea level being unity), and a uniform fall in temperature with altitude of 5°C.

t	V	h	d	t	V	h	d
0	0	0	1	20	1,800	18,000	1 : 10.63
1	90	45	—	30	2,700	40,500	1 : 28.28
2	180	180	—	40	3,600	72,000	Close to zero
3	270	405	—	50	4,500	112,500	Close to zero
5	450	1,125	1:1.13	70	6,300	220,500	0
7	630	2,205	—	100	9,000	450,000	0
10	900	4,500	1:1.653	113	9,990	574,600	0
15	1,350	10,125	—				

With a sixfold quantity of explosives, the time of explosion lasts 113 sec, at the end of which time the body acquires a velocity of 9,990 m/sec and reaches an altitude of 575 km; further ascent will be due to inertia.

The work of atmospheric resistance is extremely small; while the loss, in vertical motion, due to the force of gravity does not represent such a small quantity; namely, the first loss is 35 times less than the second. For this reason it is advantageous to incline the path of the rocket so as to increase several times over a comparatively small quantity (air resistance) and thus reduce at the same time a comparatively significant quantity: the loss of energy due to the effects of gravity.

It will readily be seen that the work of atmospheric resistance is approximately proportional to $\cos^2 (\alpha - 90°)$, where $(\alpha - 90°)$ is the angle of inclination of vehicle motion to the horizon.

The table (see page 101) gives a rather true picture for a certain deviation from horizontal flight. The table is based on the previous law.[12]

The first column indicates the deviation of flight from the horizon in degrees; the fourth, the sum of all losses when the usefulness, U, of the shape of the rocket is taken as 100; the last column gives the sum of losses if the usefulness of the shape is taken as 25.

According to the fourth column, the most advantageous inclination to the horizon lies between 10° and 15°; for shape utilization four times less, the optimum inclination will lie between 15° and 30°. In the former case, the loss will be 0.044 of the entire

[12] See Table 86 of work "Investigation of World Spaces...", 1903 (in this volume, see page 82) (Editors).

energy of rocket motion obtained from the explosive substances in a medium without gravity, or about $4^1/_2\%$. In the latter case, the loss is equal to 0.079, or about 8%.

$\alpha - 90°$	Losses due to		Sum of losses	Loss if usefulness of shape U equals 25	Sum of losses
	gravity	atmosphere $(U = 100)$			
0	0.010	—	—	—	—
2	0.014	0.0834	0.0974	0.328	0.342
5	0.020	0.0341	0.0541	0.136	0.156
10	0.027	0.0171	0.0441	0.068	0.095
15	0.035	0.0115	0.0465	0.044	0.079
20	0.045	0.00868	0.05618	0.035	0.080
30	0.057	0.00594	0.06294	0.024	0.081
40	0.070	0.00462	0.07462	0.018	0.088
45	0.075	0.00420	0.07920	0.017	0.092
90	0.100	0.00297	0.10297	0.012	0.112

Note: This table was later corrected by Tsiolkovsky (Editors).

In a medium without gravity with a sixfold quantity of explosive substances (compared with the weight of everything else), utilization is 0.63 of the entire latent energy.

If, in the worst case, 8% of this number is destroyed, we find that in inclined motion it is possible to utilize 58% of the entire chemical energy of the explosive material.

The work of air resistance may be reduced several times if the flight is started from the summits of the highest mountains or if the rocket is raised to a considerable altitude with the aid of an airship and then launched. Thus, take-off from an altitude of 5 versts reduces twofold the work of air resistance, and take-off from a ten-verst altitude reduces it four times.[13]

※ THE FLIGHT PICTURE

Relative Phenomena

Though travelling into space is a thing of the far distant future, let us suppose that everything is ready: everything has been invented, constructed and tested and we are seated in the rocket awaiting take-off, and our friends are watching.

[13] The work of air resistance has not been calculated exactly, but the qualitative conclusions are correct (Editors).

We will refer phenomena to the rocket, our friends will refer them to the earth, astronomers on Mars to their planet and so forth. All these phenomena will be relative and quite different because every phenomenon depends, among other things, on the form of motion of the body to which it refers.

We who are taking off will experience very strange, quite marvellous and unexpected sensations, which we will now describe.

The signal is given, the explosion is set off and is attended by a deafening noise. The rocket shakes and takes off. We have the sensation of terrible heaviness. Four poods of my weight have turned into 40 poods. I am knocked to the floor, severely injured and perhaps have even been killed; can there be any talk of observations? There are ways of standing up to this terrible weight, but in a, so to speak, packed-up form or in a liquid (this will be discussed later on).

Even when immersed in liquid we will hardly be inclined to observe anything. Be all that as it may, the gravity in the rocket has apparently increased tenfold. We would be informed of this by spring balances or a dynamometer, by the accelerated oscillations of a pendulum (some three times faster), a faster falling of bodies, diminished size of droplets (their diameter decreases tenfold), by all things becoming heavier, and by many other phenomena; see the formulae following (28).

If the density of the earth were increased 10 times or if we found ourselves on a planet where the attraction is 10 times greater than on the earth, we would find no difference between the phenomena in the rocket and those on the planet with enhanced gravity. It could be less in the rocket, but then the duration of explosion would be longer, though the rocket would—with the same consumption of material—rise to a lower altitude or would acquire a smaller velocity. We are examining the case of vertical ascent when the direction of relative gravity is the same as on the earth. In the case of inclined take-off we could note a change in the direction of relative gravity of not more than 90°, whereas for optimum take-off it would be 75 to 80 degrees compared with its direction on the earth at the given place.

If we should look out of the window of the rocket in this case, the earth would appear almost a vertical wall going off into the sky in one direction and into an abyss in the other.

The awful gravity that we experience will last 113 seconds, or about 2 minutes, until the explosion and the noise come to an end. Then, as dead silence sets in, the gravity will vanish instantaneously, just as it appeared. We are now out beyond the limits of the atmosphere at an altitude of 575 km. The gravity did not only diminish in force but evaporated completely without a trace: we no longer even experience the terrestrial gravitation that we take for granted in the same way we take the air for granted, though it is not at all so necessary as the air. The distance of 575 km is very little, it is almost at the surface of the earth and the gravity should have diminished ever so slightly. And that actually is the case. But we have to do with relative phenomena, and for them there is no gravity.

The force of terrestrial gravitation acts on the rocket and on the bodies in it in the same way. For this reason there is no difference in the motion of the rocket and the bodies in it. They are carried along by the same stream, the same force, and as far as the rocket is concerned there is no gravity.

There are many things that convince us of this. All objects in the rocket that are not attached have left their places and are hanging in the air, out of contact with anything; and if they are touching something, they do not exert any pressure on each other or on the support. We ourselves can have any position and be in any direction: we can stand on the floor, on the ceiling or on the wall; we can stand perpendicularly or have an inclined attitude; we float in the middle of the rocket like fish, without any effort whatsoever, and we do not come in contact with anything; no object exerts pressure on any other one if they are not pressed together.

Water does not pour out of a carafe, a pendulum does not oscillate and hangs to the side. An enormous mass hung from the hook of a spring balance does not make the spring taut—it always indicates zero.

Lever scales are also useless: the balance beam takes up any position, quite irrespective of and indifferent to the equality or inequality of the weights in the pans. Conventional ways of measuring mass cannot be employed here.

Oil shaken out of a bottle with some effort (effort because the pressure or elasticity of the air that we breathe in the rocket is a hindrance) takes the shape of a vibrating sphere; the vibration ceases in a few minutes and we have a liquid sphere of superlative precision; we break it up into pieces and get a group of smaller spheres of different sizes. All this moves slowly in different directions up along the walls and wets them.

The mercury barometer has risen upwards and the mercury has filled the entire tube.

A double-knee syphon does not convey water.

An object that is dropped does not fall; one that is pushed moves in a straight line and uniformly until it strikes the wall or some object, and again comes into motion, though with a smaller velocity. Generally it is also in rotation like a toy top. It is even difficult to push a body without imparting some rotation to it.

We feel so nice and light, as if we were on the softest feather-bed, but the blood has a tendency to flow to the head; for plethoric people this is not so good.

We can observe and meditate. Although the mighty hand of the earth is constantly retarding the ascent of the rocket with a fantastic force, which is to say that the force of terrestrial gravitation does not cease even for an instant, we experience in the rocket the same thing that we would on a planet whose force of gravity had vanished in some miraculous fashion or had been paralyzed by a centrifugal force.

Everything is so quiet, so nice, so calm. We open the outer jalousies of all windows and look out through thick glass panes in all six directions. We see two skies, two hemispheres that form a single sphere, in the centre of which are we, or so it seems. We are, as it were, inside a ball consisting of two different-coloured halves. One half is black with the stars and the sun; the other half is yellowish with a multitude of bright and dark spots and with vast spaces that are not so bright. That is the earth which we left just a short time ago. It does not appear to be convex like a sphere but quite the contrary; by the laws of perspective, it is concave like a round dish into which we are looking.

In the month of March we took off from the equator at about noon and so the earth occupies almost half the sky. If we had taken off in the evening or in the morning, we would have seen it covering a fourth of the sky in the form of a gigantic curved sickle; at midnight we would see only a zone or a ring brilliantly purple—the colour of the dawn—and dividing the sky in half: one half without stars, nearly black, a bit reddish; the other, black as pitch and studded with numberless multitudes of comparatively bright stars that do not twinkle.

As we recede from the earth's surface, increasing our altitude, the zone becomes smaller and smaller, but at the same time brighter and brighter. The globe in this form or in the form of a sickle or dish seems to get smaller, yet we see (in absolute terms) more and more of its surface. Now at last it appears as an enormous dish that gradually diminishes in size to a tiny saucer. Then it begins to look like the moon.

There is, properly speaking, no up and no down in the rocket, for there is no relative gravity and a body left without support does not tend towards any wall of the rocket, but there do remain the subjective sensations of up and down. We feel up or down, only they constantly change places as our body changes its attitude in space. We recognize 'up' in the direction of our head and 'down' where our feet are located. So if we look at our planet, it will appear to be upwards; but if we turn our feet in that direction, we plunge the earth into an abyss, for it now appears to be down. The picture is grandiose and at first terrifying; then you get used to it and really lose all notion of up and down.

Those observing us from the earth watched the rocket roar and then take off, rising upwards like a falling stone, only in the opposite direction and with 10 times more energy. The speed of the rocket increases steadily as it moves skywards. In one second the rocket reaches an altitude of 45 m; in 5 sec it has reached one verst, in 15 sec, 10 versts, and we hardly see it in the form of a fine vertical dash racing upwards and away. In half a minute it is already at a height of 40 km, but we continue to see it freely with the unaided eye because its increasing speed has boosted the temperature to white heat (like an aerolite) and its protective refractory and nonoxidizable shell shines like a star. This star-like flight continues for over a minute, and then gradually everything fades from view because when the rocket gets out beyond the atmosphere and ceases to experience friction with the air, it cools off and gradually disappears. Now it can only be located with the aid of a telescope.

The heat from the outside did not penetrate to us because we were protected by a layer that has low heat conductivity; we also had a powerful source of cold: the evaporation of liquefied gases. Protection was needed for only one or two minutes in all.

The apparent lack of gravity within the vehicle continues as long as there is no explosion and the rocket does not revolve: it is receding from the earth close to the surface; if the rocket is moving at large distances from its planet in some kind of curve, there is no gravity; if the rocket is hurtling round the sun, if it is heading for the stars and is subjected to the strong and weak effects of all suns and all planets, then gravity is not noticed; all phenomena peculiar to a medium devoid of gravity are observed in the rocket and about it, as before. This conclusion is not rigorously exact, but to an approximation it is true; the effect of its inaccuracy is unperceivable not only within the limits of rocket space, but even tens, hundreds, and sometimes thousands of versts around it. A certain slight influence is still exerted by the force of attraction of the rocket itself, its people, and the objects that have been taken along with them. But their interaction is very slight and is noticeable by the movement of strictly stationary (relatively, of course) bodies only in the course of hours. But if the things have even the slightest movement, the effect of Newtonian gravitation cannot be detected.

It is possible, by restricting the explosion, to rise only to a desired altitude; then, having lost all the speed, and so as not to allow ourselves to drop back to the planet, we turn the vehicle with the aid of bodies rotating inside the rocket and produce a new explosion in a direction perpendicular to the original direction.

Relative gravity is again generated; only this time we confine ourselves to extremely small magnitudes; all the now familiar phenomena of a medium with gravity are again repeated; they will again vanish; and silence and peace will set in, but the rocket will now already be secure from falling; it will have acquired a speed normal to the radius vector, i.e., in a circle, like the moon, and like the latter will continue eternally to revolve about the earth (this is discussed in the Chapter "Curves of Vehicle Motion and the Velocity").

Now we can calm down completely because the rocket has acquired a "firm" position: it has become a satellite of the earth.

From the rocket we see the enormous sphere of our planet in one of its phases, like the moon. We see it rotating; in a few hours it shows us in succession all of its sides. The closer it is to the rocket, the more gigantic it appears and the more concave and spread-out over the vault of the sky it seems to be and the more fanciful it is and the greater the brilliance it imparts to its satellite (the rocket) and the faster the rocket whirls round its mother, the earth. This distance may be so small that one circuit round the earth will last two hours, and in the course of several minutes we will view different points on the earth from various angles and at a close distance. This picture is so magnificent, alluring and infinitely diversified that I heartily wish you and I could see it. In such a two-hour circuit every two hours the rocket is eclipsed as it dips into the earth's shadow and into night. Night lasts less than an hour; then the sun shines for over an hour, to be followed by darkness again.

If we wanted to take advantage of more light, i.e., a longer day, we would either have to recede from the earth or revolve not round the equator but in the direction of a meridian, so that our path would lie over the poles of the earth. In that case, i.e., when the orbit of the rocket is normal to the sun's rays, even at a comparatively small distance from the planet we will have the advantage of a long day lasting a month or more: and the pictures of the earth are still more multifarious, more enchanting and surprising, for then we will clearly see the borderlines of the illuminated parts of the earth, which are in fast motion. We would get a particularly good view of the poles.

We are not conscious of the rocket motion just as we are not conscious of the movement of the earth (when we are on the earth), and we have the impression that the planet itself is racing round us together with the entire enchanting vault of the sky: as far as our senses go, the rocket is the centre of the universe, just as once the earth was!..

✳ CURVES OF VEHICLE MOTION AND THE VELOCITY

When a rocket is ascending vertically in the absence of rotation of the earth, the relative path of the rocket will be the simplest: it will be a straight line of more or less greater length, depending on the quantity of explosive substances.

Such is the path of a rocket when it is launched from the poles of a rotating planet, the effects of other celestial bodies being neglected. When the quantity of explosive material is 8 times the mass of the vehicle, the path of the rocket, after take-off from the earth's surface, has no end in the other direction; it is infinite, and the rocket will never return to the earth, if we assume of course that there are no other celestial bodies and hence no gravitation.

As applied to the earth, the least velocity for complete escape to infinity is 11,170 m/sec, or over 10 versts a second.

The slight rotation of a planet, as is the case of all medium and small planets of the solar system, including the earth, exerts a very modest change in the straightness of the path; namely, the path of the rocket turns into an extremely elongated ellipse if the vehicle is expected to return to the earth, and into a parabola or hyperbola in the case of infinite recession.

When speaking of the trajectory of the vehicle, we did not have in mind its comparatively short part (this corresponds to the duration of the explosion), which incidentally is also close to a straight line if the direction of explosion does not change.

At first, during explosion, the rocket undergoes rapid acceleration. After that the velocity varies more slowly—solely due to the effects of the force of gravitation, namely: during ascent and recession from the centre of the planet, the velocity acquired by the vehicle during explosion diminishes; when it is approaching and falling towards the planet, it increases.

In the case of infinite recession, in the course of endless time, the velocity of the vehicle more and more approaches zero or some constant value. In both cases the rocket will never stop and will never return to the earth, irrespective of the resistance of the ether and the attraction of other celestial bodies.

But vertical take-off is not advantageous, an inclined take-off is better. And in the case of an initial (i.e., during explosion) horizontal flight of the vehicle, we have one of the second-degree curves tangent to the globe at the take-off site. A focus of the curves will lie at the centre of the earth. If the relative quantity of explosive substances is insufficient (less than 3 or 4), the flight will not take place and the rocket will touch the earth or will fall onto the planet, like an ordinary cannon-ball fired horizontally.

If the speed of the vehicle due to the action of the explosive materials is $\sqrt{2}$ ($\sqrt{2} = 1.41...$) times less than the least speed needed for escape to infinity (11,170 m/sec), then the path of the rocket will be a circle coinciding with a great circle of the globe (with the equator or a meridian). Also, this case does not have any application because a vehicle flying constantly in the earth's atmosphere would quickly lose its speed due to air resistance and would fall to earth. But if there were no atmosphere or if the vehicle began its flight from mountain tops projecting beyond the limits of our ocean of air, the path of the rocket would be circular and eternal; it would never fall back to earth, just like the moon. Obviously, this too is impossible.

From what has been said, the speed needed for circular motion can be calculated roughly at 8 km/sec, or 7,904 m/sec.[14]

If we take advantage of the earth's rotation and launch the vehicle from the equator in the direction of motion of the equatorial points of the globe, the necessary speed will be reduced by 465 m/sec (such is the maximum speed of rotation of terrestrial points), and thus will be equal to 7,441 m/sec. So we see that the advantage is not great. The required relative quantity of explosive substances will be expressed by a number between 3 and 4 (if the weight of the rocket is taken as unity).

The work required for circular motion is exactly half that needed for escape from the planet to infinity.

An increase in the speed of the rocket will yield an ellipse that gradually goes out beyond the limits of the atmosphere. Further increases in the speed will extend the ellipse until it finally becomes a parabola; in that case the work and velocity that the vehicle would need to fight the force of gravitation will be the same as for eternal escape in the direction of a planetary radius (11,170 m/sec for the earth).

For a still greater velocity, the path of the rocket will be a hyperbola. In all these cases the vehicle loses too much from

[14] More exact values of the first (orbital) and second (escape) velocities for the earth are: $V_1 = 7,912$ m/sec and $V_2 = 11,189$ m/sec, respectively (Editors).

atmospheric resistance; and therefore this rocket trajectory (tangential to the earth) is not practicable.

We have seen that the most advantageous path of the vehicle is inclined to the horizon 10° to 15°. In this case, the loss due to the action of gravitation and atmospheric resistance is only $4^1/_2\%$ of the energy acquired by the rocket in airless space that is devoid of gravity as well. In this case, the path of the rocket would be the same as one of the second-degree curves (ellipse, parabola and hyperbola), but a curve no longer tangential to the surface of the earth. If the quantity of explosive material is insufficient or altogether small, then the rocket will describe a portion of an ellipse and will return to the earth. Here, the vehicle will have to explode a new quantity of substances so as to slow down and not be destroyed outright. The total quantity of explosives for ascent and safe return in the case of a small trip from the earth is twice as much as for the ascent alone; for greater ascents, it is three times as much, and for still greater ones, four times, etc.; see formula (66).

If we wanted to leave the rocket forever in airless space and make it a permanent satellite of the earth, then at greatest distance from the earth (in apogee) a certain small extra amount of substance has to be exploded to increase the speed of the vehicle. When this point is close to the surface of the earth, the velocity the rocket must gain is close to 8 km/sec, and the total amount of explosives will exceed the weight of the remaining mass of the vehicle by a factor of only 3 to 4. Incidentally, no matter how far away we set up our observational station, even at a distance of one million versts from the centre of the earth, the quantity of explosive substances will be less than that needed for escape from the planet to infinity in a straight line or in a parabola. Namely, it will be expressed by a number less than 8.

Of course it is possible, by a new explosion, to turn a circular orbit into an elliptical one and this, as has been described, into a circular one again but with greater radius. Thus we can at will alter the radius of our circular motion, that is, we can recede from the earth or come closer to it as we desire.

If, when we have already achieved circular motion, we fire very weakly but constantly and in the direction of motion of the rocket, its path will be a spiral orbit, the equation of this orbit depending on the law of the explosion.

The subsequent trajectory of the rocket, when the explosion is terminated, will be some second-degree curve, say a circle, which depends on us. In an explosion that retards the motion of the vehicle, the spiral will loop round inside the original circular orbit and the rocket will approach the earth.

In the case of spiral motion almost perpendicular to the direction of gravitation, nearly the same per cent (up to 65%) of the energy of the explosives is utilized as in a medium without gravity; the same thing happens when an elliptical orbit is turned into a circular one.

When the rocket takes off at an incline, the moon will exert on its elliptical path the greater influence, the more elongated the orbit and the closer the vehicle is to the moon, which, in turn, will depend on the comparative quantity of explosives consumed and the relative position of the moon and the rocket. It may happen—or the motion of the vehicle may be computed in such fashion—that due to lunar attraction the vehicle will leave its orbit completely and will fall onto the moon.

The speed of fall will be at least 2,373 m/sec, which is twice the speed of a cannon-ball. But this velocity is not so killing as in the case of a fall to earth. The energy of fall onto the earth is 22 times that onto the moon.

Taking into account the speed of motion and the rotation of the moon and the motion of the vehicle as well, we can also compute the small quantity of explosives that will be needed for a safe stop on the surface of the moon. I can state that the total quantity of explosives needed for a safe trip to our moon is expressed by a number that does not exceed 8. At a comparativel y small distance from the moon the speed of the rocket must be constantly reduced by means of firing the rocket. Everything should be calculated and controlled in such fashion that at the instant of contact with the surface of the lunar soil this relative speed should equal zero. Of course this is a rather delicate problem, but quite a feasible one. The error in its solution may be corrected by a fresh explosion as long as there is a sufficient supply of explosive substances.

In the case of a miss, that is, if the rocket flies close by the moon without touching the surface, the vehicle will not become a satellite of the moon but will approach again and then recede revolving round the earth in an extremely complex curve that passes sometimes near the earth and sometimes near the moon. There remains the possibility of falling either onto the earth or onto the moon. During closest approach to the moon it is possible to fire the explosive material in order to slow down the rocket and become an eternal satellite of the moon or great-grandson of the sun. It is also possible, in a variety of ways, to leave this circular orbit and reach the moon or move away from it.

From the description of the flight it is evident that the rocket can become an eternal satellite of the earth moving round it like the moon. The distance of this artificial satellite, or little brother of the moon, from the earth's surface may be arbitrarily small or great; it will be in eternal motion because the resistance of the ether has not been detected even for small and low-density bodies, like the majority of aerolites, which most likely are components of comets. If small bodies experienced resistance on the part of the ether, then (among other things) how could such things as Saturn's rings, which astronomers conclude must consist of just such tiny separate solid bodies in amazingly rapid revolution about Saturn, exist for millions of years?

Vehicles in revolution about the earth and with all the accessories for the existence of intelligent beings may serve as a basis for the further expansion of humanity. People inhabiting the vicinity round the earth in the form of a multitude of rings like those of Saturn (perhaps these, too, are living rings, for otherwise it would be difficult, nearly impossible, to account for their existence; if it weren't for something intelligent controlling them, the rings should have formed a moon for Saturn) would increase 100- to 1,000-fold the reserves of solar energy that are allotted to them on the surface of the earth. Even so, man may not be satisfied, and from this conquered base he may extend his hands to capture the rest of the solar energy, which is two thousand million times greater than what the earth gets.

In that case, eternal motion round the earth will have to be superseded by the same kind of motion round the sun. To do this we will have to go farther away from the earth and become an independent planet, a satellite of the sun and a brother of the earth. To put it precisely: a rocket, via explosions, will have to gain a velocity in the direction of motion of the earth round the sun when the vehicle is moving with maximum velocity relative to the sun. The energy needed for this purpose depends on the distance that the rocket is from the earth: the greater it is, the less is the work; and the total sum of the energy required for circular motion round the earth and for the subsequent almost complete escape from it does not exceed the energy needed to recede from the earth for all time, on the assumption that there is no sun and no other celestial bodies, i.e., a sevenfold (7) or eightfold (8) quantity of explosive substances (relative to the remaining mass of the vehicle).

As more energy is expended the circle will pass into a more or less elongated ellipse, the perihelion (closest distance from the sun) of which will be roughly at the earth-sun distance.

In the first case, for average energy expenditure (7-8), the vehicle will at first (on account of a fresh thrust) fly much faster than is needed for circular motion round the earth and even round the sun; then because of the action of terrestrial gravitation (that of the moon is neglected) this velocity will fall off gradually and will at the very end and at a considerable distance from the earth (roughly at 1,000 earth diametres) become equal to the velocity of the earth round the sun. The earth and the rocket will be in the same circle with the same velocity and therefore may not see each other for hundreds of years. However, there is little chance for such an equilibrium over the centuries, and in order to keep a respectful distance the rocket will have to be alternately accelerated and slowed down so that neither the earth nor the other planets should disrupt this distance. Otherwise, there will be the danger of its falling onto the earth.

In the second case, when more energy is expended and when the path of the rocket is elliptical, there is likewise some chance of encountering the earth, but one could take advantage of the recession of the rocket in order to land on some of the superior planets: Mars or its satellites, or Vesta, or some other of the 500 small planets (planetoids, asteroids).

I do not speak of reaching the most massive planets such as Jupiter, Saturn, and the others because a safe landing on them would require such fantastically large quantities of explosive substance that today no descent could even be dreamed of. But it is easier to become their satellites, in particular more distant satellites, and it is easier to reach and join up with Saturn's ring. The quantity of energy needed to reach a planetary orbit (but not including a descent to the planet) depends on the distance of its orbit from the orbit of the earth: the greater this distance, the greater, naturally, will be the energy consumption. But no matter how great this distance is, its work is less than that needed to escape from the solar system to infinity and wander about among the stars. Even this work is not so enormous as might appear at first glance. Indeed, it is obviously no joke to overcome the mighty attraction of the sun whose mass is 324,000 times the mass of the earth! But calculations show that if we launch a vehicle at the instant of its maximum speed round the sun or directly from the surface of the earth at the favourable moment and in a favourable direction, then the velocity relative to the earth and necessary for complete escape from the earth and the sun does not exceed 16.3 km/sec (about 15 versts), which is attended by the consumption of explosive substances expressed (relative to the mass of the vehicle) by the number 20. For the most unfavourable launching of the rocket this speed will be 76.3 km/sec, and the quantity of explosives would be truly terrible compared with the remaining mass of the rocket. The absolute velocity (what I want to say is the velocity relative to the sun) for escape is the same no matter in what direction we launch the rocket. And if the energy we need for this purpose in the favourable case is 25 times less, this is because we borrow some from the motion of the earth, which should in such a case slow down by an imperceptible amount.

The circular path of the rocket round the sun may be made elliptical by increasing or reducing the speed of the vehicle by means of an explosion.

In the latter case (reduction of speed), the perihelion of the rocket will be less than the earth-sun distance and then the vehicle will be able to reach any of the inferior planets: Venus or Mercury. Their masses are not so great and landing would not require such impossibly large quantities of explosive material as a safe landing on Jupiter, Saturn or Neptune would. The landing energy on Mercury or on Mars is about 5 times less than on our own planet; the energy for landing on Venus comes out to 0.82 of the energy needed to land on the earth. As for asteroids and most of the planetary satellites (moons), the mass of explosive material consumed for a safe landing on their surfaces is simply negligible.

Theoretically, a closer approach to the sun is possible and even falling onto it with complete loss of speed relative to the sun. If a rocket is already revolving round the sun like the earth and at the same distance from it, then to stop the motion we need a relative (reverse) speed of about 30 km/sec. The amount of explosive material will be 200. The fall onto the sun will continue for $64^1/_4$ days, or about two months.

From this it is clear that falling into the fiery ocean of the sun requires 10 times more sacrifice (in the sense of consumption of explosive material) than escape from our sun and approach to some other one.

As in the case of orbiting the earth, it is possible to put a rocket into any kind of trajectory by a continual and exceedingly weak explosion; it is possible to compel it to describe some path relative to the sun, say a spiral path, and in this way to attain the desired planet, approach the sun or recede from it, fall into it or leave it completely, to become a comet wandering for many thousands of years in blackness among the stars until approach is made to one of them, which will become a new sun for the travellers or for their future generations.

It will be noted that in all cases of reducing the speed of the rocket, the explosive material has to be fired in the direction of motion of the earth; but the motion of the vehicle relative to the sun will remain as before, i.e., in the direction of the motion of our planet.

The plan for further exploitation of solar energy will probably be as follows.

Man will launch his vehicles to one of the asteroids and will make it a base for the initial work. He will use the material of the tiny planetoid (decomposing it and carrying the material away, down to the very centre) for building structures that will make up the first ring round the sun. This ring will be inhabited by intelligent beings and will consist of mobile parts like the ring of Saturn.

After taking apart and utilizing the other minute asteroids, intelligent beings will form another series of rings somewhere between the orbits of Mars and Jupiter in the space cleared of all asteroids.

Some rings may be located closer to the sun between the orbits of the inferior planets for certain different technical and other needs.

When the energy of the sun is exhausted, intelligent beings will leave it and go off to another luminary that will have just come to peak force. This may even occur before: some of the beings may want other light or may want to inhabit deserts.

Perhaps humanity will thus be born many times over.

There is no need to deal with the surface of the sun even when it is covered over with a cold crust. There is not even any need to be on the heavy planets, except to study them. It is difficult to reach them; to live on them means to bind oneself with heavy chains that are often stronger than our terrestrial ones, and to set up multitudes of barriers, to attach oneself to a tiny area and live a miserable life in the mother's womb. Our planet is the cradle of intelligence, but one cannot eternally live in a cradle.

✳ LIFE-SUPPORT FACILITIES IN FLIGHT

Food and Respiration

The first thing that is needed is oxygen for breathing; a great deal of it is taken for explosion, so we could take some more to cover the needs of respiration for a certain interval of time.

Pure oxygen is hardly suitable for a human being even in a state more rarefied than usual. Indeed, in that case the pressure of it on the body will be insufficient, and the result may be hemorrhages from purely mechanical causes.

The best way would be to use a mixture of oxygen with some gas that is harmless in respiration: nitrogen, hydrogen, but not carbonic acid that prevents the release of carbon dioxide from the lungs and skin of a living thing and poisons it. It is easy to breathe a mixture of 20% oxygen and 80% nitrogen under a pressure of 1,000 to 500 mm of mercury. Nitrogen is preferable to hydrogen because it does not present any danger of explosion.

The compartment for passengers must naturally be hermetically sealed and strong enough to withstand the pressure of gases not exceeding 1 kg per cm^2 on the walls of the chamber when the latter has reached the rarefied layers of the atmosphere and has got out beyond. The elongated fish-like or bird-like shape of the rocket makes for cleaving the air with ease and also helps to retain intact the gases and the vehicle, particularly during the explosion period when everything increases in weight tenfold. Metal prevents the loss of gas due to diffusion.

But a mixture of oxygen and nitrogen is not all; we have to add more oxygen, which turns into carbon dioxide, and eliminate or, to put it more exactly, separate the products of respiration: carbon dioxide, ammonia, excess humidity, etc. There are many substances that absorb carbon dioxide, water vapour, ammonia, etc. We therefore have to be supplied with these substances too. Of course, if the trip is one that will take only a few minutes or hours, then such supplies together with, say, a lunch, will not overload the rocket. But the situation is radically different if the mission is to last for weeks and years or is not planned for any return at all; then these facilities will have to be rejected.

In order to exist during an indefinitely long time without our atmosphere and our planet, we will have to take advantage of the strength of the sun's rays. Just as the earth's atmosphere is purified by plants with the aid of the sun, so our artificial atmosphere can be regenerated in the same way. Just as on the earth plants use their leaves and roots to absorb impurities and yield food, so here, too, plants that we take along on our trip will work constantly for us. Just as all living things on the earth exist with one and the same quantity of gases, liquids and solid bodies, of which there is no decrease or increase (if one discounts the falls of aerolites), so we can live eternally with the same supply of matter that we take with us. Just as on the earth's surface there is an endless mechanical and chemical cycle of matter, so in our little world there will be one too. From the scientific point of view, this is all quite possible; now let us see how feasible it is for the future—perhaps a far distant future.

According to Langley, 1 m^2 of surface normal to the direction of the sun's rays receives 30 calories of solar energy in one minute. This means that 1 kg of water spread out over 1 m^2 of surface illuminated by perpendicularly falling solar rays will heat up 30°C in one minute, if we disregard loss of heat due to radiation, thermal conduction, etc.

Converting this thermal energy into mechanical energy, we get 12,720 kg-m. Thus, every 24 hours we will obtain 18,316,800 kg-m, or 43,200 calories, at the sun-earth distance. (We obtain 0.5 calorie, or 212 kg-m, per second, which is a constant work of nearly 3 horsepower.)

According to Timiryazev, physiological experiments with plants show that only 5% of the solar energy is utilized; this is 2,160 calories per day stored up in the roots, leaves and fruit of plants.

On the other hand, according to Lebon, 1 kg of flour contains almost twice that energy; so the 24-hour reserve of potential energy of a plant corresponds to 0.5 kg of flour, or nearly 1 kg of bread (without the crust).

That same gift of the sun utilized on 1 m² of surface continuously illuminated by the sun's rays may be expressed by one of the following quantities: 4 kg of carrots, 5 kg of cabbage, 2/3 kg of sugar, over 0.5 kg of rice.

In the foregoing experiments the 5-per cent economy was accumulated in all parts of the plant. There will of course be less in the fruit. These experiments were conducted in the most favourable conditions, but our artificial atmosphere and plant nutrition may be placed in still more favourable conditions. According to Timiryazev, plants in the field utilize, at best, 5 times less, or only about 1% of the solar energy. From this we see that artificial conditions are even 5 times more advantageous.

Let us see what actual practice has to say. A dessiatine, or approximately a hectare (10,000 m²), has an annual yield of up to 25,000 poods of bananas, which corresponds to 0.11 kg per day per square metre of orchard area.

But there are clouds on the earth and there is a thick layer of air and water vapour that absorb a good deal of energy; then on the earth we have night and the sun's rays impinge at an angle; as experiments show, the quantity of carbon dioxide in the air is unfavourable (the most favourable according to Timiryazev is 8%, whereas the air doesn't even contain a tenth of one per cent). Finally, can we consider favourable the primitive culture of plants cultivated by almost wild tribes? Taking all this into consideration, one would have to increase at least tenfold the gifts of the sun and take the productivity per square metre in our artificial garden at no less than 1.1 kg of bananas. According to Humboldt, the breadfruit tree is nearly as productive as bananas.

From the foregoing it therefore follows that one square metre of greenhouse facing the sun's light is already sufficient for the feeding of one person.

But what is there to prevent taking along an extensive surface in packed-up form, i.e., in a small volume! When our vehicle has settled into circular motion round the earth or the sun, we assemble our hermetically sealed cylindrical boxes with various plant seeds and suitable soil and extend them from the rocket. The sun's rays stream through the transparent cover of the green-house and prepare our magnificent food at a fabulous rate. The sunlight gives us oxygen and at the same time purifies the soil and air of animal excretions. Neither objects nor people will experience gravity here and therefore the vessels containing the plants will be designed only to withstand the elasticity of the gases within. The principal gases are carbon dioxide and oxygen. In the earth's atmosphere, carbon dioxide makes up not more than one two-thousandth (1/2,000) of the whole volume. Nitrogen and the other gases also play a role in plant nutrition, but their density, like the density of oxygen, which (according to Timiryazev) they consume in quantities 20 times less than carbon dioxide, may be extraordinarily small without harming the plants.

Thus, the atmosphere of our greenhouses may be so rarefied that the gas pressure on the walls will be 1,000 times less than the pressure of the air at sea level.

From this it is evident that not only will there be any fight against gravity, but there will hardly be any struggle with the elasticity of the gases, so that per passenger we can take, if the need arises, hundreds of square metres of these narrow glass boxes with growing vegetables and fruit.

There is every opportunity while still on the earth to work out and test facilities for respiration and nutrition of human beings in an isolated space.

It is possible to determine the smallest surface area illuminated by sunlight and sufficient for a person relative to his respiration and nutrition; it is also possible to select and test various plants suitable for this purpose. True, the conditions on the earth are different by far from those in the ethereal medium far away from our planet, but still they may be made very much like our ter-restrial conditions. For one thing, it is easy to make day and night in a medium without gravity; all one needs to do is impart a slow rotational motion to the greenhouses. Then light and darkness will alternate and the duration of the alternation is arbitrary. The motion will be eternal, by inertia. In my opinion, the condi-tions there will even be much more favourable than on the earth. Indeed, terrestrial plants suffer more and even perish because of unfavourable drops of temperature during night or winter, and also due to bacteria, parasitic fungi, worms, insects, rodents, birds; they suffer from insufficient moisture and exhaustion of the soil. Now in ethereal space there are no such enemies because everything taken from the soil is returned to it, and also because temperature fluctuations depend on us just like the duration of the night does; there will be no seasons if the rocket is in circular motion; there will be no harmful bacteria and insects in the small greenhouse compartments because they may be destroyed by filling the compartments with a gas that will kill off undesirable beings and embryos, or elevated temperatures could be employed, or even the simple constant light of the sun, which kills bacteria and malignant embryos. Moisture cannot escape from the hermetically closed spaces either.

It is rather difficult to construct such experimental greenhouses on the earth, especially well insulated from the external air and with a favourably rarefied medium, because this would require very strong material and massive structures to withstand the outer pressure of the atmosphere and to stand up to gravity. In experimental greenhouses we will first have to be content with outside and inside pressure being the same, and with only the most favourable ratio for the mixture of gases useful to the plants. The sum of the internal pressures will be equal to one atmosphere. But in ethereal space, one can rarefy the gas mixture up to the most suitable degree. In terrestrial experiments, light rays not only pass through the glass, as in ethereal space, but also through a thick layer of atmosphere loaded with water vapour, fogs and clouds that make it hard for solar energy to reach the plants unchanged. Actually, we are quite unacquainted with the true energy of sunlight that has not yet come into contact with air. It may be quite unusual as to chemical properties.

✳ PROTECTION FROM ENHANCED GRAVITY

At the very beginning of the flight, when we still hear the roar of the exploding substances, the relative gravity in the vehicle will, as we have seen, increase several times over, say tenfold.

The question is whether a person can withstand it for several minutes without inflicting harm on himself. This question can be resolved on the earth and at the same time the most favourable conditions can be worked out so that a person can withstand this or even a greater gravity without doing harm to his health. I have been experimenting for a long time with different animals, subjecting them to the effects of enhanced gravity on special centrifugal machines. I did not succeed in killing a single being, and that was not my purpose, but I thought that that would happen. I remember that I increased the weight of the common cockroach caught in the kitchen three-hundred-fold, the weight of a baby chicken tenfold; I did not find at that time that the experiment did them any harm.

The easiest way to increase apparent gravity in preliminary experiments with man is by means of the centrifugal machine with vertical axis of rotation and with the greatest possible radius, that is, the largest possible dimensions in the horizontal direction. The greater the distance from the axis of the experimental chamber with the human subject, the better, because the smaller the angular velocity of the device, the less the test subjects will suffer from dizziness. Rotation is particularly harmful to the organism even in the case of a small centrifugal force or for a low absolute speed if the angular velocity is great, i.e., when the radius of revolution is small. Everyone has experienced this slight harm, when, as a child, he turned round and round in the yard.

Incidentally, the rotation and, hence, the attendant discomfort does not occur in the case of an increase in gravity in a rocket moving rectilinearly. That a certain slow rotation does not inflict painful sensations and is not even noticeable is evident from the uninterrupted rotation of the earth to which we are all subjected from birth; the same may be concluded when observing how long children and even adults can ride merry-go-rounds.

From 2 to 10 minutes suffices for each experiment involving increases in gravity because this is the duration of explosion in a rocket.

I will not give the derivations of familiar formulae from which we can conclude the following.

It is possible, experimentally, to obtain artificial gravity of any desirable intensity; the slower we want to make the rotation, the greater must be the speed of the chamber to obtain the same gravity. For instance, a radius of 100 m and a speed of 100 m/sec and a complete circuit in 6.3 sec yield a tenfold force of gravity; if the radius is one tenth of this, then for the same artificial gravity the number of revolutions or the angular speed has to be increased some 3 times; there will be just as big a decrease in the translational, or absolute, velocity.

By experimenting with a centrifuge or with the aid of rapid circular motion of a railway car on inclined tracks, we can determine the highest value of gravity that is not harmful to the health of a subject during a certain period of time. If, contrary to expectations, we found from these experiments that even a small, say, doubled gravity is the highest safe value, even then we should not consider our case lost: firstly, because a rocket in inclined motion can advantageously utilize the work of explosives even for such a small relative gravity inside it; secondly, because by immersing a person in water and performing increased-gravity experiments with such a person swimming in a favourable position, we would surely obtain incomparably more comforting results.

The explanation is this. We take a very strong open or closed vessel filled with a liquid and put in a delicate figurine made of very feeble material, but with the density equal to that of the liquid in the vessel. Now let the figurine be so brittle and delicate by itself, that is, outside the liquid, that it could not be dropped without breaking or even taken into one's hands without being dented or broken. Now let us take it with the vessel, in the liquid of which it is so well balanced that it stands motionless in the place and position that we want it (like an oil drop in wine in Plateau's experiment).

If the centrifuge experiments are conducted not with a person but with a tiny delicate figurine, which outside the liquid is hardly capable of withstanding its own weight, the results will be really brilliant: the figurine will remain intact and even motionless despite any increase in relative gravity.

And without the centrifuge we can strike the vessel against the desk or hammer the vessel, and as long as the vessel remains intact and the liquid does not spill out, our figurine will not be damaged; but as soon as the experiments are conducted without liquid, the entire effect vanishes; even sturdy objects will break if the rotation is sufficiently fast or if the blows are strong enough. The same experiments with the same success can readily be performed with small fish immersed in water. From the foregoing it is evident that the liquid surrounding the body is of the same density and apparently eliminates the destructive effects of gravity, no matter how great the latter is. So if we take a liquid whose density is equal to the mean density of a human being and immerse the man in the liquid, then in enhanced-gravity experiments we should in part get the same good results. I say in part because what has been said refers to bodies, all particles of which have one and the same density. The different organs of an animal do not possess this property in full measure by far, particularly, the density of the bones and air-filled cavities of the animal differs from the density of its other structures. The bones, when immersed, will pull downwards in the direction of relative gravity, while the lighter parts will strive upwards: a tension will be set up between the different tissues that may tear them and even kill the organism if the increase in gravity is sufficient.

To summarize, then, the maximum tolerable gravity is still quite limited even when man is immersed in a proper liquid. The limit here is, I believe, at least 10 and may be determined for each subject only by experiment. It is best if during the experiment the person lies horizontally in a casing of approximately the same shape and size as the subject under test; then only small quantities of liquid will be needed to fill the empty spaces, and this is an important consideration for actual rocket flight. The mouth, nose and ears should be closed tightly with a casing and pipe for free breathing.

There can be no doubt that even in the absence of a liquid a man is capable of standing up to enormous gravity for a small fraction of a second. Indeed, when a body falls from a height, it strikes the ground, which—to destroy the speed acquired by the person in his fall—imparts to him (via its own elasticity) an acceleration in the opposite direction. True, the elasticity of the body of the animal is also a factor, in particular the elastic cartilage between bones and—in a neat jump—the muscular force of bending legs as well. Here, an apparent gravity should develop that is extremely great because the duration of the impact is small, and so the reverse accelerated motion at this instant is very great.

In such cases and in the case of heavy blows from outside, nature itself takes advantage of this property of a liquid to eliminate the destructive effect of relative gravity and so with great care immerses all delicate organs of animals in special liquids poured into tough natural vessels. Such is the brain which floats in a liquid in the skull; such also is the embryo of a mammal surrounded by a liquid right up to the time it is born. Even in the handling of delicate fruit, use is made of loose material, which is a rough substitute for a liquid; for example, grapes are covered with sawdust or cork-dust.

✳ FIGHTING THE ABSENCE OF GRAVITY

Now that the explosion in the rocket is over and the terrible gravity is no more, we can safely climb out of our casing, wipe away the remaining liquid and put on some clothes. As if by way of reward for the multifold gravity that we have just withstood, we are now completely free of all gravity.

Immediately the question comes to mind, will not this absence of gravity adversely affect our health? Should we not take some protective measures here too?

In a fall or a jump on this planet, we are in a medium free of gravity relative to our clothes and the objects on and with us so long as we have not yet touched the soil with our feet, but this phenomenon lasts only half a second; during this time the parts of our body do not press upon one another, the coat does not weigh upon our shoulders, our watch does not pull in our pocket and the eye-glasses on one's nose do not press into the flesh. When swimming on the earth, the weight of the body is likewise almost paralyzed by the counter-action of the water. We can stand this absence of weight for an indefinitely long time so long as the water is rather warm. We thus see that there is hardly any need for special experiments to prove that a medium devoid of gravity is harmless.

But even if it were found that people cannot live without gravity, it would be easy to create artificial gravity in a medium where it is absent. For this purpose, man's dwelling, say a rocket, would have to be set into rotational motion; then, through the centrifugal force, an apparent gravity would be established and of the desired magnitude, depending on the size of the dwelling and the rate of its rotation. This transformation of the medium will cost us nothing because rotation of a body in airless space and in a medium free from gravitation will continue eternally without any contribution. This gravity is particularly convenient because it may be made arbitrarily small or great and can at any time be eliminated and restored again; but, like natural gravitation, it requires stronger structures and objects, for it strives to destroy them; also, the motion is inevitably curvilinear and this has a harmful effect on the organism if a complete circuit is made in a short time.

The action of enhanced gravity on plants has long since been tested but nothing in particular has been noticed; only a change in its direction alters the direction of growth; namely, the stem points in a direction exactly opposite to that of the artificial gravity. It will be interesting to know which way it will grow when gravity has been eliminated; most likely its direction will then be a matter of chance and of the influence of light.

✳ DREAMS

The Future of Reactive Vehicles

In our first publication about reactive vehicles we dreamed of future, still undiscovered, and more elementary substances whose combination would be attended (on the basis of general chemical findings) by a still more tremendous release of energy than the union of familiar simple bodies like hydrogen and oxygen. Here, the volatile product of the union would acquire a greater velocity (W) when exiting from the reaction pipe.

From formula (35) [page 90] it is seen that an increase in W brings about a proportional increase in the velocity of the rocket, V_2, for the same relative consumption of explosive material (M_2/M_1).

It is believed that as radium disintegrates continually into more elementary matter it liberates particles of different masses moving with amazing, unconceivable velocities close to that of light. For example, helium atoms are released here with speeds from 30 to 100 thousand km/sec; helium atoms are four times as heavy as hydrogen atoms; other particles released by radium are 1,000 times lighter than hydrogen, but they move with speeds of 150-250 thousand km/sec; the total mass of these particles (negative electrons) is much smaller than the mass of helium atoms (positive electrons). These speeds (in km) are 6 to 50 thousand times greater than those of gases emerging from the muzzle of our reaction pipe.

And so if it were possible to accelerate the disintegration of radium or other radioactive bodies, and probably all bodies are of this kind, then its employment might yield—all other conditions being equal, see formula (35)—a velocity of the reactive vehicle such that to reach the closest sun (star) would be possible in 10 to 40 years.

Then only a handful of radium, see formula (16), would be enough for a rocket weighing a ton to break all ties with the solar system.

Subsequent advances of science will of course demonstrate that all this is not so by far, but one thing is good and that is that even today we can dream about such things.

It may be that with the aid of electricity it will be possible, in time, to develop tremendous velocities for particles ejected from a reactive vehicle. Today we know that the cathode rays in the Crookes tube, like the rays of radium, are accompanied by a flux of electrons whose mass, as we have mentioned, is 4,000 times less than that of the helium atom, and whose velocity reaches 30 to 100 thousand km/sec, which is 6 thousand to 20 thousand times the speed of the combustion products emerging from our reaction pipe.

✳ WHAT IS IMPOSSIBLE TODAY BECOMES POSSIBLE TOMORROW

There was a time—and very recently—when the idea of the possibility of learning the composition of the celestial bodies was considered senseless even by prominent scientists and thinkers. That time has now passed. The idea of the possibility of a closer, direct, study of the universe will today, I believe, appear still wilder. To step out onto the soil of asteroids, to lift with your hand a stone on the moon, to set up moving stations in ethereal space, and establish living rings round the earth, the moon, the sun, to observe Mars from a distance of several tens of versts, to land on its satellites and even on the surface of Mars—what could be more extravagant! However, it is only with the advent of reactive vehicles that a new and great era in astronomy will begin, the epoch of a careful study of the sky. The terrifyingly enormous force of gravitation—does it not frighten us more than need be?

A cannon-ball hurtling with a speed of 2 km/sec does not amaze us. Why should a vehicle flying at 16 km/sec and leaving for ever the solar system to wander in the depths of the universe, overcoming the force of gravitation of the earth, the sun and the whole solar system—why should this plunge us into horror? Is there such a gulf between the numbers 2 and 16? It is only that one is greater than the other by eight times.

If a velocity of one unit is possible, what is so impossible about a velocity of 8 such units? Isn't everything progressing, advancing, and with a rapidity that amazes us? Was it so long ago that our grandmothers stood in wonder at the inconceivable speed of ten versts an hour; yet today automobiles do 100 and 200 versts an hour, which is 20 times faster than people rode in the days of Newton. And was it so long ago that it would seem strange to make use of any other force than that of the muscles, the wind and the water? Speaking in this vein, we could go on forever.

At the present time, the more advanced layers of humanity strive to put their life in frameworks that are more and more artificial. Does not this represent progress? The fight against inclement weather, high and low temperatures, the force of gravity, beasts and harmful insects and bacteria—do not all these activities create about man a situation that is purely artificial?

In ethereal space this artificiality will simply be extended to the very limit, but then man too will find himself in conditions that are most favourable for him.

Over the course of the centuries, new conditions will create a new species of beings, and the artificiality which surrounds them will be diminished and perhaps will disappear completely. Wasn't it like this that aquatic animals once crawled out upon the land and little by little turned into amphibians and then into land animals; the latter, but perhaps also the aquatic animals (flying fish, for example) started the line of animals of the air, the flying birds, insects, and bats. Perhaps the conquest of the air will be followed by the conquest of ethereal space: will not the creature of the air turn into a creature of the ether?

These creatures will be born citizens of the ether, of pure sunshine and the boundless expanses of the cosmos.

✳ THE REACTIVE VEHICLE WILL SAVE US FROM CALAMITIES THAT AWAIT THE EARTH

What is this globe? It is an extremely incandescent mass, solid inside because of pressure of the upper layers, but fluid and molten closer to the crust. Inside it is still a tiny sun, and only on the outside has it calmed down and covered over with a thin cold crust.

Chemical processes that are still continuing under it, the effects of water, the compression of the central mass must from time to time give rise to volcanic eruptions that even today on occasion shake the thin crust of the earth.

Who can be sure that in the course of thousands of years the potential energy of the masses of the globe will not exhibit itself some terrible day with a force that will wipe from the face of the earth all living things. The cause of the explosion may be certain movements of the internal masses of the earth, their chemical union, attended by the liberation of tremendous quantities of heat and an increase in volume. The result would be a cataclysm that would destroy the organic world mechanically or by an increase in the temperature of the soil and the air. Finally, the higher animals might perish due to noxious gases being liberated into the atmosphere. In this case, the reactive vehicle will save the seed of mankind.

If an aerolite several versts across hit the earth, it would kill people; and this could happen quite unexpectedly, for such an aerolite as a nonperiodic comet coming from the murky depths of stellar space along a hyperbolic path cannot be foreseen by astronomers much in advance of the catastrophe. People will then perish because of earthquakes, rising temperature of the earth and air, and due to a multitude of other causes.

We see a star flare up as if being born, and then die down to extinction; this dark body, like the earth, an outwardly extinct sun, was struck by a calamity either in the form of gigantic bolides falling onto it, or, more likely, due to inner chemical processes in the terribly hot inside of the celestial body.

A sudden increase in temperature could instantaneously destroy all living things that had come to life in the atmosphere of the planet in the course of thousands of years during which the crust of the earth was calm. Comets have long been expected to bring

125

an end to the earth, and not without reason, though the probability of this end is extraordinarily small; still and all, it might happen tomorrow or in trillions of years. It will be rather difficult for a comet and other accidental, highly improbable but terrible and unexpected enemies of living beings to strike down in one blow all creatures that have formed—thanks to reactive vehicles—circular habitations round the sun....

The population of the earth is continually and rather rapidly on the increase, despite hosts of unfavourable conditions. During the past century this build-up has come out to at least 1% per annum.

If we take this percentage to be constant in the future as well, then in 1,000 years the population of the earth will increase about 1,000-fold.

What then will happen to the human race, which will be too much for the surface of the earth to feed?

Reactive vehicles will conquer limitless spaces for us human beings and will provide two thousand million times more solar energy than that which humanity has here on earth.

But there is not one sun, there are numberless luminaries and therefore not only limitless space will be captured, but also limitless energy of the rays of numberless suns will be available for the life of creatures.

That it is possible to reach other suns is seen from the following reasoning: suppose a reactive vehicle is in uniform motion at a velocity of only 30 km/sec, which is 10,000 times slower than the speed of light.

That is the speed of the earth moving round the sun; such also is the speed of certain aerolites, from which it is evident that this speed is possible (without decrease) for small bodies as well. Since from the closest stars it takes light several years to reach us, reactive trains will travel that distance in the course of several tens of thousands of years.

For the life of one person this period of time is of course very great, but for the whole of humanity and for the light-giving life of our sun it is negligible.

During tens of thousands of years in its trip to another star, the human race will live by the stores of potential energy borrowed from our sun.

If transportation of mankind to another sun is possible, then why our fears about the light-giving span of life of our presently bright sun? Let it grow dim and become extinct! During hundreds of millions of years of its glory and brilliance man will be able to build up supplies of energy and emigrate with them to another seat of life.

The gloomy views of scientists about the inevitable end of all living beings on the earth and its cooling off due to the loss of the heat of the sun should not now have the merits of indisputable truth.

In all likelihood, the better part of humanity will never perish but will move from sun to sun as each one dies out in succession. Many decillion years hence we may be living near a sun which today has not yet even flared up but exists only in the embryo, in the form of nebulous matter designed for eternity and for high purposes.

If today we are able to believe somewhat in the infinitude of mankind, what will it be like several thousand years from now when our knowledge and reason will have increased?

Thus, there is no end to life, to reason and to perfection of mankind. Its progress is eternal. And if that is so, one cannot doubt the attainment of immortality.

Advance boldly, great and small workers of the human race, and you may be assured that not a single bit of your labours will vanish without a trace but will bring to you great fruit in infinity.

Investigation of World Spaces by Reactive Vehicles

(Supplement to first and second parts, 1914)

I am seeking support for my strivings to be useful and that is why I am here presenting everything known to me that may inspire faith in my work.

It is hard to work by oneself many years and under unfavourable conditions and not experience any gratification or support at all.

From all the articles on the "rocket" it is quite clear that with our present-day technical facilities we are very far from attaining the required speed.

Here I would like to popularize my ideas and make some remarks relative to them and to refute the view taken of the "rocket" as something extremely removed from us.

Here are some theorems that I have proved earlier and that I now give explanations to if they have not been quite convincing.

Theorem 1. *Suppose the force of gravity does not diminish with the distance of a body from a planet. Suppose this body has been sent to a height equal to the radius of the planet; then it will perform work equal to that which is necessary for a complete overcoming of the gravitational force of the planet.*

For the earth, to take an example, and for a ton of material, this work is 6,366,000 ton-metres.[1] If a vehicle, as Esnault-Pelterie

---

[1] 6,371,000 ton-metres to be precise (Editors).

has stated, operates for 24 minutes and weighs 1 ton, it is easy to calculate that in 1 sec its engine will supply, to the vehicle, work to the amount of 4,420 ton-metres, or 58,800 horsepower, and not 400,000 as Esnault-Pelterie computed.[2]

In my case, the explosion is faster and continues only 110 sec. Thus, in one second a vehicle weighing one ton should liberate 57,870 ton-metres, which is 771,600 horsepower. Everyone will say: Is this possible? A vehicle of only one ton, or 61 poods, and produces almost a million horsepower!!

Today, the very lightest engines do not generate more than 1,000 horsepower per ton (1,000 kg) of their weight.

But the point is that we are not speaking here about ordinary engines but about vehicles resembling a cannon.

Imagine a cannon 10 metres long launching a one-ton shell with a speed of 1 km/sec.

This is not so far from reality. What work does the explosive perform and convey to the cannon-ball? It is the easiest thing to calculate that it comes to about 50,000 ton-metres—and all in the course of a small fraction of a second. The mean speed of the cannon-ball in the gun is at least 500 m/sec. Hence, the ball covers a distance of 10 metres in 1/50 sec. This means that the work of the cannon per second comes out to 2,500,000 ton-metres, or about 33,300,000 horsepower.

From this it is evident that the useful work of an artillery piece is 566 times greater than required by the rocket of Esnault-Pelterie and 43 times more than demanded by my reactive vehicle.

And so, quantitatively, there is nothing in common between reactive vehicles and ordinary motors.

Theorem 2. *In a medium without gravity, the terminal speed of a "rocket", provided the direction of explosion is constant, does not depend on the force and order of explosion, but only on the quantity of explosive material (relative to the mass of the "rocket"), its properties and the design of the explosion pipe.*

Theorem 3. *If the quantity of explosive material is equal to the mass of the "rocket", then nearly one half of the work of the explosive substance is conveyed to the rocket.* This is easy to believe; all you have to do is imagine two spheres of the same mass and an expanding spring between them. In extending, it will divide equally, between the spheres, the work contained in it.

If for instance, we have a cannon-ball with a pipe and a mass of hydrogen at zero temperature emerging from it, the latent

[2] See K. E. Veigelin's article in "Priroda i lyudi" (Nature and People), 1914, No. 4. Without a doubt I have corrected a misprint here and not any errors of Esnault-Pelterie (Author).

energy of the hydrogen will be divided in half, one half being imparted to the cannon-ball. As we know, hydrogen molecules have a speed of about 2 kilometres a second. The ball will thus acquire a speed of about 1,410 m/sec. But if we take into account the thermal capacity of hydrogen or the rotational motion of the two atoms that make up each molecule of hydrogen, then the ball will acquire about 2 km of speed per second.

After this, one can readily believe my calculations, which show that when hydrogen and oxygen combine chemically the speed of the newly formed molecules of water emerging from a stationary pipe comes to more than 5 km/sec; consequently, the speed obtained by a stationary pipe of the same mass is over $3^1/_2$ km/sec. Indeed, if the entire heat of combustion were transmitted to the compound, i.e., the water vapour, then its temperature would reach 10,000°C (if there were no expansion); the velocity of particles of vapour will be approximately 6 times more than at zero ($+273°$ of absolute temperature).

The speed of molecules of water vapour at zero is known to be over 1 km/sec, consequently, when water vapour is formed out of oxygen and hydrogen, the chemical reaction gives rise to a speed of up to 6 km/sec.

I am of course making only a rough and pictorial check of my earlier calculations.

And so when the mass of detonating gas is equal to the mass of the "rocket", its speed of $3^1/_2$ km per second is extremely reasonable and the number is very modest.

Theorem 4. *When the mass of the rocket plus the mass of the explosive substances carried by the reactive vehicle increases in a geometric progression, the speed of the "rocket" increases in an arithmetic progression.*

We will express this law by two rows of numbers:

Mass . . .	2	4	8	16	32	64	128
Velocity . .	1	2	3	4	5	6	7

Let us suppose, for example, that the mass of the rocket and the explosives is 8.

I eject 4 units of explosive and obtain a speed which we will take to be unity.

Then I eject 2 units of explosive and get another unit of speed; finally, I eject the last unit of mass of the explosive and gain another unit of speed; this makes a total of 3 units of speed.

From this theorem it is evident that the velocity is by far not proportional to the mass of the explosive material: it increases very slowly but without bound.

There is a most advantageous relative quantity of explosive substances at which their energy is utilized in the best manner. This number is close to 4.

But still the absolute speed of the "rocket" increases with the supply of explosives. Here are the quantities of explosives and the corresponding speeds (km/sec):

Mass of explosive	1	3	7	15	31	63	127	256
Velocity	$3^1/_2$	7	$10^1/_2$	14	$17^1/_2$	21	$24^1/_2$	28

Theorem 5. *In a gravitational medium, say on the earth, and in vertical ascent of the "rocket", part of the work of the explosives is lost; the loss is the greater, the closer the pressure of the emerging gases on the rocket is to the weight of the rocket.*

If, say, the rocket and its contents weigh a ton and the pressure of the explosives on the vehicle also comes to a ton, then utilization is absent or equal to zero, which means that the explosion has been without result, because the rocket stands still and no energy is conveyed to it.

That is why in my projects I take the pressure on the rocket 10 times the weight of the vehicle with all it contains.

Esnault-Pelterie takes the weight of the rocket at one ton and allots one third, or 20 poods, for the explosive substances. If this is radium and if it releases its energy a million times faster than is actually the case, then interplanetary flight is ensured.

I myself have dreamed of radium. But I have recently carried out the calculations that have demonstrated to me that if the particles (alpha and beta) emitted by radium are directed in a parallel beam in one direction, its own weight will be cut by approximately one millionth....[3]

After that I gave up the idea of radium. All kinds of discoveries are possible, and dreams may suddenly come to fruition, but I would like to stand as far as possible on practical ground.

Esnault-Pelterie calculates that 20 poods of detonating gas can transfer to the rocket only 1/130 of the required work necessary to escape from the force of gravity.

In my calculations, even a smaller part is transmitted, namely 1/540. The reason is not only that the relative quantity (1/3) of explosives is small, but mainly that the pressure of the gases on the vehicle in the case of Esnault-Pelterie is taken at only one tenth more than the weight of the "rocket". This difference is 100 times less than I take.

---

[3] At the time this paper was written, it was not sufficiently clear how intra-atomic energy could be utilized and the possibilities of controlled chain reactions were unknown (Editors).

On the basis of the last theorem (5), we saw that explosion in a gravitational medium may even be without any result if the pressure of the gases on the vehicle is equal to its weight.

Indeed, the relative quantity of explosives (1/3) in Esnault-Pelterie's case is far from the most favourable one (4); therefore, according to my tables, a vehicle would acquire a speed not exceeding $1^1/_2$ km/sec, and this only for gas pressure as in my case. But since his pressure is 9 times less, the utilization will be less by a factor of 10, and the speed will be only about 0.5 km/sec. But to overcome the earth's gravity one needs over 11 km/sec; consequently, the speed has to be 22 times higher and the energy required for this purpose will have to be 484 times greater.

I repeat that the errors I have detected in Esnault-Pelterie's report are probably simple misprints, as is often the case, but I think that it is worth correcting them.

In my view as well, the successful construction of a reactive vehicle involves tremendous difficulties and requires many years of preliminary work and theoretical and practical investigations, but still and all these difficulties are not so great as to be confined to dreams about radium and about as yet nonexistent phenomena and bodies.

Is it possible to carry a supply of explosives that exceeds the weight of the rocket tens of times?

Suppose half of the elongated spindle-shaped rocket is filled with liquid, readily evaporating explosive substances.

These substances are subjected to enhanced relative gravity due to the accelerated motion of the rocket, and therefore the walls of the rocket experience more pressure from the liquids than when the rocket is stationary on the earth. Calculations show that in the case of a steel rocket 10 metres long having reliable (6) strength and with gravity exceeding terrestrial gravity 5-fold, the weight of the explosive substances may be 50 times that of the rocket with all its contents.[4] And this is for very common material and a large margin of safety. Theory also states that with increasing dimensions of the rocket the relative supply of explosives falls off, and the converse is true. It is therefore advantageous to make the rocket small: 10 metres in length is quite sufficient.

Another important problem is that of the temperature of the explosive materials. Calculations show that for a free (as in our explosion pipe) expansion of the combustion products of detonating gas, their highest temperature should reach 8,000°C.

---

[4] At the present time, the ratio of propellant to dry rocket weight does not exceed 10-12 in single-stage rockets (Editors).

But actually even lime does not melt in burning detonating gas. Consequently, the temperature is not so high by far. This is due to dissociation.

When hydrogen and oxygen begin to combine chemically, the temperature rises so high that it prevents the greater part of the molecules from forming a chemical compound, because this is impossible at high temperatures. Water begins to decompose into hydrogen and oxygen already at 1,000°C. Deville has found that the temperature of decomposition of water vapour lies between 900° and 2,500°C.

Therefore one may take it that the maximum temperature of burning detonating gas does not exceed 2,500°C.

It will not be an insurmountable barrier to find materials capable of withstanding such a temperature.

The following is a list of the melting temperatures of materials that I know of: nickel 1,500°, iron 1,700°, indium 1,760°, palladium 1,800°, platinum 2,100°, iridium 2,200°, osmium 2,500°, tungsten 3,200°, carbon does not melt even at 3,500°C.

On the one hand, the explosion pipe must be cooled as much as possible, and on the other, investigators will have to search for high-strength refractory materials.

Investigations should also be directed at finding the most suitable substances for explosions. Of all known chemical reactions, the union of hydrogen and oxygen yields the greatest quantity of heat.

The amounts of heat liberated per unit weight of substances taken when they combine with oxygen are as follows: hydrogen in the formation of water yields 34,180 and in the formation of steam, 28,780, coal in the formation of carbon dioxide, 8,080, and hydrocarbons, from 10,000 to 13,000 calories. But these are not the important figures; the important ones are those expressed per unit mass of the combustion products: only they give us some idea of the suitability of fuel for the rocket. Per unit mass of water vapour we find 3,200 calories, of carbon dioxide, 2,200, and of petrol, 2,370. Generally, the combustion of hydrocarbons per unit mass yields a bigger number than that of carbon, that is, greater than 2,200, but one that does not reach 3,200. The more hydrogen there is in the hydrocarbon, the better it is for the rocket. Materials that yield nonvolatile products, say calcium oxide or lime, are not suitable.

One of the gases in the liquid form (preferably oxygen) is useful as a means for cooling the explosion pipe. Hydrogen in the liquid form may be replaced by liquid hydrocarbons (or those that are easily condensed). One must seek compounds of hydrogen and carbon, which, while containing as much hydrogen as possible, are formed from their elements with the absorption of heat, as, for instance, acetylene, which unfortunately contains little hydrogen. In this respect, turpentine is better, and methane (or marsh gas) is still better, though the latter is deficient in that it does not readily condense into a liquid.

It would not be bad to find similar compounds for oxygen as well.

The idea is to find unstable compounds of oxygen with itself (like ozone) or with other bodies that would yield stable volatile products when combined with the elements of a hydrocarbon and would release considerable heat.

If for the rocket in place of hydrogen we use benzene or petrol, then for the case when the mass of explosives is equal to the mass of the rocket with its contents, we will find the speed of particles emerging from the pipe to be only 4,350 m/sec instead of 5,700 m/sec. And the speed of the rocket will only be 3,100 m/sec. Thus we now have the following table of masses of explosive materials and rocket speeds:

Mass	1	3	7	15	31	63	127
Velocity, km/sec	3	6	9	12	15	18	21

These velocities are also sufficient for interstellar voyages.

Hydrocarbons have the advantage that they yield highly volatile products: water vapour and carbon dioxide; besides, liquid hydrocarbon at ordinary temperatures does not absorb substantial quantities of heat when heated, like liquid and very cold pure hydrogen do.

An important problem is the weight of the explosion pipe. We have to know the pressure of gases inside it. The problem is very complicated and requires a thorough mathematical exposition (which I am preparing for the press). Here we will only touch on the question.

Imagine the intake of the explosion pipe into which the gases (say hydrogen and oxygen in a definite ratio) in liquid form flow. Only a part of the atoms combine chemically because the increasing temperature (to 2,500°C) inhibits the combination of the other atoms. Assuming the density of the mixture of gases to be unity, we find that their elasticity (taking into account their high temperature) does not exceed 5,000 atmospheres or about 5,000 kg/cm² on the pipe surface at the intake.

As the gases move in the pipe and expand, their temperature should fall; but for a short time this will not occur because the lowered temperature will straightway enable the chemical reaction to proceed, and this will again raise the temperature to 2,500°C.

And so to a certain degree of expansion of the gases, their temperature remains constant, since it is restored by the heat of combustion.

After all atoms have combined and formed water vapour, the
temperature will begin to fall rapidly. Calculations show that
a sixfold increase in the volume brings about a twofold reduction
in the absolute temperature. On this basis we compile the following table of expansions and corresponding absolute and ordinary temperatures (approximately):

Expansion	1	6	36	216	1,296	7,776
Temperature, absolute	2,800	1,400	700	350	175	87
Temperature, °C	+2,500	+1,100	+400	+50	−125	−213

From the foregoing it is evident that an expansion of about
200 times liberates nearly all the heat, which is converted into
the work of the translational motion of the gases and the rocket.
In further expansion, the vapour is transformed into liquid and
even into ice crystals hurtling from the pipe at amazing speeds.

That is a rough picture of phenomena that occur in the explosion pipe.

Let us suppose, for the sake of simplicity, that the pipe is
cylindrical in shape; we determine its maximum thickness and
the area of the bottom.

Let the weight of the rocket with a man and with all components
and supplies, except the explosives, be one ton; let there be
9 tons of explosives.

We put the pressure on the rocket at 5 times its weight. The
relative gravity (of both the rocket and all the objects in it) will
be 5, which is five times the gravity on the earth. The man has
to be supine and immersed in a casing containing water. This
will ensure complete safety of his body.

And so the pressure of the gases on the rocket or on the bottom
of the pipe will come to 50 tons, or 50,000 kg. Since the gases
at the intake of the pipe yield 5,000 kg of pressure on one square
centimetre, the area of the base of the pipe is 10 cm². We calculate
the wall thickness of the pipe in the case of the best steel and
an ordinary safety factor (6) at 4.5 cm for an internal diameter
of 3.6 cm. This makes the external diameter less than 13 cm,
and the internal, less than 4 cm.

The weight of a decimeter length of such piping will come
to about 10 kg, one metre will weigh 100 kg; but bear in mind
that the weight of the pipe should fall off rapidly with distance
from intake because the gases expand rapidly and their pressure
diminishes proportionally, to say nothing of the fall in tempera-

ture that does not set in at once, but some distance from the intake of the pipe.

Still and all, it is clear that the pipe accounts for a great deal of the weight of the rocket. Therefore investigations should be made to find materials stronger than ordinary steel, which may not satisfy our aims, one of its drawbacks being that it is a low-melting metal.

It is difficult to determine the total weight of the pipe without resorting to higher mathematics. We shall leave this question for a more detailed treatise.

Some method must be employed to press the explosive materials into the pipe; this will require an enormous amount of work, thus constituting one of the difficulties of the problem. But we must not close our eyes to it. If the rocket weighs one ton, the explosives 9 tons, the acceleration of the rocket, 50 m/sec^2, then the pressure on it during inclined ascent (which is more advantageous) will come to about 50 tons.

The initial elasticity of the gases and the pressure on the bottom of the pipe will be 50 tons. The gas pressure per cm^2 was taken at 5 tons. Now, from all these data we find that to obtain a velocity of 10 km/sec the explosion will have to last about 200 sec; we will have to supply about 45 kg of explosive material to the pipe every second.

Assuming the mean gas density to be unity, the speed of the gas flow will be about 45 m/sec. Given the enormous pressure at the intake, the work of gas injection will come to 2,250 ton-metres per second, which amounts to 30,000 horsepower!!

We have obtained a result that is inconceivable for engines at the present state of technology. Thus, pumping by conventional methods is obviously out of the question. The simplest thing is to place a certain charge in the pipe and allow it to explode and disperse. Then, in the absence of pressure in the pipe, insert another charge, and so forth. This will have to be done by machine and with extreme rapidity. Here too we foresee difficulties.

Note that the useful work of explosive substances in our vehicle will average at least 400,000 horsepower, which is 13 times the work of injecting explosive material into the pipe. Perhaps the material could be injected by the work of the explosion itself, like Giffard's injector injects water into the boiler by the pressure of the steam in it.

Right at the intake of the pipe there must be a branch pipe through which the gases turn back again to the intake and, by virtue of their speed, entrain and inject the explosive material (in a continuous jet) into the intake of the explosion pipe.

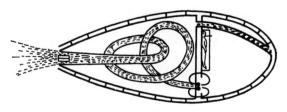

FIG. 1 *Rocket (schematic)*

This would be feasible without a doubt if suitably strong and refractory structural materials were found.

If one takes into account the tremendous force of gas pressure on the rocket, which comes up to 5 tons and more per ton of rocket, the problem of control of the rocket will not appear to be easy. By turning the exit end of the explosion pipe and changing the direction of the emerging gases, we bring about a lateral pressure and a change in the attitude of the rocket. But the general pressure on it is so great that before turning back the flared end of the pipe (or the rudder in it), the rocket will have already deviated greatly or even turned over. Rockets and shells designed for military purposes are made to rotate rapidly about the longitudinal axis in order to ensure stability of direction. We cannot do this to our rocket because rotation will cause a centrifugal force, which is detrimental to all living things. But stability can be attained by installing two rapidly rotating bodies in the rocket, the axes of rotation of the bodies being mutually perpendicular. This will increase the weight of the rocket, which is not desirable. The same thing can be achieved more simply and more economically if the explosion pipe is coiled (see Fig. 1); some of the coils will be parallel to the longitudinal axis of the rocket, while the others will be perpendicular. Though the mass of the gas jet is negligible, the reward lies in its amazing speed, which reaches 5 km/sec.

If for example the density of the gases is 400 times less than the density of a rotating disc and their speed is 20 times that of the disc, the resistance of the rocket to rotation will, thanks to the action of the gases, be just the same as that caused by the disc, if their masses are the same.

Even educated people have very hazy ideas about phenomena that occur in a rocket during its ascent. Science fiction writers either avoid giving descriptions of such phenomena or give them incorrectly.

The apparent gravity in a rocket depends on the acceleration it gets from the pressure of the gases. If the acceleration of the rocket is 50 m/sec², the relative gravity in it will be 5 times terrestrial gravity, the latter being 10 m/sec². And so during explosion in the rocket, the enhanced gravity will last 3 or 4 minutes; when the explosion is terminated the gravity is destroyed, as it were, because acceleration due to explosion will be zero. It is easy to withstand enhanced gravity by getting into a strong casing (in the shape of a human being) containing just a little water. Preliminary experiments are necessary with the aid of a large centrifuge, which also generates relative gravity.

These experiments are necessary to determine the conditions for breathing and eating when the rocket is flying through the void of outer space.

The foregoing already gives us some idea of the design of a reactive vehicle for cosmic missions. Now is the best time to refer to the schematic drawing of a rocket (Fig. 1) and to give a description of it.

The left, aft, half of the rocket consists of two chambers divided by a partition not shown in the drawing.

The first chamber contains the freely evaporating liquid oxygen. It has a very low temperature and surrounds a part of the explosion pipe and other components subject to high temperatures.

The other compartment contains hydrocarbons in the liquid state. The two black dots at the bottom (almost in the middle) indicate pipes in cross-section that carry the explosive materials to the explosion pipe. At the intake of the explosion pipe (around the two dots) are two branch pipes with high-speed gases that entrain the liquid components of explosion and inject into the intake (this is similar to a Giffard injector or a steam-jet pump).

In the gaseous and cold state, the freely evaporating liquid oxygen flows through the intermediate space between the two shells of the rocket and in this way prevents the inside of the rocket from heating up during its high-speed transit through the air.

The explosion pipe executes several rotations along the rocket parallel to its longitudinal axis and then a few rotations perpendicular to this axis. The aim is to reduce tumbling of the rocket and to simplify its control. These rotations of high-speed gas take the place of massive rotating discs.[5] The right-hand nose compartment is isolated, i.e., closed on all sides, and contains:

1. Gases and vapour needed for respiration. 2. Devices for protecting living beings from fivefold or sixfold gravitational forces. 3. Food supplies. 4. Control devices for a person in a supine position in water. 5. Substances that absorb carbon dioxide,

[5] Tsiolkovsky subsequently gave up this idea (Editors).

noxious emanations and, generally, all harmful products of respiration.

Here, we will perform some rough calculations[6] to compare artillery guns with the rocket pipe.

Though I have read about experiments in which cannon-balls have reached speeds of 1,200 m/sec, ordinary speeds are in the vicinity of 500 m/sec. Then, if we disregard air resistance, the cannon-ball will rise vertically to a height of $12^1/_2$ km. Launched 45° to the horizon, it will cover a maximum distance in the horizontal direction, namely 25 km. In the former case, the flight lasts about 100 seconds, in the latter, 70.

For a speed of 1,000 m/sec, the greatest ascent is 50 km, and the maximum horizontal distance is 100 km. The time of flight will be doubled.

With a 14-inch gun 10 metres long and a shell weighing 1 ton, we find that the mean pressure in the barrel per square centimetre comes out to about 1,250 kg, or 1,250 atmospheres. If the speed of the shell is doubled, the mean pressure reaches 5,000 atmospheres. The maximum pressure is of course much greater. Therefore, in a cannon the pressure is close to that which we have taken for our rocket (5,000 atmospheres).

Taking the mass of explosives in our rocket at one ton and the time of flight of the shell in the barrel at 1/25 sec (the terminal speed being 500 m/sec), we find that on the average 25 tons is consumed in one second.

In our rocket, only 45 kg is consumed; this is 555 times less. Obviously, the rocket explosion pipe is not very massive.

The explosion pipe of the rocket ejects only gas molecules and not heavy cannon-balls. Quite naturally, their velocity is much greater than that of the cannon-ball—5 km/sec. The velocity acquired by the rocket is about the same order of magnitude. The hot gases transmit their work to the cannon-ball only while in the barrel, but by far not all the work is transmitted. Emerging, they still have tremendous elasticity and high temperature, as is evident from the boom and flash when a gun is fired. The gradually flaring explosion pipe of the rocket is so long that the temperature and elasticity of the gases emerging from it are quite negligible. Thus, the rocket utilizes the energy of the chemical reaction almost completely.

---

[6] Atmospheric resistance is disregarded and the gravitational field is considered homogeneous (Editors).

The Spaceship

(1924—1926)*

If pressure is exerted on a body from below that is greater than its weight, the body will not only rise but will be constantly accelerated. After a certain time it will receive a velocity that is sufficient for escape from the earth and even the sun forever.

That is the basis for interplanetary and interstellar (intersolar) voyages.

For a vehicle to escape the earth and settle into the annual path (orbit) of our planet, it needs a relative speed (that is to say, relative to the earth when the earth is considered stationary) of 11.2 km/sec, and for escape from the sun for all time one needs a relative speed of $16^1/_2$ km/sec.[1] In this case, it is necessary to take advantage of the diurnal and, particularly, annual motion of the earth. Otherwise the needed velocities will have to be fantastic.

To effect eternal flight round the earth beyond the limits of the atmosphere, a speed not less than 8 km/sec is necessary. Then our vehicle will resemble a tiny moon.

These speeds will not appear to be excessive if we recall that a shell leaving the barrel of a cannon attains speeds of 2 km/sec, while the exit velocity of the most energetic explosive substances in a void is 5 km/sec.

---

* The present translation is based on Tsiolkovsky's article written in 1924 and amended in 1926 (Editors).

[1] All the figures and arguments given here are based on my published and unpublished works (Author).

140

And so the problem reduces to exerting on a body a pressure several times its weight. For example, a 2-, 3- and 10-ton pressure on a one-ton vehicle.

What facilities are available to achieve this?

First of all, cannons come to mind: with explosive materials (powder, for example), with compressed gases, with superheated volatile liquids, electromagnetic, etc.

But here we encounter no small number of insuperable obstacles.

Let us suppose, for the sake of simplicity, that the gas pressure in a cannon is the same for the duration of the explosion. Let the shell weigh one ton and let the pressure of the gases on it be 2 tons. Acceleration (the increment of speed in one second) will be twice the acceleration of the earth, and so the cannon-ball will acquire an apparent relative gravity twice the earth's. In a word, then, the apparent gravity of a cannon-ball exceeds the earth's gravity just as many times as the gas pressure on the ball exceeds the ordinary weight of the ball. Then the cannon would have to be 3,000 versts long in order to obtain sufficient speed to overcome gravity.

If the cannon is 60 km long, the pressure required to produce the necessary speed will be 100 times greater than the ordinary weight of the ball with all its contents. In this case the weight of the bodies in it will increase 100 times. A traveller of 100 kg would weigh 10 tons during the period of explosion and attendant gas pressure. One hand, weighing 10 pounds, would increase to 25 poods. This gravity is probably too much for any living being, even with the very best protective facilities.

With a cannon 600 km long, the mean apparent gravity increases tenfold. This gravity is also hardly tolerable for a human being, and then only when he is immersed in a liquid of the same density as the mean density of his body.

Let us explain the value of a liquid as a protective means. Suppose you are immersed in a liquid having the same density as the mean density of your body and you are breathing through a pipe extending out into the air. Your weight vanishes, as it were; it is balanced by the pressure of the water, you neither rise nor fall, you are in equilibrium at any depth (compression of bodies is disregarded). Now let the gravity increase a million times. As before, you will be in equilibrium and will not feel the enhanced gravity. Apparently, it does not exist for you. Indeed, although the gravity of your body has increased 1,000,000 times, the water pressure has increased just as many times. And so the equilibrium is not upset. And the liquid protects a person, as it were, from the terrible consequences of any increase in gravity. No wonder then that nature takes just such precautions when it wishes to protect delicate organisms from the crude force of gravitation and jolts. Nature places the embryos of animals in a liquid and surrounds the brain of higher animals with a liquid. That would be the case if man's body were quite uniform in density. But the crux of the matter is that, unfortunately, this is not so. Bones are much denser than muscles, and the latter have a higher density than fat. As the force of gravity increases, the bones will pull downwards, and the fat will strive upwards. This pressure difference is capable of destroying any organism if the force of gravitation is sufficient.

Only experiment can determine the maximum relative gravity that may be safely sustained by a human being. We believe that a tenfold increase is possible; then the cannon would have to be 600 km long. For such a length, it would unavoidably have to be in a horizontal position. The cost would be prohibitive and the feasibility almost unlikely. The air resistance in horizontal (or slightly inclined) flight and the enormous initial velocity would destroy the greater part of the kinetic energy of the missile and it would not reach its goal.

Electromagnetic or other types of cannons would inevitably yield the same deplorable results.

It is also possible to acquire speed using the support of the air, like an aeroplane or dirigible. But such speeds are much too far from what is needed. The 100 m/sec speed of an aeroplane (360 km/hr) amounts to only 1/120 (or less than 1%) of that required to overcome the earth's gravity completely. The speed isn't even enough to get out of the atmosphere.

It is hard to hope that an ordinary, unmodified aeroplane would be able to acquire a cosmic velocity. First of all the strength of the best structural materials does not permit a wheel or air screw (irrespective of its diameter) to have a peripheral speed greater than 200-400 m/sec. Thus, aeroplane speeds will be confined to 100-200 m/sec (360-720 km/hr).[2]

But they can be modified and propelled in other ways, without air screws, by the ejection of air by special complex turbines. This method has certain advantages for it provides an unlimited quantity of material for ejection (taken from the atmosphere) and oxygen for the fuel. Incidentally, at considerable altitudes (100 to 200 km) oxygen almost disappears, giving way to hydrogen.[3]

[2] Modern turbopropeller aircraft have speeds up to 1,000 and 1,100 km/hr (Editors).
[3] According to recent experimental data, the composition of the atmosphere hardly at all changes up to altitudes of 120-130 km. Artificial-earth-satellite observations have established that at altitudes greater than 250 km, the atmosphere consists of atomic oxygen and nitrogen (Editors).

Perhaps it will be possible to make use of hydrogen as a fuel.

A still simpler method is to propel aircraft by exploding supplies of explosive substances. But then the aeroplane is transformed into a gigantic rocket. This way would seem to be worse than the previous one, for one has to store not only fuel but oxygen as well, the weight of which is eight times that of the lightest propellant, hydrogen. A device of this kind is loaded down with nine times more supplies of potential energy (in the form of explosives). Theoretically, at a certain altitude we should get an explosive mixture of oxygen, nitrogen and hydrogen. True, this mixture is highly rarefied, but it may be condensed by means of complicated centrifugal pumps. Then the rocket can take off without large supplies of propellant and, without cost, acquire high velocities in the rarefied layer of air.

And finally, the third and most attractive method of obtaining speed. This is to transmit energy to the vehicle from outside, from the earth. The vehicle itself need not store up material energy (that is, ponderable energy—in the form of explosive or fuel). The energy is transmitted to it from the planet in the form of a parallel beam of electromagnetic rays of short wavelength. If its size does not exceed a few tens of centimetres, this electromagnetic "light" can be directed as a parallel beam with the aid of a large concave (parabolic) mirror to a flying aeroplane and there perform the work needed for ejecting particles of air or supplies of "dead" material in order to acquire cosmic velocity while still in the atmosphere. This parallel beam of electric or even light (solar) rays should exert pressure by itself (there can be no doubt that such pressure exists);[4] such pressure can give the vehicle a sufficient speed. In that case, one would not need any supplies for ejection.

The last method would seem to be the most refined. Indeed, on the earth we could build a power station of almost unlimited size with the generation of many millions of units of electric energy. The station transmits energy to a flying vehicle which does not need to carry any supplies of special energy (energy to produce speed). The vehicle would only carry passengers and life-support facilities for the trip or for permanent residence in the ether. This would greatly simplify the problem of interplanetary communications and colonization of the solar system.

But all this is much too hypothetical and not even enough for calculations. Besides, if we find a supply of "dead" ejection

_____
[4] The effect of light pressure was experimentally established by the noted Russian physicist P.N. Lebedev in 1899 (Editors).

material for the vehicle, would it not be more reasonable to replace it with explosive material, which in addition to the support role it could play would also contain valuable energy. Incidentally, it would be more advantageous at high altitudes in the atmosphere to make use of rarefied air for ejection purposes; the air would of course have to be condensed in complicated centrifugal compressors. When a speed of about 8 km/sec is developed in this terrible rarefaction, the vehicle would spiral out of the atmosphere altogether and would revolve like the moon. And from there it would be quite easy to obtain increments of speed.

Now if we only make use of the pressure of a light beam, then will such pressure be sufficient and will the light not burn our vehicle or destroy the people inside it?

At the earth-sun distance, the pressure of sunlight does not exceed 0.0007 g/m^2. To produce a pressure of 10 tons (assuming that the vehicle, without explosives, weighs only one ton), or 10,000,000 grams, we need a mirror surface of at least 16 million square metres.

Then one side of a square parabolic reflector would have to be 12,600 metres long, or 12.6 km. This is obviously not feasible, particularly at the present time. The point is that a beam of rays would instantaneously melt the most refractory material of the celestial ship. Also, how would one keep the energy flux fixed on a vehicle that is constantly changing its position? This mode of motion poses a number of difficult problems, the resolution of which we shall leave for the future. But the pressure of sunlight, electromagnetic waves, electrons and helium particles (alpha rays) may even today be applied in the ether to vehicles that have already conquered the gravitation of the earth and only require further propulsion in outer space.

We have pointed to the magnitude of speeds needed to overcome the gravity of the earth, the planets and the sun, but we have not calculated the work needed to obtain these speeds.

Only after we have determined the work of gravitation will we be able to see the power that will have to be generated by celestial vehicles.

Simple integration shows that it is equal to that which a vehicle or other body requires to go a distance of one earth radius on the assumption that gravity is constant, nondiminishing.[5]

Indeed, at a distance of one earth radius, gravity diminishes 4 times, at two radii it falls off 9 times. In short, then, it falls off just as fast with distance from the centre of the planet as the

---

[5] And equal to the gravity at the earth's surface (Editors).

attraction of a magnet, which becomes unnoticeable only a few steps away. From this it is clear that the work of gravitation is not infinite; quite the contrary, it has a definite and not very considerable magnitude (like the work of moving a nail away from a magnet).

If a body has a mass of one ton, the total work of the gravitation of the earth in moving this ton will come to 6,367,000 ton-metres. This figure expresses the radius of the earth in metres.[6]

Now let us compare this energy with that presently available to man.

A ton of hydrogen, when burnt in oxygen, liberates 28,780 ton-degrees (large calories) or 12,300,000 ton-metres.

What this means is that if all the energy could be converted into mechanical work, it would be twice that needed to liberate one ton of fuel from the force of the earth's attraction.

Petroleum gives up to 13,000 calories, or 5,560,000 units of work, which means that the energy of petroleum is just slightly less than that needed for complete escape of its mass from the earth.

True, there is no oxygen in ethereal space and so if it is a question of a rocket vehicle, we should take oxygen with us. Generally speaking, we have to lift: fuel, oxygen, and the ship itself with all the people and all accessories.

A ton of a mixture consisting of hydrogen and oxygen, which form water when combined chemically, liberates 1,600,000 ton-metres of work. This energy amounts only to one fourth that needed for complete escape from gravity of the combustion products (water) alone.

Petrol and oxygen yield 1,010,000 ton-metres per ton. This is already less than one sixth of the required energy.

The energy of radium and other similar substances is enormous, but it is released so slowly as to be totally unsuitable.[7] Thus, a ton of radium releases in 2,000 years about a billion (10^9) ton-metres, which is a million times that released by coal in the formation of a ton of combustion products (carbon dioxide).

But 1 kg of radium yields only 130 calories per hour. Consequently, 1 kg of radium yields the continuous work of a workman under ideal employment. In the same conditions, a ton of radium produces about 100 horsepower. Hence, even in weight, radium is 10 times less productive than aeroplane motors. There can be no question that the needed quantities of radium cannot now

---

[6] A more precise value for the earth's radius is 6,371 km (Editors).

[7] This article was written at a time when the idea of utilizing intra-atomic energy was not sufficiently elaborated, and the possibilities of controlled chain reactions were unknown (Editors).

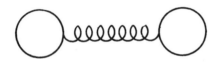
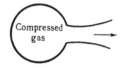

FIG. 1   FIG. 2

be found over the whole world, and that its cost is so stupendous that there isn't even a radium engine in existence.

But it is possible to use negative and positive electrons, i.e., cathode and anode rays, particularly the latter (their lowest velocities reach several hundred kilometres per second), if it is possible to reduce their speeds many times (say 100 times). I am speaking of the use of electricity, the action of which is always attended by the ejection of helium nuclei and electrons.

The Franklin-wheel phenomenon shows that their speeds may be greatly reduced by the surrounding medium; they produce perceptible pressure. In particular this pressure can be utilized in the atmosphere, even in a very rarefied atmosphere. It is more difficult to utilize it (pressure) in empty space, because it becomes immeasurably small. On the contrary, the force of electricity is boundless and for this reason can yield a powerful flux of ionized helium which can be made to serve in a celestial ship.[8]

For the time being, however, we shall leave these dreams and return to our prosaic explosive materials.

It turns out that the most energetic explosive materials under ideal conditions are not powerful enough to achieve a complete victory over their own gravity.

Still, we shall now prove that explosives, if taken in sufficient quantities, will, under certain conditions, be capable of transmitting to celestial ships any desirable velocity and thus to accomplish space travel.

For the time being, let us suppose there is no gravity. We have two bodies of equal mass and between them a compressed spiral spring (Fig. 1).

The spring opens up and both bodies, which had been stationary up till then, acquire identical speeds. Approximately the same thing will occur if we replace one of the bodies with an equal mass of compressed gas directed by a pipe in one direction. In this case we confine ourselves to one hollow sphere with a flared cone and to the compressed gas or superheated volatile liquid in it (Fig. 2). The gas emerges in one direction and an equal mass of the vessel moves off in the other. The speeds, as I have said, are only approximately equal.

---

[8] These arguments are inexact (Editors).

To obtain greater speed, in place of a gas or steam we can take some explosive substances like powder, pyroxylin, dynamite, etc.

With a long enough pipe, the speeds of emerging explosive substances can reach (in empty space) 5 km/sec. Which means that our vehicle, if it has the same mass as the exploding material, can obtain the same speed.

But suppose the mass of explosives is three times the weight of the rocket with everything it contains. We take the weight of the rocket as unity; the weight of the explosives will be 3 $(2^2 - 1 = 3)$.

First we explode two units. The remaining two units receive a speed of 5 km/sec. We then explode another unit. We get an increment of 5 km/sec. The vehicle will then have a speed of 10 km/sec. Now imagine that the explosive supply of the rocket is 7 $(2^3 - 1 = 7)$. We explode 4 units. The remaining 4 units acquire 5 km/sec of speed. We explode 2 more units. The remaining ones get another 5 km/sec, making a total of 10 km/sec. Finally, a third explosion yields 5 km/sec, bringing the total to 15 km/sec. Also, the supply of explosive substance relative to the mass of the rocket may be as follows: $2^4 - 1 = 15$; $2^5 - 1 = 31$; $2^6 - 1 = 63$; $(2^n - 1)$.

The corresponding speeds (per second) of the ship will be $5 \times 4 = 20$; $5 \times 5 = 25$; $5 \times 6 = 30$; $5 \times n$.

They obviously increase without bound, yet even for interstellar flights the speed need not exceed 16-17 km/sec.

In this discussion we have disregarded the force of gravity. In a medium of gravitation, part of the work of the explosive materials is lost. This part is the smaller, the faster the explosion takes place and the closer the vehicle flies to the horizon.

In the case of an instantaneous explosion there is no loss of energy. Likewise there is no loss if the explosion is normal to the action of gravity, no matter how feeble the explosion.

But here we have two grievous drawbacks. In the case of an instantaneous explosion the relative gravity in the vehicle will be infinitely great and for this reason must kill all living things in the celestial ship. In a horizontal explosion, the rocket will fall back to the planet before acquiring the necessary velocity to wipe out gravitation (8 km/sec. At this speed the centrifugal force becomes equal to the force of gravity, so that the vehicle describes innumerable circles, like our moon).

Moreover, in horizontal flight there is a multiple increase in the layer of atmosphere that is traversed. For this reason, most of the work of the explosive substances is actually squandered on the air. Which means that both extremes are inapplicable.

Calculations show that the most advantageous angle of direction (to the horizon) lies between 20 and 30°.[9]

In this case, the atmospheric resistance is not very great, the relative gravity in the rocket is small, and the loss of energy of the explosives due to the force of gravitation is slight.

Apparently, then, a vehicle of any mass can acquire a cosmic velocity with even a relatively small supply of explosives (4-10). But here too we will be sorely disappointed. Calculations show that if the explosion occurs gradually but just as in an ordinary rocket, the weight of the vessel containing the explosive material will be very great with respect to the mass of the vessel.

Indeed, in all the rocket systems I am acquainted with, the pressure of the gases during explosion is transmitted to the whole internal surface and compels us to make it very strong. Can a rocket like that be lightweight?

The gas pressure during the explosion of the most energetic substances reaches 5,000 atmospheres, or 5 ton/cm². Suppose we have used one or several vessels of the best cylindrical-spherical shape made of the strongest and lightest material with a resistance of 100 kg/mm² (density = 8; light alloys of magnesium and aluminium readily melt and for this reason are absolutely unsuitable), the safety factor is moderate (4) and this strength will not suffer from enhanced temperatures. Then calculations will show us that the weight of the vessel (or boiler) will be 30 times the weight of the explosive material in the vessel. Here, the density of the explosives is taken at unity (the density of water).

If, for instance, explosive substances of the density of water weigh one ton, then the best boiler holding them will weigh 30 tons.

If the density of the substances is doubled, the vessel will weigh 15 times more. On the contrary, if the explosives (in the form of liquid oxygen and hydrogen) are on the average three times lighter than water, the vessel will be 90 times heavier than they are. Thus, the explosive material is at least 15 times lighter than the rocket. To put it otherwise, the mass of explosive material cannot make up more than 1/15 the weight of the rocket consisting of vessels only. We take the pressure at only 2,500 atmospheres and the density of the explosives as unity, then the vessel will weigh 15 times more. Disregarding the weight of the remaining components of the rocket and all accessories and the weight of the people with their necessary supplies, let us ask ourselves about the maximum height to which this most

[9] If the rocket is guided, it is best to traverse the atmosphere at a 90° angle and then settle into the desired flight path. The best angle for jet aircraft depends on the ratio of initial thrust to initial weight (Editors).

elementary rocket can ascend. Calculations give 360 m/sec or a height of 6,605.5 m, or less than 7 km.

The pressure generated by powder, pyroxylin and other explosives in use is less, but so is their action. At any rate, a more substantial relative supply of explosives is possible and a greater speed.

The complex rocket of Goddard and Oberth does not alter the matter at all. Theory shows that the number of vessels (even if they are inserted one in the other) and the order of their explosion do not yield any reduction in weight.[10] Compressed gases, no matter how elastic they are, give the same result. But there may be substances of high density which develop small pressures. For instance, heated water may yield one, ten, one hundred, etc. atmospheres instead of 5,000.

Here too the most accurate calculations show that for the most favourable conditions, superheated water cannot raise itself and its boilers higher than 60 km. And note that we have not taken into account the fact that the use of superheated water (up to 200°C) has not yet been tested and therefore that these calculations may not be justified for other, purely practical, reasons.

Though this is far from cosmic velocities, water heated to 150°-200°C may prove suitable for the first experiments.

Where is the way out? It would seem to be very simple. Have a supply of the most powerful explosives but explode them gradually in a definite very strong and small vessel, which we will call the explosion chamber, or the intake of the explosion pipe. Only this chamber and its continuation (explosion pipe) will experience the pressure of the gases; it is into this pipe that the products of the explosion will stream, gradually expanding and cooling off due to the conversion of the random thermal energy into kinetic energy, i.e., into an ordinary gas jet. The pipe and the explosion chamber are very small in volume, and so their mass cannot be very great. It is definite and does not increase with increasing supplies of explosive substances. The vessels do not experience any pressure whatsoever, with the exception of that produced by their enhanced relative weight. Such vessels, especially if they are of a multi-chamber design, may weigh very little.

But the design of such a rocket becomes complicated. A constant pumping of explosive materials into the explosion chamber is necessary. Explosion in a gravitational medium must take place very rapidly (no delays are permissible).

[10] This assertion is incorrect. In his article "Cosmic Rocket Trains Tsiolkovsky gives formulae for more exact estimates of composite (mult-stage) rockets; see this volume, page 187-218 (Editors).

The quantity of materials exploded in one second is great, the pressure is several thousand atmospheres. Naturally, there is a great deal of work in the pumping. We will now see what it is and whether it is possible.

Thus, a celestial rocket will definitely become more complicated. In addition, there will be continually operating pumps and engines to drive them.

This idea cannot be applied to superheated water because it develops pressure throughout its mass. And it is impossible to heat water as it is pumped into the fire chamber because of the extraordinary and inevitable rapidity of the process (the formation of steam, that is). Thus, superheated water is suitable only for the first experiments and exercises that yield modes and methods of control, regulation of explosion, variation of speed, etc. This will be comparatively cheap and may be accomplished without hindrance; in other words, we do not visualize any insuperable engineering difficulties here.

Let us now return to our modified rocket. Its design compares to the earlier one just like the first boilers of Watt's time compare to the steam generators of Serpolet with small heated pipelines into which water was fed and instantaneously evaporated. The pipes had very low capacities and therefore the weight of such steam generators could, theoretically, be small indeed compared to the big-belly cylindrical boilers still in use in places.

My calculations show that when a space rocket is flying at 30° to the horizon, the gravity and air resistance absorb a small amount of energy and the efficiency is almost the same as without attraction (in a medium devoid of gravity).

For the rough calculations of this article, we neglect the aforementioned losses and take the acceleration of the rocket at 30 m/sec². The relative gravity in it will be three times the earth's gravity. A healthy young person in a supine position should be able to withstand it without being immersed in water. But under no circumstances should one disregard precautions.

The table given below shows (like everything else in this article, it is of an approximate nature) the time in seconds from the start of motion, the corresponding speed in kilometres per second, the distance traversed, and the altitude of ascent in kilometres. The fifth column indicates the density of the atmosphere, the dominant gas and the force of the earth's gravity.[11]

A careful examination of the table will give us a picture of the rocket's flight.

[11] The figures for the atmosphere are out of date (Editors).

Table 1

Time, sec	0	1	2	3	5	7	10	15	20	30	40	50	60	70	80
Speed, km/sec	0	0.03	0.06	0.09	0.15	0.21	0.30	0.45	0.6	0.9	1.2	1.5	1.8	2.1	2.4
Distance, km	0	0.046	0.183	0.413	1.15	2.25	4.6	10.3	18.3	41.3	73.4	115	165	225	294
Altitude, km	0	0.023	0.091	0.26	0.57	1.12	2.3	5.1	9.1	20.6	36.7	57.5	82.5	112	147
Air density	1	Troposphere. Normal composition of air, water meteors, clouds						0.5	0.3	0.06	0.006	0.000020	Stratosphere. Falling stars. Noctilucent clouds. Hydrogen		

Table 2

Time, sec	90	100	120	150	170	200	220	250	260	270	280	290	300	320	350
Speed, km/sec	2.7	3	3.6	4.5	5.1	6	6.6	7.5	7.8	8.1	8.4	8.7	9.0	9.6	10.5
Distance, km	371	459	660	1,030	1,330	1,830	2,220	2,870	3,101	3,340	3,596	3,858	4,130	4,700	5,620
Altitude, km	185	230	330	515	665	915	1,110	1,435	1,550	1,670	1,798	1,929	2,065	2,355	2,810
Air density and gravity	0.000006		0.000002	Geocoronium Black sky			Empty space — ether		0.66		0.61			0.50	

Table 3

Time, sec	370	380	390	400	420	450	470	500	520	550	570	600	620	650	700
Speed, km/sec	11.1	11.4	11.7	12.0	12.6	13.5	14.1	15.0	15.6	16.5	17.1	18.0	18.6	19.5	21.0
Distance, km	6,184	6,235	6,287	7,339	7,980	9,290	10,140	11,470	12,460	13,880	14,900	16,510	17,600	19,380	22,480
Altitude, km	3,100	3,117	3,143	3,669	3,990	4,645	5,070	5,735	6,230	6,940	7,450	8,255	8,800	9,690	11,240
Gravity	0.45			0.41	0.38		0.31		0.26		0.21		0.18		0.13

The rocket is constantly undergoing acceleration at an angle of 30° to the horizon. In 15 seconds the velocity reaches 0.45 km/sec (450 m/sec), but the atmospheric resistance has already fallen off by one half because the rocket has reached an altitude of 5 km, where the air density is half that at sea level. Within another 5 seconds the density has diminished by a factor of three; the rocket reaches an altitude of 9 km with a speed of 600 m/sec. After this the composition of the atmosphere begins to change perceptibly. The lighter gases are predominant, and the percentage of nitrogen increases. We have now traversed all the clouds, all accumulations of ice crystals and the entire realm of water meteors (troposphere). Everywhere about is utter dryness and cloudless sky.

Thirty seconds from take-off, the speed has reached 0.9 km/sec (900 m/sec); the air resistance is very weak because the rocket has attained a height of 20 km where the density is 0.06: the air is 17 times more rarefied than down below. We are flying through the stratosphere where we sometimes encounter cirrus clouds. This is the sphere of falling stars (where they burn up) and noctilucent clouds. We pass through it about one minute after take-off and reach 80 km with air that is rarefied by a factor of 50,000. The air is almost imperceptible. According to Wegener, the blue colour of the sky disappears here; its composition is hydrogen and geocoronium, with insignificant quantities of other gases. The rocket is now moving at 1.8 km/sec (1,800 m/sec, which is the highest speed of an artillery shell as it emerges from the barrel). From now on we can forget about the resistance of the atmosphere, and for this reason the rocket can more and more bend towards the horizon setting its path more in the form of a circle, like the moon. In the table we left the inclination unchanged. But it is enough for the rocket to get outside the atmosphere. The extreme ascents indicated in the table are superfluous: the first problem is to reach the status of an earth satellite, that of a small moon orbiting close to the earth. From there it is easy to travel anywhere, even to leave the solar system and fly out among the stars. And so we have passed through the hydrogen sphere surrounded by the black sky with the burning bright points of the stars. Rising up above 80 km brings us to the sphere of the geocoronium with a small additional percentage of hydrogen, into the mysterious realm of the aurora borealis.

In 150 seconds, or $2^1/_2$ minutes, we have passed through this sphere and are entering the absolute void, the space of the light-bearing ether where the motion we have acquired becomes eternal in the same way that the motions of the celestial bodies are eternal. The speed of the rocket has reached 4.5 km/sec and we are 500 km from the earth's surface. But this speed is not enough to become a reliable satellite of the earth. The rocket bends into a circle, all the time accelerating with an explosion lasting another 2 minutes, making a total of 270 seconds from take-off and—by explosion—attaining a speed of 8 km/sec after reaching an altitude of 1,700 versts. Here the gravity of the earth has perceptibly diminished (by about 35 per cent). Therefore, the rocket would have reached much greater heights if it had not been inclining more and more to the horizon.

We can calm down now, stop the explosion and take a look around; but let us suppose that the explosion were continued, then the table shows us what subsequent results there would be. The table indicates the results of subsequent explosions, but altitudes are given with diminishing gravity disregarded.

The important thing, however, is not the altitude of ascent but the acquired velocity. That is what enables us, after 370 seconds of explosion is over, to recede from the earth and fly in an annual orbit as a brother of our planet. In a longer explosion (550 seconds or 9 minutes from take-off) the speed will not only be sufficient to reach any planet (provided the direction of rocket velocity coincides with the annual motion of the earth) but will even be enough to overcome completely the attraction of the sun and wander out among other suns of the Milky Way.

In earlier publications we calculated that for a celestial ship to attain the first cosmic velocity of 8 km/sec, it has to carry a supply of the most energetic explosive substances that exceeds fourfold the weight of a fully loaded rocket (minus the explosives).

If a rocket containing people and other things weighed a ton, the explosives would weigh 4 tons, or 4,000 kg, and would be consumed in 270 sec, the average rate of consumption being 15 kg/sec.

As stated, the pressure on the space rocket will be three times the weight of the rocket with all it contains, including the unexploded material. Thus, if the acceleration is constant, then at the beginning of the flight when the rocket weighs 5 tons (1 + 4), the pressure will be 15 tons (5 × 3). At the termination of the explosion, when the material is consumed and the rocket weighs only 1 ton, the pressure will then be only 3 tons. Which means that the consumption of explosives at the beginning is 5 times that at the end.

Though this is very inexact, we will assume, for the sake of simplicity, that the average consumption is 15 kg, and the average pressure is 9 tons.

153

Then at the start of motion, the rocket would move more slowly, and at the end, faster. This would be useful relative to reducing losses due to resistance of the atmosphere. It also simplifies the design of the explosion pipe and the explosion chamber.

Let us take the maximum pressure of the exploding gases at 3,000 atmospheres. The pressure on the bottom of the pipe will thus be equal to 3 tons per square centimetre of bottom. But we have to have 9 tons. Consequently, the bottom of the explosion pipe should have a base area of 3 cm². The speed of flow of explosives when consumption is 15 kg/sec, taking the density of the gases to be equal to that of water, will come out to (15,000 : 3 = 5,000 cm/sec) 50 metres per second. The work of their expulsion will be (9 tons × 50 m = 450 ton-metres) 450 ton-metres or 4,500 metric horsepower (a metric horsepower is equal to 100 kg-m).

Now this means that among other things we need an engine of 4,500 horsepower for pumping explosives into the explosion pipe. At present this is not feasible. Indeed, even if we put one half the weight of the rocket in this motor (500 kg), our motors will then have to be 9 times lighter than existing ones.

That is one of the many difficulties inherent in the rocket.

An idea comes to mind of periodically inserting ready-to-explode cartridges into the explosion pipe (or chamber); that is, first one cartridge is put in, exploded, and time elapses until the pipe is free from gases and pressure, and then a second cartridge is put in, and so on. Then the rocket will advance in spurts in nonuniformly accelerated motion. This is tolerable. But the speed of inserting the cartridges will be unattainably great. Every second we would have to insert a 50-metre cylinder of explosive material, or 100 cartridges each half a metre long. But if we expand the pipe 10 times and make the base 30 cm² (6.2 cm in diameter), the weight of the explosion pipe will increase by a factor of at least 10. Then it will be necessary to put in 10 50-cm cylinders of explosives every second. Aside from all these obstacles, the jerks due to explosions will increase tenfold and will become intolerable for human beings and dangerous to the integrity of the rocket itself. The weight of the vessels containing the explosive supplies and, generally, the mass of the rocket will have to be increased tenfold.

Giffard's injector pumps water into the steam boilers by the force of the steam itself. Couldn't this principle be employed for pumping materials into the pipe, using the energy of the explosives themselves—their monstrous pressure and enormous speed?

The work of the explosive materials, i.e., 4 tons of substance (assuming the energy of chemical union of hydrogen and oxygen), will be (1,400,000 × 4 = 5,600,000 ton-metres) 5,600,000 ton-metres. This means that in one second they liberate (5,600,000 : 270 = 20,700) 20,700 ton-metres, which is equivalent to the work of 207,000 metric horsepower. This will be 46 times the work required to inject materials into the pipe.

From this it is evident, firstly, that the work of pumping amounts to 1/46 of the entire work of the explosives, secondly, it is clear that the work of explosion is tremendous and cannot in any way be compared with the power output of ordinary engines, for it generates continuously, that is, every second, 207,000 metric horsepower.

Yet the explosion pipe that performs this stupendous work is extremely light, weighing only a fraction of a ton.

Is this possible? Quite possible. The proof may be seen in the operation of artillery pieces. It is easy to calculate that a gun throws a ton of iron with an initial speed of 1,000 m/sec, performing work to the amount of 50,000 ton-metres, and all this in the time of 1/50 sec, which means that in one second it will come to 2,500,000 ton-metres, or 25,000,000 metric horsepower. This is 121 times the work of the explosion pipe. If the gun weighs 20 tons, our explosion pipe will weigh less than 200 kg, which is attainable, as my calculations show.

But how are we to handle the delivery of the materials? Invent an injector. Before that, one can only dream of space travel.

Here is a drawing (which I made in 1914, 11 years after the first design) of a space rocket (see Fig. 1, p. 137).

The foregoing already gives some idea of the design of a reactive vehicle for space travel. It is best at this juncture to recall the schematic drawing of the rocket of 1914 and to give an appropriate description. The left rear (aft) half of the rocket consists of two chambers separated by a partition not shown in the drawing.

The first chamber contains liquid, freely evaporating oxygen. It has a very low temperature and surrounds part of the explosion pipe and other components subject to high temperatures.

The other compartment contains hydrocarbons in the liquid state. The two black dots at the bottom (almost in the middle) denote the cross-section of the pipes that deliver the explosive materials to the explosion pipe. From the intake of the explosion pipe (see the vicinity of the two dots) go two branch lines with gases flowing at high speeds that entrain and push the liquid explosive components into the intake, like a Giffard injector or a steam-jet pump. Freely evaporating liquid oxygen in the gaseous and cold state bathes the intermediate space between the two shells of the rocket and thus prevents burning of the inside of the rocket when the latter is in high-speed flight through the air.

The direction-and-turning rudders are like those of an aeroplane. They are positioned on the outside opposite the exit end of the explosion pipe. They function in the air and in empty space as well. They deviate, and so does the rocket, due to the pressure of high-speed gases. A similar rudder, but away from the others may also serve for rotation control, that is, it can make the rocket rotate in one direction or in the other, slower or faster, and it can stop any undesired rotation of the rocket caused by incorrect explosion and air pressure. Its operation depends upon the helical-like bevel of the rudder blade located along the flow of gases in the pipe. Because of the bevel, the rudder takes the shape of an Archimedean screw, and thus makes the explosion products rotate; that is what causes the rocket to rotate on its long axis or to stop rotating.

The purpose of course is to stop any rotation of the rocket that is detrimental to human beings.

Let us describe the sensations of travellers taking off in a space rocket to circle round the earth like the moon and also the observations of those seeing them off. It is assumed that the rocket is well-equipped and fulfils its functions normally.

The rocket has several case-forms in the shape of a human being, one for each passenger. Each traveller lies horizontally relative to the apparent gravity and a very small amount of water is poured in. The hands are also in the liquid, but are free so that they can attend to the instrument controls, which are also located in water. These instruments regulate the direction of rocket flight, the composition of the air, temperature, humidity in the rocket, the explosion process, and so forth.

During the 270 seconds of explosion, the travellers in this position are not able to see very much.

Their weight is greatly reduced by the water. The water is warm. There is no cold. The windows are tightly sealed with opaque shutters so that it is impossible to see outside the rocket. That is the way things have to be. But suppose the travellers are standing or sitting in chairs and looking out transparent windows, calmly observing everything around. Then even in the 270 seconds, or $4^1/_2$ minutes, one can notice quite a bit.

At first the rocket is brought to a special railed track. A place high up in the mountains has been selected. The ground is inclined 20° to 30° to the horizon. The terrain has been evened and rails have been laid. The rocket is now resting on the rails.

The altitude of this locality is 5 to 6 km, the air density one half (0.5), the track extends up to 100 versts.

The rocket on the track is in an inclined position, and so is the floor with the attached seats. The passengers have entered the rocket, which is then hermetically sealed. Their position is extremely inconvenient. It is impossible to sit in the chairs, the walls of the chamber are inclined everywhere. One cannot walk either. The only way to get seated is in lightweight rope seats in the form of trapezoids, and that is what our travellers have done after a lot of turning and twisting. Out the windows one can see mountains, buildings floating in the dark blue sky, higher up are clouds—in short, the ordinary picture of a mountain scene. The explosion has started. The noise is terrible and affects the nerves; but let our heroes be tough and let them pay no attention to the terrifying howling.

The rocket hurtles along the track, the travellers feel a jolt and the horizon—so it appears to them—turns through 60°. To them it becomes almost a vertical precipice. But the floor of the rocket becomes nearly horizontal. The hanging chairs tilt and become nearly parallel to the walls. The gravity nearly doubles and the people fall back into their chairs. To raise oneself requires the exertion of every effort, but as yet there is no need for this. Everything is perfectly visible through the windows. Everything round about—the vertical horizon and the mountains, lakes and rivers that stud it—is nearly in a vertical position. It is as if a relief map of the earth were tilted at a 60-degree angle to the horizon.

The sun has just risen and it appears high above one's head.

The pressure on the rocket was constant (at 9 tons), but since the quantity of explosives decreased, the acceleration of the vehicle increased. This brought a continuous build-up in gravity: from 1 (the gravity of the earth = 1) at take-off, to 9 at the end. This was obvious from observations of spring scales. A one-pound weight on the scales indicated about 2 pounds, which was more than it should, because the pan and the spring now weighed more than usual. This weight continued to grow right before their eyes, pulling the spring more and more.

Two minutes had hardly passed when the rocket rose from the rails and flew freely and far from the ground. The passengers could not feel the motion but it seemed to them that the enormous up-turned horizon with all its mountains, lakes and cities was falling down and away from the rocket.

The clock with the weight pendulum was shamelessly running ahead, the pendulum hurried in jerks and in place of two oscillations was doing three. This was noticeable at once and could be checked with a pocket watch that continued to keep correct time. The mercury in the barometer had dropped by half, though the aneroid barometer continued to show the same air pressure inside the rocket. Lever scales did not show an increase in weight,

though all bodies had become twice as heavy. This was under-
standable because the weights had become heavier themselves.
It was very instructive to see this continual build-up in weight,
which we are accustomed to consider as something constant.
A centrifuge could demonstrate that the masses of all the bodies
remained the same without the slightest change. Things began
to fall precipitously. Droplets became half-size in diameter and
8 times smaller in volume. Waves were propagated faster. The
faces of the passengers paled, and if it weren't for their youth
and good health, they would have lost consciousness. Still they
wanted very much to stretch out on the beds and take what they
thought to be a horizontal position. Meanwhile they stood it.
But the chairs gave way more and more under their weight.

The sky was getting dark. The planets came into view and
so did the larger stars, despite the full brilliance of our sun.
It too shone more brightly. The moon, which before had hardly
been noticed, was now all golden and brilliant, as if thoroughly
washed. The sky had long since become quite cloudless, while
the clouds slopingly covered the inclined horizon in places and here
and there prevented one from seeing the upturned earth and sea.

The sky got darker and darker, and the stars came out in ever
larger numbers. The moon became brighter and the sun more
brilliant. The troposphere and stratosphere had long since been
passed.

We are entering the region of hydrogen and geocoronium. The
sky is totally black, there are multitudes of stars, and everything
seems close at hand. The vault of the sky has become more sphere-
like, more regular in shape, and it would be terrible indeed if
it weren't for its toy-like appearance. The stars have become
bright and multicoloured but they do not twinkle. A person with
good eyesight sees only bright points on a black background.

The region of the geocoronium is past and we are out beyond
the atmosphere. The stars are brighter still and clear-cut. The
shades and shadows of objects in the rocket are sharply outlined,
but the half-lights remain due to reflection of light from the
walls of the rocket and from objects within. The Milky Way is
visible. The earth, which just a while ago was in the form of an
enormous vertical wall, has now become a dish occupying half
the sky. It appears to be to one side. One half of the vault of
the sky is black and studded with silvery and multicoloured dots
of stars, the other is like an immense concave moon occupying
nearly half the sky.

The gravity is so great now that one of the passengers has
lost consciousness, another has stretched out on the floor, and
a third—the toughest and most muscular—suggests that the one

on the floor get into a bath with water to save himself. First, with great difficulty, they put in their friend who had lost consciousness, and then get in themselves holding the head of the weak one above the water.

All at once they felt like they were in paradise, and the one who had fallen unconscious woke up without even noticing his faint. One's body lost weight, only the head was much heavier and seemed to belong to someone else, as if it were an object outside oneself. They tossed their heads about unintentionally, as if they wanted to throw them off. But even this unpleasant feeling was easily got rid of. All one had to do was to put his head into water. They first put on special goggles that permitted seeing under water and each one took into his mouth a tube that fitted closely over lips and nose and calmly went under in the bath. Marvellous it was. And still better to lie down flat on the bottom of the bath-tub. It was softer to the body than the softest feather beds or specially built arm-chairs. A fish finding itself in this water swam about as if nothing were happening. Only the surface of the liquid rippled from the vibrations, and there was a general shaking of everything.

At the end of the explosion period came a ninefold increase in gravity, but no one was afraid now.

The rocket was under almost completely automatic control, and only occasionally did they have to move the indicating pointers of the regulators and the instrument levers. Fine connecting wires and control buttons were located in the water or close-by. But when one tried to stretch a hand or leg out of the water, the effort was awful, for his limbs felt loaded with lead.

About 4 to 5 minutes after take-off a sudden and absolute silence set in—the explosion period was over. After the deafening howl and noise and vibrations that made ordinary speech quite impossible, this silence was just as amazing as the horrendous boom at take-off from the earth. Their ears were ringing and they were in a daze as if shot into a new world. Their faces filled with blood, but this was not dangerous because in the water almost the same thing happened. Blood vessels would not break. There was only a slight contrast in the blood pressure.

Now what was there to do? They all continued to sit in the water without moving as if in a stupor. But the water, now no longer weighing anything, began gradually to climb out of the tub, taking on fanciful shapes. This brought them to their senses. They jumped to their feet and began to fly about the rocket. They banged their heads and other parts of their bodies against the ceiling and walls of the rocket, and that more than anything else brought them to their senses. Their first movements in the bath-tub threw the water about in different directions; now it was flying about in the chamber in the form of big lightweight balloons. Or perhaps like flitting soap bubbles. But these were dense spheres, massive and enormous-size drops. The spheres incidentally soon gave up their wanderings. They stuck to the walls and to other objects and enveloped them. Solid things, sometimes wet or covered with a thick massive layer of water, like chunks of glass, were moving back and forth together with the passengers. The things slowed down little by little, but the people tried to move and therefore were tossed about backwards and forwards like jumping shadows.

The travellers now had only one feeling, that of surprise because the happenings amazed them more than their description (which had been read before the flight).

The ringing in their ears subsided, the rocket appeared to be standing still, but they knew that it was racing round the earth like a new moon with a speed of 6 to 7 versts a second. It was outside the atmosphere 3 to 4 thousand versts from the surface of the earth. It could not stop by itself, for it was a satellite of the earth.

When our heroes had completely recovered their senses, they began to put things into order. They cleared away the water and attached the objects that had been torn from the walls during the period of enhanced gravity.

They experienced blissful calm and silence. Their bodies and all other things had three principal stable kinds of motion: rectilinear, rotational, and combinations of the two. Quite often there was an additional irregular oscillatory rotation, but it soon turned into ordinary stable rotation about a free axis, of which there were at least three to be found in any body.

The barometer rose and the mercury occupied the whole tube; there was no empty place left. Scales were now powerless. There was no gravity. One could judge mass only by the effort needed to move it from its place and give it some speed.

A person or any object could be at rest in any position. Motion did not cease unless there were obstacles. 'Up' was where the head was, 'down', where the feet were. Each person therefore had his own 'up' depending on his position.

The earth occupied nearly half the sky and was in the shape of a concave hemisphere, in the centre of which was the rocket; but one part of the earth was illuminated like the moon and looked like an enormous curved lunar crescent, the other part was dark, of an ashy colour. The strength of the terrestrial light was twice that of the moon, while its absolute intensity at full earth was 30,000 times that of the full moon. The bright crescent continued to grow and in a few minutes became a full circle. The terrestrial phases came and went quickly: from a bright red circle inside a dark one, to a brilliant half-sky. The earth was then clearly visible: all its continents, seas, oceans, islands and even cities. Only part of it was covered over with snow-white clouds and the limbs were not clear-cut. The earth was like a map but in a strange projection never seen before. All the forms of the limbs were flattened and fuzzy. Maps like these are not in use. The vertical position of the earth had of course disappeared.

Now for one person it appeared to be overhead, for another, it seemed to be to the side, and for a third, down below, all depending on their own positions. Now our heroes had all come to rest at different places in the rocket and in all kinds of positions without touching any objects, like fish in water. They moved about with the greatest of ease, using hardly any effort at all. When they turned about, the impression was that the rocket, the sun, stars and the earth were turning. When they were in motion, they could not rid themselves of the idea that it was the rocket moving. And so to some it appeared that the rocket was stationary, to others that it was in slow rotation, to some, that it was in rapid rotation, to someone else that it was both turning and moving away, to another person, that it was only receding, and so forth, all depending on their own diversified motions.

Chairs, mattresses and pillows and even one's feet seemed quite superfluous. Neither was there any need of tables or various supports. But all things had to be attached in some way, of course, or protected by nets so that they should not go floating about the chamber. For indeed, the slightest motion of the air, the slightest jolt was capable of setting an object into motion and rearranging things generally. Without precautions there would be the most awful mix-up and disorder imaginable.

If it weren't for the warmth of the earth nearby, one could vary the temperature at will from 270°C below zero to 150°C above zero. But the heat radiated by the earth prevents attaining these extremes in the rocket. Still, it is possible to get down to about 100°C below zero.

Temperature changes are handled by the changeable sheath outside the rocket: it is brilliant, then black, or both together. By turning appropriate levers, it is possible to freeze all the people or to fry them like fish in a pan.

Likewise, there is no need of kitchens or furnaces. Different compartments of the rocket can have different temperatures depending on the requirements. A few mirrors set in the right positions can bring the temperature up to that of a smith's furnace or even higher.

An extended rocket, in the form of a specially designed green-house, can be made to yield oxygen and food for the passengers. It will indeed be a haven for the most fruitful of plants. That is where food and oxygen will be obtained. But that is a topic of very great extent and is out of place here.

Every 100 minutes the rocket goes into the shadow of the earth. Then the stellar sky is particularly clear. And the earth too shines brightly like an immense red corona, dark on the inside. It takes up nearly half the sky. The sun is of course not in view. This is a solar eclipse or night, whatever you want to call it. Here, the daylight period lasts about 100 minutes, and night about 40. The moon passes through its phases in the usual time. Only it is twice as bright because there is no atmosphere.

The starry sky, the sun, the Milky Way and the planets are all just as they should be, but more clear-cut, without twinkling and without "rays", twice as bright, and much more populous, more varicoloured and all situated (it would seem) on a tiny black and strictly spherical surface.

This is paradise indeed for astronomers whose chief enemy is the atmosphere, of which there is none here. Astronomers here would make numberless great discoveries with their gigantic telescopes, spectroscopes and photographic equipment.

The friends that remained on the earth and saw our heroes off did not, quite naturally, experience anything like this. All they saw was the rocket disappearing from view in a few seconds after roaring horrendously for a short time.

A minute or two later, an even roll of thunder was heard. First it grew in intensity, and then fell away and vanished. The rocket was cleaving the air as it built up to cosmic speed. And when the air came together again it reinforced the air wave, which spent quite some time in covering the distance back to the take-off point of the rocket.

In about 2 or 3 minutes the rocket again came into view as a tiny star. It was glowing now due to friction in the air. Then the star soon disappeared from view.

When the travellers got quite some distance away from the earth, they thought that they were in an absolute void, but they were mistaken, for traces of the atmosphere were found there as well.

Therefore since the rocket experienced a slight resistance, it described a spiral path with a very small pitch, which brought it ever closer to the earth, but very slowly. They made so many turns round the earth that they had long since lost count. But still a return to the earth was unavoidable. At first the speed of the rocket increased and the centrifugal force balanced the earth's gravity despite the increase in gravity. Then the speed of the spaceship began to diminish because of the increasing resistance of the atmosphere. Then the travellers went into a glide by raising the nose of the rocket with a rudder that functioned like an aeroplane rudder. Now they were able not only to reduce falling but even convert it into a lifting force so long as the speed had not yet been shed. But lifting was superfluous for it might end in a loss of motion upwards and the rocket would perish, turning into a wingless aeroplane. They descended but slowly, coming closer and closer to the earth.

The travellers prayed to fate that the impact would be at sea and not on land.

Indeed, the re-entry was more dangerous than the descent of an aeroplane because there were no wings, and a very high speed was needed to offset gravity.

Fate heard their request and they came into the sea almost horizontally.

The speed was still great (200 to 300 m/sec) and they skimmed across the water a considerable distance before coming to rest; they were then taken on board a passing steamship.

Only precise calculations can give answers concerning spaceships. Calculations will also indicate what requirements will have to be met by explosives, the properties of the materials and mechanisms suitable for flight and life in the ether.

I have made many such calculations, but I have not yet been able to overcome everything. Nevertheless it is desirable to have a complete edition of these works published with all their formulae and tables. Only then will we be able to do something.

I have also accumulated material that points to ways of achieving success in a practicable way. This is the result of experiments and explorations under the impulse of theoretical conclusions.

The condition that I make with the publishers is to put out the manuscripts little by little, otherwise I will not have strength enough. Each published part will supply me with vitality to look over carefully the next one. It is useful to put out earlier publications that have not yet reached many readers.

I think to play the part of initiator. Mathematicians who know more and are more powerful will perhaps finish the solution of the problems I have posed. Experienced and knowledgeable technicians will help them to design and construct the spaceship itself.

A High-Speed Train

(1927)[1]

Application: high-speed train. General idea. The friction of the train is nearly eliminated by the excess pressure of the air between the floor of the car and the railway bed close to it. Work is needed for pumping air, which is constantly flowing out along the edges of the slits between the car and the roadway. The work is great and the lifting force of the train may be enormous. Thus, if the excess pressure is one tenth of an atmosphere, then there will be a lifting force of one ton on every square metre of the bottom of the car. This is five times that needed for lightweight passenger cars.

No wheels or lubrication is needed of course. The thrust is maintained by the rearward pressure of the air escaping from an opening in the car. The work of pumping is also rather moderate here (if the car has a good streamline shape like that of a bird or a fish). There is a possibility of attaining tremendous velocities.

As a result, the train overcomes all inclines and gets to the very tops of mountains without any thrust, by acceleration and sheer momentum (inertia).

From here we can imagine that in time it will be made to skip over all rivers, precipices and mountains no matter what size

---

[1] This is an abstract from the article by K. E. Tsiolkovsky "Resistance of the Air and High-Speed Trains", first published in Russian in 1927. The first part, which contains a general analytical treatment of the air resistance of various bodies, has been omitted (Editors).

they are. There will be no need of bridges, tunnels, and large-scale earth-moving jobs. There will be the difficulty of landing the trains after a jump.

The inconvenience of high speeds is the impossibility of frequent stops. The higher the speed, the fewer the stations and the greater the distance between them.

Deceleration consists in reducing or eliminating the extra air pressure under the car. Braking of this kind is easy only for ordinary train speeds. It is more economical to effect stopping at the summits of elevations or hills. Here, gravity does the stopping and the car performs the useful work of lifting. At high speeds, the train races along of itself even without any participation of thrust, jumps across ditches, lakes, swamps and elevations. There is also the difficulty of high initial speeds that occasionally are lost unproductively during stops.

Quite naturally, experiments will begin with small speeds. The route will not be very steeply inclined. Bridges and tunnels will remain at first.

A clearer conception of high-speed trains may be had from the following drawings, calculations and tables.

Description of drawings. Drawing 1 (Fig. 1) shows the cross-section of a car (*B*), half-pipes (*TT*) at its base, rails (*P*) and the roadbed between them forming a single plane with the rails. Separate motors pump air into *T* and *T*; the air flows into the narrow slip between the car and the roadbed. It lifts the train a few millimetres and escapes along the edges of the base of the car, which no longer touches the roadbed but hovers on a thin layer of air experiencing only a very slight air friction, like an object in flight. Thanks to flanged edges, the car cannot leave the rails. This also diminishes air leakage because the air flow here takes a sharp change in direction.

Drawing 2 (Fig. 2) portrays a roadbed (man-made road) and the base of a car. The base is fine-corrugated with two channels open downwards (*T*, *T*) into which air is pumped. The corrugated under-floor surface of the train likewise retards loss of air and, hence, reduces the work of pumping. The air enters from the outside through a forward vent (*Ve*) of the car and partially flows out through slits round it, and also in part through a rear opening (*Op*) where it exerts pressure on the train, making it move by reaction (or recoil). *B, B* are extended ends of the car that reduce air resistance. The motor that pumps air into the rear opening can also be independent of the other motors. If this opening does not communicate with the channels (*T, T*), the pressure at the opening may differ from the pressure in the channels (*T, T*).

165

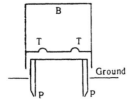

FIG. 1

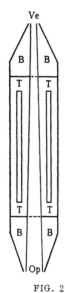

FIG. 2

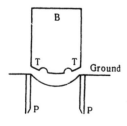

FIG. 3

Drawing 3 (Fig. 3) shows in cross-section another design of the roadbed and the car base with a circular cylindrical floor. No flanged edges are needed here. Besides, since the centre of gravity of the car is generally lower than its geometric centre, the car possesses stable equilibrium like a steamship in water. But the construction of such a road would seem to be more difficult. Other forms are also possible. We have only indicated the more characteristic ones.

Calculations. We assume a roadway that is straight and horizontal.

For the lifting force (Y) of a rectangular car base we have the expression:

$$Y = lb\,(p_1 - p), \qquad (70)$$

where the second factor gives the difference between the air pressure under the floor of the car and the external air pressure. The lifting force per square metre will be $p_1 - p$. An excess pressure of 0.1 atmosphere is quite sufficient; this yields over one ton of lifting force per square metre of floor surface. Even 0.02 atmosphere is enough (that is, 200 kg/m²). For this reason, in subsequent formulae we shall disregard the work of compression of the air and the slight increase in temperature that it causes. We consider it to be a noncompressible medium, as it were. This reduces the work (or will be in error) by no more than 5%.

For the magnitude of resistance of streamline bodies we have the formulae (33), (34) and (20).[2] For the sake of brevity, in place of (33) we put[3]

$$X_{tot} = Kv_{tr}^2, \qquad (71)$$

where[4]

$$K \cong \frac{\pi D^2}{8g} \rho f \left(\frac{C_{X_{sp}} \cdot K_{sh} \cdot C_{X_{pl}}}{\lambda^2} + \frac{4\eta \delta_1}{D} \right). \qquad (71_1)$$

In the formulae we can take

$$h = b, \qquad (72)$$

that is, the height and width of the car are the same,

$$D = \sqrt{\frac{4}{\pi} \cdot bh} \qquad (73)$$

or

$$D = \frac{2}{\sqrt{\pi}} h, \qquad (74)$$

where D is the diameter of a circle of area bh.

On the other hand, the pressure of the reactive air jet at the rear of the car, which is fed by a separate motor and by pumps, will be

$$p_2 = (p_{jet} - p) \cdot S_{jet}, \qquad (75)$$

where the notations signify, in order, reactive pressure, difference in jet pressure, and cross-sectional area of jet. The established uniform motion of the train requires the equality

$$p_2 = X_{tot}, \qquad (76)$$

i.e., the reactive pressure should be equal to the total air pressure (X_{tot}). From this, using (75) and (71) we get

$$(p_{jet} - p) \cdot S_{jet} = Kv_{tr}^2, \qquad (77)$$

---

[2] The numbering of the formulae has been left unchanged. The symbols used in formulae (71)-(149) are explained either in the text or in the footnotes (Editors).

[3] X_{tot} = total air resistance due to friction and inertia, v_{tr} = velocity of the train (Editors).

[4] D = diameter, g = acceleration due to gravity, ρ = air density, $f = \left\{ 1 \pm \ln \left(\frac{l}{v} \right) \right\}^{\pm 1}$ = time dependent function of δ, $C_{X_{sp}} (=0.4)$ = friction coefficient of a sphere, K_{sh} = correction factor depending on the equation of the generatrix curve, $C_{X_{pl}}$ = correction factor for the friction of a plate, approximately equal to 1.5, η = correction factor that allows for the narrowing of the rotational body to its ends ($\eta < 1$), δ = thickness of the air layer adhering to the surface of the body (Editors).

whence

$$S_{jet} = K v_{tr}^2 \cdot (p_{jet} - p).\qquad(77_1)$$

From this we can calculate the area and the diameter of a circular cross-section of the jet or the opening in the rear wall of the car.

We now find the speed (v_{jet}) of the reactive air jet. The normal wind pressure is known from formula (9). The reactive pressure is approximately expressed by this same formula. From (9) we obtain

$$v^2 = \frac{2g X_{pl}}{lb\rho C_{X_{pl}}}\qquad(78)$$

But here

$$v = v_{jet};$$
$$X_{pl} = p_2 = (p_{jet} - p)\, S_{jet}.\qquad\text{(see 75)}$$

and

$$lb = S_{jet}.$$

From this and from (78) we find

$$v_{jet} = \sqrt{\frac{2g\,(p_{jet} - p)}{\rho C_{X_{pl}}}}.\qquad(79)$$

There will be three kinds of work of motors in the train: (1) air pumping to maintain the car in a hovering position over a layer of air compressed under the floor; (2) air pumping at a different pressure to obtain pressure at the rear in order to overcome the resistance of oncoming air (in a calm atmosphere, i.e., without a wind), and, finally, (3) we have to impart to the oncoming air a speed equal to the speed of the train (v_{tr}). But since the pressure difference of the gases $(p_1 - p,\ p_{jet} - p)$ gives an additional speed $(v_{jet},\ v_{slit})$, the additional work will correspond to the speeds: $v_{tr} - v_{jet}$ and $v_{tr} - v_{slit}$. In the latter case, it is assumed that the entire slit air emerges rearwards, but actually this is not so. It is therefore better simply to add v_{tr}. Incidentally, it is necessary to determine all these items of work. The area of the slit openings round the circumference of the car will be

$$S_{slit} = 2\,(b + l)\,c.\qquad(80)$$

Here, c denotes the gap, or the mean distance between the floor of the car and the roadbed. We find the amount of air leakage from the cross-section of the slits (80) and the rate of slit leakage

(v_{slit}). The latter may be found from formula (79). To do this we only need to replace the difference of jet pressures $(p_{jet} - p)$ by the difference of under-floor pressures $(p_1 - p)$. We then get

$$v_{slit} = \sqrt{\frac{2g\,(p_1 - p)}{\rho c_{x_{pl}}}}.\tag{81}$$

Hence, the volume of air leaking through the slits (V_{slit}) will be

$$V_{slit} = 2\,(b + l)\,c \cdot v_{slit}.\tag{82}$$

Actually, the rate of leakage will be much less because of the enormous friction of the gas between the roadbed and the corrugated surface of the base of the car. The loss will be normal, that is, in accordance with the formula, only when the gap (c) is increased or the car raised. This raising is useful in that it will require a less even roadbed and car base.

Likewise, the volume of air leaving through the rear opening will be

$$V_{jet} = v_{jet} \cdot S_{jet}.\tag{83}$$

It is now easy to determine the least work for both. One compressor operates to maintain the car in a hovering position (a sort of flight). It will have to overcome a pressure $p_1 - p$ per unit area and its work per second will come to

$$R_{slit} = (p_1 - p)\,V_{slit}.\tag{84}$$

The other pump will give a different pressure, $p_{jet} - p$, and its work will be

$$R_{jet} = (p_{jet} - p)\,V_{jet}.\tag{85}$$

The third kind of work—the work of inertia—will be slit work and jet work. The former is equal to

$$R_{in.\,slit} = \frac{V_{slit}\rho}{2g} \cdot v_{tr}^2.\tag{86}$$

The latter is

$$R_{in.\,jet} = V_{jet}\,\rho\,\frac{(v_{tr} - v_{jet})^2}{2g}.\tag{87}$$

In view of the complexities of the formulae, we will for the

169

time being express all four kinds of work separately. We assume

$$l = D\lambda, \tag{88}$$

where λ is the elongation of the train, or the ratio of length to the diameter of its median cross-section. In this way, and with the aid of (72) and (74) in place of (80) and (70) we get

$$S_{slit} = \left(\sqrt{\pi} + 2\lambda \right) Dc \tag{89}$$

and

$$Y = \frac{\sqrt{\pi}}{2} \lambda D^2 \left(p_1 - p \right). \tag{90}$$

We determine all four kinds of work per unit of lifting force. From (84), (82), (81), (89) and (90), we obtain

$$\frac{R_{slit}}{Y} = \frac{2c}{D} \left(\frac{1}{\lambda} + \frac{2}{\sqrt{\pi}} \right) \sqrt{\frac{2g \left(p_1 - p \right)}{\rho c_{X_{pl}}}}. \tag{91}$$

In order to shorten the formulae, we will express constant and almost constant quantities by the letters A, B, Q, etc. Thus, in (91) we put

$$\sqrt{\frac{2g}{\rho}} = A \tag{91$_1$}$$

and

$$\frac{2c}{\sqrt{c_{X_{pl}}}} \left(\frac{1}{\lambda} + \frac{2}{\sqrt{\pi}} \right) = B. \tag{91$_2$}$$

Then in place of (91) we find

$$R_{slit} : Y = \frac{AB}{D} \sqrt{p_1 - p}. \tag{91$_3$}$$

Hence, the slit work diminishes with increasing car dimensions and reduction in pressure under the floor.

The additional slit work by inertia (per unit of lifting force) will be

$$\frac{R_{in.\,slit}}{Y} = \frac{V_{slit} \cdot \rho}{2gY} : \left(v_{tr} - v_{slit} \right)^2, \tag{92}$$

or, more exactly,

$$\frac{R_{in.\,slit}}{Y} = \frac{V_{slit} \rho}{2gY} v^2, \tag{92$_1$}$$

since the air flows from the slits in all directions.

From this fact and from formulae (82), (88), (72), (73) and (90) we derive

$$\frac{R_{in.\,slit}}{Y} = \frac{2c}{D} \sqrt{\frac{\rho}{2gC_{X_{pl}}(p_1 - p)}} \left(\frac{1}{\lambda} + \frac{2}{\sqrt{\pi}}\right) v_{tr}^2. \tag{93}$$

And on the basis of the simplifications (91_1) and (91_2) we find, in place of (93),

$$\frac{R_{in.\,slit}}{Y} = \frac{B v_{tr}^2}{AD \sqrt{(p_1 - p)}}. \tag{93_1}$$

Whence it is evident that this additional slit work also diminishes with increasing dimensions (D) of the car and its elongation (λ), and likewise with diminishing pressure under the floor. But high train speeds are very disadvantageous.

From (91_3) and (93_1) we determine the total slit work $(R_{tot.\,slit})$:

$$\frac{R_{tot.\,slit}}{Y} = \frac{B}{D} \left(A \sqrt{p_1 - p} + \frac{v_{tr}^2}{A \sqrt{p_1 - p}}\right). \tag{93_2}$$

Using formulae (85), (83), (79), (77_1) and (90), we find the reactive work of jet pressure. We obtain

$$\frac{R_{jet}}{Y} = \sqrt{\frac{2g\,(p_{jet} - p)}{\pi \rho C_{X_{pl}}}} \cdot \frac{K v_{tr}^2}{\lambda D^2\,(p_1 - p)}. \tag{94}$$

Here, K is known from (33) and (71_1). If in these formulae we assume that

$$C_{X_{sp}} \cdot K_{sh} \cdot C_{X_{pl}} : \lambda^2 + 4\eta \delta_1 : D = E, \tag{94_1}$$

then

$$K = \frac{\pi D^2}{8g}\,\rho E f. \tag{94_2}$$

Now from this fact and from (92_1) and (94) we obtain

$$\frac{R_{jet}}{Y} = \sqrt{\frac{\pi\,(p_{jet} - p)}{4C_{X_{pl}}\,(p_1 - p)^2}}\,\frac{E \cdot f}{A\lambda} \cdot v_{tr}^2. \tag{95}$$

It is seen from this that the reactive work of a jet diminishes with the jet pressure and the speed of the train. It also diminishes with increasing elongation (λ) and pressure under the floor of the car.

Indeed, the greater it is, the greater the lifting force and the smaller the work per unit of load. From (94₁) and (20), E and f depend on λ, but they do not change drastically.

Now let us calculate the relative additional work of inertia of the jet. It is expressed by the formula (87). From (87), using formulae (83), (79), (77₁) and (90), in place of (87) we get the following:

$$\frac{R_{in.\ jet}}{Y} = \sqrt{\frac{2\rho}{\pi g C_{X_{pl}}(p_{jet}-p)} \cdot \frac{K v_{tr}^2}{\lambda D^2 (p_1-p)}}\,(v_{tr}-v_{jet})^2. \quad (97)$$

From this, using (94₂) and (91₁), we find

$$\frac{R_{in.\ jet}}{Y} = \frac{E \cdot f}{2A^2\lambda} \sqrt{\frac{\pi}{C_{X_{pl}}}} \cdot \frac{v_{tr}^2 (v_{tr}-v_{jet})^2}{(p_1-p)\sqrt{p_{jet}-p}}. \quad (98)$$

From this it is clear that the work of inertia of the jet increases in proportion to the fourth power of the train speed, if the speed of the rear air jet is insignificant. On the contrary, all the work of inertia vanishes when the relative speed of the jet becomes equal to the speed of the train. Generally, the work diminishes with increasing elongation (λ) of the car and the jet pressure under the car floor.

The total work of the jet ($R_{tot.\ jet}$) is obtained from (95) and (98):

$$\frac{R_{tot.\ jet}}{Y} = \frac{E \cdot f}{2A\lambda} \sqrt{\frac{\pi}{C_{X_{pl}}}} \left\{ \sqrt{p_{jet}-p} + \frac{(v_{tr}-v_{jet})^2}{A^2 (p_1-p)\sqrt{p_{jet}-p}} \right\} \frac{v_{tr}^2}{p_1-p}. \quad (99)$$

It has a minimum if

$$v_{jet} = v_{tr}. \quad (100)$$

But then we have a condition that follows from formula (79). This and (100) yield

$$p_{jet} - p = \frac{\rho C_{X_{pl}}}{2g} \cdot v_{tr}^2. \quad (101)$$

From this it is seen that for minimum work the jet pressure should increase in proportion to the square of the train speed. Consequently, under the conditions of (100) and (101) we find— in place of (99) ['see (91₁)]—

$$\frac{R_{tot.\ jet}}{Y} = \frac{E \cdot f \sqrt{\pi}}{2A^2\lambda} \cdot \frac{v_{tr}^3}{p_1-p}. \quad (102)$$

Hence, with ultimate efficiency the jet work is proportional to the cube of the train speed. But the speed diminishes with increasing elongation and pressure under the car floor. Equations (93_2) and (102) tell us that the slit work increases with increasing train speed more slowly than the jet work. If we equate both kinds of work, we find that

$$v_{tr} = \sqrt{M \left(1 + \frac{v_{tr}^2}{A^2 (p_1 - p)} \right)}, \qquad (103)$$

where

$$M = \frac{2A^2 B\lambda}{\sqrt{\pi}\ E f D} (p_1 - p)^{3/2}. \qquad (104)$$

Let us assume:

$$c = 0.001;\ C_{X_{pl}} = 1.5;\ \lambda = 10;\ C_{X_{sp}} = 0.4;$$

$$p_1 - p = 1;\ K_{sh} = 1;\ K_{jet} = 0.75;\ \delta_1 = 0.0084;$$

$$D = 3. \qquad (105)$$

Then from formulae (91_1), (91_2) and (94_1) we calculate: A = 123; $A^2 = 15,130$; $A^3 = 1,861,000$; B = 0.002; E = 0.0173 and $M = = 813,000 : f$.

The first approximation for the car speed will be

$$v_1 = \sqrt[3]{M} = 116 : \sqrt[3]{f}. \qquad (106)$$

From formula (20), $f = 0.53$.

Hence, $v_1 = 144$ m/sec. The second approximation will be $v_2 = 187$ m/sec. The third, more than 200 m/sec.

In view of the fact that the fraction in (103) is greater than unity, for the first approximation we can suppress unity; then in place of (103) we get

$$v_{tr} = M : \{A^2 (p_1 - p)\}. \qquad (107)$$

From this we find $v_1 = 158$ m/sec. The subsequent approximations are then found from (103). The second approximation will now be close to the truth: $v_2 = 220$ m/sec. This method will bring us to our goal quicker. And so for the velocity found, the slit work will become equal to the jet work. Consequently, for small velocities, up to 50 m/sec, we can count only the slit work, and for velocities greater than 400 m/sec, only the jet work (102). But do not forget condition (100). From formula (101) we calculate approximately

$$p_{jet} - p = \frac{C_{X_{pl}}}{A^2} \cdot v_{tr}^2 = 0.0001 \cdot v_{tr}^2. \tag{108}$$

For instance

$$\left.\begin{array}{lccccccc} v_{tr}, \text{ m/sec} & \ldots & 10 & 30 & 50 & 100 & 200 & 300 \\ p_{jet} - p, \text{ ton/m}^2 & \ldots & 0.01 & 0.09 & 0.25 & 1 & 4 & 9 \end{array}\right\} \tag{109}$$

The speed (in km/hr) will be from 36 to 1,080, while the jet pressure will vary from 0.001 atmosphere to 0.9 (9 tons). At a speed of 1,000 m/sec it will reach 10 atmospheres. This increases the work and makes our formulae of work unsuitable.

The formulae are fully valid for submarines and ships with jet devices where the medium—water—is only slightly compressible.

From formula (103) it is seen that the critical speed of the train may be increased if M is increased. Now M increases (104) when we increase the elongation of the train or the pressure under the floor.

We shall not consider the case when the jet velocity is not equal to the speed of the train, as being uneconomical.

Then for the total work (R_{tot}) of the train we have the formulae (93_2) and (102). From them we find

$$\frac{R_{tot}}{Y} = \frac{B \cdot A}{D} \sqrt{p_1 - p} + \frac{B}{AD} \frac{v_{tr}^2}{\sqrt{p_1 - p}} + \frac{\sqrt{\pi} E f}{2A^2 \lambda} \cdot \frac{v_{tr}^3}{p_1 - p}. \tag{110}$$

Given condition (105), we calculate that

$$BA : D = 0.082; \tag{111}$$

$$B : (DA) = 0.0000054; \tag{112}$$

$$\sqrt{\pi} E : (2A \cdot \lambda) = 0.000000101. \tag{113}$$

This will suffice to compile a table of work values for various velocities.

From Table 114 (row 15) we see that the total work per ton of lifting force varies from 1.8 to 27 (in metric horsepower). This is in one second. Per unit distance (row 16), it fluctuates between 1.8 kg-m (for a speed of 100 m/sec) and 6.8 kg-m (speed 400 m/sec). And the utilization lies between 556 and 12 (row 17). For a speed of 1 m/sec, the utilization in distance covered is just the same as on poor railways, but more than by an aeroplane. The table also shows that up to 50 m/sec (row 15) the engine power (per second) may be considered constant, irrespective

TABLE 114

	1	10	20	25	30	35	40
1	1	10	20	25	30	35	40
2	3.6	36	72	90	108	126	144
3	86.4	864	1,728	2,160	2,592	3,024	3,456
4	0.05	5	20	31.25	45	61.25	80
5	0.14	14	56	88.8	126	173.6	240
6	0.035	3.5	14	22.2	31.5	434	56
7	4.40	2.10	1.41	1.18	1	0.870	0.781
8	1	100	400	625	900	1,225	1,600
9	0.029	1.41	3.78	4.96	6.03	7.13	8.37
10	0.00001	0.001	0.004	0.00625	0.009	0.01225	0.016
11	0.29	2.9	5.8	7.25	8.7	10.15	11.6
12	274,600	5,640	2,180	1,660	1,320	1,117	952
13	0.82	0.82	0.85	0.85	0.87	0.89	0.91
14	—	0.0021	0.0113	0.0184	0.027	0.037	0.05
15	0.82	0.82	0.86	0.87	0.90	0.93	0.96
16	82	8.2	4.3	3.5	3.0	2.7	2.4
17	12	122	233	286	333	370	417
18	0.000054	0.025	0.12	0.18	0.24	0.30	0.36
19	0.0102	1.02	4.08	6.08	9.18	12.50	16.32
20	0.02	2	8	12	18	25	32.6
21	—	—	24.5	19.6	16.3	14.0	12.2
22	—	10	40	60	90	120	160
23	—	4.9	2.5	2.0	1.6	1.4	1.2
24	10	100	200	250	300	350	400
25	0.014	1.4	5.6	8.88	12.6	17.36	24

	50	60	70	80	90	100	150
1	50	60	70	80	90	100	150
2	180	216	252	288	324	360	540
3	4,320	5,184	6,048	6,912	7,776	8,640	12,960
4	125	180	245	320	405	500	1,125
5	375	512	735	908	1,148	1,400	3,150
6	87.5	128	171.5	227	287	350	787.5
7	0.662	0.592	0.541	0.505	0.476	0.453	0.383
8	2,500	3,600	4,900	6,400	8,100	10,000	22,500
9	11.08	14.22	17.79	21.64	25.84	30.35	57.72
10	0.025	0.036	0.049	0.064	0.081	0.1	0.225
11	14.5	17.4	20.3	23.2	26.1	29.0	43.5
12	717	561	447	369	309	262	138
13	0.98	1.01	1.09	1.17	1.26	1.36	2.04
14	0.0825	0.128	0.186	0.259	0.347	0.453	1.28
15	1.06	1.14	1.276	1.429	1.607	1.813	3.32
16	2.1	1.9	1.8	1.8	1.8	1.8	2.2
17	481	526	556	556	556	556	453

TABLE 114 (continued)

18	0.47	0.56	0.63	0.69	0.73	0.77	0.86
19	25.50	36.72	49.98	65.28	82.62	102.00	229.5
20	51	73	100	131	165	204	459
21	9.8	8.2	7	5.4	6.1	4.9	3.3
22	250	370	500	650	830	1,020	2,300
23	0.98	0.82	0.7	0.54	0.61	0.49	0.33
24	500	600	700	800	900	1,000	1,500
25	37.5	51.2	73.6	90.8	114.8	140	315
1	200	300	400	500	600	800	1,000
2	720	1,080	1,440	1,800	2,160	2,880	3,600
3	17,280	2,592	34,560	43,200	51,840	69,120	86,400
4	2,000	4,500	8,000	12,500	18,000	32,000	50,000
5	5,600	12,600	24,000	37,500	51,200	90,800	140,000
6	1,400	3,150	5,600	8,750	12,800	22,700	35,000
7	0.345	0.303	0.279	0.26	0.245	0.23	0.22
8	40,000	90,000	160,000	250,000	360,000	640,000	1,000,000
9	92.46	18.27	298.8	452	583	984	1,473
10	0.4	0.9	1.6	2.5	3.6	6.4	10.0
11	58.0	87.0	116.0	145	174	232	290
12	86.1	43.6	26.7	17.6	13.7	8.1	5.4
13	2.98	5.68	9.48	16.8	19.8	35.8	54.8
14	2.72	8.10	17.9	32.5	52.8	117.8	220.0
15	5.70	13.78	27.38	49.3	72.6	153.6	274.8
16	2.8	4.5	6.8	9.86	12.1	19.2	27.5
17	355	222	147	101.4	82.6	52.1	36.4
18	0.90	0.93	0.95	0.958	0.964	0.971	0.976
19	408.00	918.00	1,632	2,550	3,672	6,528	10,200
20	816	1,836	3,264	5,100	7,344	13,056	20,400
21	2.45	1.63	1.22	0.98	0.803	0.612	0.490
22	4,080	9,180	16,320	25,500	36,700	65,300	102,000
23	0.25	0.16	0.12	0.098	0.080	0.061	0.049
24	2,000	3,000	4,000	5,000	6,000	8,000	10,000
25	560	1,260	2,400	750	5,120	9,080	14,000

of the speed (8 to 10 metric horsepower). As we have seen, for a speed between 200 and 250 m/sec, the slit work and jet work become equal. At a speed of 200 m/sec and higher the first term may be neglected, and for 800-1,000 m/sec, it is sufficient to take only the third term, that is, the jet work alone.

From formula (110) it is evident that, on the one hand, the work increases with increasing pressure under the car floor, and, on the other hand, it diminishes. Clearly the work has a minimum. In formula (110) let us put

$$B \cdot A : D = Q, \tag{115}$$

$$v_{tr}^2 B : (AD) = U, \tag{116}$$

$$\sqrt{\pi} \, E f v^3 : (2A^2 \lambda) = J \tag{117}$$

and

$$\sqrt{p_1 - p} = Z. \tag{118}$$

Then in place of (110) we find

$$\frac{R_{tot}}{Y} = Q \cdot Z + UZ^{-1} + JZ^{-2}. \tag{119}$$

Differentiating and equating the derivative to zero, for the minimum work we find

$$Z = \sqrt[3]{\frac{2J}{Q} + \frac{U}{Q} Z} \, . \tag{120}$$

On the basis of (115-117) we calculate

$$\frac{U}{Q} = \frac{v_{tr}^2}{A^2} \tag{121}$$

and

$$\frac{2J}{Q} = \frac{\sqrt{\pi} \, E f D}{A^3 \lambda B} \cdot v_{tr}^3. \tag{122}$$

From the conditions given in (105) we find

$$\frac{U}{Q} = \left(\frac{v_{tr}}{123} \right)^2 \tag{123}$$

and

$$\frac{2J}{Q} = 4.59 \left(\frac{v_{tr}}{123} \right)^3. \tag{124}$$

For a speed greater than 123 m/sec we can disregard the second term. Then from (120) and (124) we find

$$Z = \sqrt{\frac{2J}{Q}} = 0.0135 \cdot v_{tr}. \tag{125}$$

This is the first approximation. For example, at a velocity of 123 m/sec, $Z = 1.66$, at 100 m/sec, $Z = 1.35$.

The second approximation is obtained from formula (120). For a velocity of 123 m/sec, $Z_2 = 1.84$, whence, from (118) $R_{id} = 3.39$. This comes to about 0.34 atmosphere, which has an advantage but is not practicable. The third approximation yields almost the same thing.

12—67

For high speeds, the optimal pressure under the car floor is nearly proportional to the square of the speed [(125) and (118)]. And for very low speeds, disregarding the first term in (120), we find

$$Z = v_{tr}/123. \tag{126}$$

From this, $R_{id} = Z^2 = 0.00066 \cdot v_{tr}^2$. Thus, for

v_{tr}	10	20	30	40	50	100
R_{id}	0.066	0.264	0.594	1.056	1.65	6.6

The table is only suitable for low speeds. Thus, for 30 m/sec we have about 0.6 ton, or 0.06 atmosphere. The law of increasing pressure is the same as for high speeds.

Now what is the utilization of the actual work (R_{tot}), i.e., the slit work, jet work and inertia as compared with the ideal work (R_{id}) needed to overcome the resistance of the medium in the translational motion of a train or ship?

From (71) it is seen that the work of resistance is

$$R_{id} = K v_{tr}^3. \tag{127}$$

The ideal work per unit of lifting force will be

$$\frac{R_{id}}{Y} = \frac{K}{Y} v_{tr}^3. \tag{128}$$

On the basis of (94_2), (91_1) and (90) we obtain

$$\frac{K}{Y} = \frac{\sqrt{\pi}\, \mathrm{E}f}{2\mathrm{A}^2 \lambda R_{id}}. \tag{129}$$

Now from (129), (128) and (110) we find

$$\frac{R_{tot}}{R_{id}} = 1 + \frac{2\mathrm{AB}\lambda \sqrt{R_{id}}}{\sqrt{\pi}\mathrm{E}\, fDv_{tr}} \cdot \left\{ 1 + \left(\frac{\mathrm{A}}{v_{tr}}\right)^2 \cdot (p_1 - p) \right\}. \tag{130}$$

From the data of (105) we get

$$\frac{R_{tot}}{R_{id}} = 1 : \varepsilon = 1 + \frac{16.08 \sqrt{R_{id}}}{fDv_{tr}} \cdot \left\{ 1 + \left(\frac{123}{v_{tr}}\right)^2 \cdot (p_1 - p) \right\}. \tag{131}$$

This quantity is the inverse of the utilization of work that corresponds to the utilization of an air screw or propeller. The greater the ratio (131), the lower the utilization. Hence, the utilization increases with increasing size of the vehicle (D), the speed of the train and with diminishing pressure under the floor.

When the difference $p_1 - p$ is close to 1 and the speed is great, the slit work may be neglected and the utilization (considering the medium noncompressible and $v_{jet} = v_{tr}$) will be unity and the use 100%. In formula (131) let us put $p_1 - p = 1$; $D = 3$, and take f from formula (20). (132)

We then compile row 18 of utilization (114) for different car speeds by the formula

$$\frac{R_{tot}}{R_{id}} = 1 + \frac{5.36}{fv_{tr}} \left\{ 1 + \left(\frac{132}{v_{tr}} \right)^2 \right\}. \qquad (134)$$

For low speeds, the utilization may be taken equal to

$$\varepsilon = f \cdot v_{tr}^3 : 81,000. \qquad (135)$$

Then the utilization is negligible because in that case the air resistance is unnoticeable compared with the tremendous amount of slit work. At 50 m/sec, utilization reaches 47%. After that it continues to increase, approaching unity. At 400 m/sec it is already 95%.

The curvature of path—whether horizontal or vertical—cannot be arbitrary. Horizontal curvature can generate a centrifugal force that will overturn the train or carry it off the tracks, while vertical curvature (the vertical component of the inclined radius of curvature) can either kill the passenger with its centrifugal force or temporarily eliminate weight and carry the train off the tracks.

Suppose that the increase in relative gravity due to the vertical curvature is not greater than the earth's gravity, so that the total relative gravity is either doubled or made equal to zero. In the latter case the car hardly at all touches the roadbed and just barely stays on the tracks. Then we have

$$v_{tr}^2 : r = g, \qquad (136)$$

where r is the vertical radius of curvature. From (136) we find

$$r = v_{tr}^2 : g. \qquad (137)$$

This is sufficient to fill the 19th row of Table 114. The vertical curvature of the roadway should not exceed these magnitudes, that is to say, the radii must not be less, otherwise either the relative gravity will be more than doubled (in the case of a concave roadway) or the resultant gravity will be reversed (in the case of a convex roadbed) and the train will rise from the rails. We see that even for high velocities such curvature is still rather practicable. Let us try to visualize this curvature. For instance, take the speed of 1,000 m/sec. Using the formula

$$\sigma = l^2 : (2r) \qquad (138)$$

we can calculate approximately what the height of elevation (the height is equal to σ) or the depth of depression will be for a given track length (l) and for a given radius of curvature. For a speed of 1,000 m/sec, $r = 10,200$ m (137). This radius is less than that of the earth by a factor of 6,000. Let $l = 1$ km $= 1,000$ m. Then from formula (138) we find $\sigma = 49$ m, which is 49 m or 4.9% of the distance for every verst of depression or elevation. This is a great curvature and is a rare occurrence in flat country.

When the additional gravity is half the earth's gravity, the radii of curvature double (row 20).

From (138) and (137) we get

$$\sigma = \frac{g}{2} \left(\frac{l}{v_{tr}}\right)^2 , \qquad (139)$$

whence we can obtain the height of the path directly as a function of the ratio $l : v_{tr}$. If, for example, a portion of the pathway and the speed per second are equal, the height will come to 4.9 metres, which in percentage of the pathway will be expressed by row 21.

The horizontal curvature for a given bed profile (Fig. 1) generates the friction of solid bodies and is impermissible; for a different profile (Fig. 3) it tilts the car and may carry it off the tracks. Curvature here is permissible, but it should be much less, say such as to generate an additional gravity of 0.1 the earth's gravity or 1 m/sec² of acceleration. Then the radii of curvature will turn out to be 10 times greater (137).

The magnitude of height for $l = v_{tr}$ will, according to (139), be 10 times less. The percentage of distance is given by row 22. Thus, for a speed of 100 m/sec and the same pathway, the height will be half a per cent, which is only 50 cm.

We now give a general explanation of Table 114.

1. Speed of train in metres per second. We take the interval from 1 to 1,000.

2. The speed in kilometres per hour: from the speed of a pedestrian to 3,600 km/hr. The speed of a railway train from 10 to 30 m/sec, of an aeroplane, from 30 to 40, and a top speed of 100 m/sec.

3. Daily speed in kilometres. At 500 m/sec, it exceeds the speed of equatorial points on the earth. At this speed, the earth executes a circuit in less than 24 hours. This is the speed of a bullet. The top speed (km/sec) approaches that of a cannon-ball.

4. The numbers indicate the height in metres that the train can cover by momentum when moving up a hill. At the record speed of an aircraft (100 m/sec), hills 500 metres in height are surmountable, and at 400 m/sec, the train can climb from sea level to the summits of the highest mountains on the earth.

5. Maximum (for an initial incline of 45°) horizontal jump of a car in metres with air resistance neglected. Because of the special elongated shape of the car, the air resistance does not appreciably change these numbers. Even for a record aircraft speed (100 m/sec), the horizontal jump is 1,400 m, at 400 m/sec, it is 24 km, and at 1,000 m/sec, it is 140 km. This would enable us to fly over rivers, ravines and mountains (no bridges needed, naturally) if it weren't for the danger of such jumps. What is needed is a perfectly exact pathway both at the start and finish of the aerial flight. How can one impact at a precise spot if the direction cannot be absolutely true, and the flight itself in the atmosphere is constantly changing due to air resistance and winds? To a certain extent, it is possible to reach a specific site if the train is controlled in flight like an aeroplane. In that case it will have to have controls like those of an aeroplane. These would be put in operation only when the vehicle is in flight.

6. Maximum elevation during a jump. For a record aircraft speed, it would come to 350 m, which is just a bit higher than the Eiffel Tower; but at speeds of 500 m/sec the rise will already exceed the altitudes of the highest mountains on the earth.

7. The magnitude of f from formula (20).

8. The square of the train speed.

9. Resistance of the medium in kilograms, or the required thrust. This is the magnitude of the rear reactive jet pressure. We make use of formulae (71), (94_2), (20) and (94_1). At first the rear pressure is slight, but at velocities of 1,000 m/sec it is more than a ton. Use is made of formulae (71), (129). Row 12 is more interesting.

10. From formula (101) we determine the difference of jet pressures or simply the jet pressure $(p_{jet} - p)$. This we give in metric atmospheres. Up to 100 m/sec it does not exceed 0.1 atmosphere, but at 300 m/sec it is just under a whole atmosphere, and at 1,000 m/sec it is equal to 10 atmospheres.

Actually it may be the desired magnitude, but we have bound ourselves by the condition of least work, and the speeds of jet and train have to be equal.

The area of the jet opening is computed from formula (77_1). From (77_1) and (101) we find

$$S_{jet} = \frac{2gK}{\rho C_{x_{pl}}}. \tag{140}$$

As may be seen from the formula, this is a constant quantity equal to 0.29 m², or 2,900 cm². A round opening will have a diameter of 60.8 cm.

11. From (83), (77₁) and (101) we get the volume of the jet emitted per second:

$$V_{jet} = \frac{2Kv_{tr}g}{\rho C_{X_{pl}}}.$$ (141)

Hence, the loss of air per second (or the ejected air) is proportional to the speed of the train, which is obvious in the case of a constant rear opening.

The 11th row gives this quantity in cubic metres. Incidentally, formula (83) suffices for calculations. The ejected air amounts to 0.29-29 m³ for speeds of 100 m/sec and even up to 290 m³ for a speed of 1 km/sec. It will be noted that as the speed is increased, these figures deviate more and more from the true figures. Here we have disregarded compression of air. But if we take into account a slight definite jet pressure, say one ton (0.1 atmosphere) per square metre, it is easy to give the formulae and numbers that correspond to reality for high train speeds as well. But then there will be no minimum of work.

We determine the area of the slit openings from formula (89). Applying the condition of (105) we get 0.065 m², or 658 cm². The corresponding diameter of an imaginary circular aperture will be 28.8 cm. The slit area is one third the area of the jet aperture. The speed of the slit jets is likewise constant. From formula (81) it is found to be 103 m/sec. But since in actual practice the speed will be much less due to the appreciable friction in the narrow slits between the corrugated base of the car and the roadway (Fig. 2), the car will rise with the same loss of air and the distance between the car and the roadway will increase. The quantity of slit air pumped in per second is found (82) to be 6.7 m³. It is constant for a constant pressure under the floor of the car and does not depend on the speed of the train.

12. The figures in this row indicate the number of times the thrust (9th row) is less than the lifting force. The latter is a constant and is determined from formula (90). We find 79.65 tons, or 79,650 kg. At first, when the speed is low, the thrust is hardly noticeable in comparison to the lifting force. But even for a speed of 35 m/sec it is less than 0.1% of the lifting force, while for 150 m/sec it is less than 1%, and only at a speed of 400 m/sec does it reach 3.7%. However, at 1,000 m/sec it becomes prohibitively great, attaining 18.5% of the lifting force.

From (93₂) and (102) we find

$$\frac{R_{tr}}{Y} = \frac{BA}{D} \sqrt{p_1 - p} + \frac{B}{AD} \frac{v_{tr}^2}{\sqrt{p_1 - p}} + \frac{\sqrt{\pi} Ef}{2A^2\lambda} \frac{v_{tr}^3}{p_1 - p}.$$ (142)

Taking into account the conditions of (105) we calculate

$$BA : D = 0.082, \qquad (143)$$

$$B : (AD) = 0.0000054, \qquad (144)$$

$$\sqrt{\pi}E : (2A^2\lambda) = 0.000000102. \qquad (145)$$

This is sufficient to supplement our table with the quantity of work per ton of lifting force. The first term in (142) expresses the constant slit work minus the work of inertia of the air injected under the car. It amounts to 0.082 ton-metre, or 0.82 metric horsepower per second per ton of train. The sum of the two first terms makes up the total slit work needed to support the car on a thin layer of air, that is to say, to wipe out contact with the roadbed and eliminate the friction of solids.

13. This slit work is expressed in metric horsepower in the 13th row. It is nearly constant up to a speed of 100 m/sec and is close to one metric horsepower per ton. But at 400 m/sec it reaches ten horsepower, and at 1,000 m/sec, 55. It would not vary at all for any velocities if we made use of material stored in the car for injection.

14. This row indicates the jet work, or the magnitude of the third term of the formula. This work is negligible at low speeds. Only at 200 m/sec does it come close to the amount of slit work. At higher speeds it exceeds the slit work: at 1,000 m/sec it is four times greater, for example. And this work would be much less if the air supply were at first in motion with the train itself.

15. This row yields the total amount of work per ton of lifting force. In the table it varies between 0.8 and 275 metric horsepower. The weight of light aeroplane engines does not take up more than 28% of the lifting force. Higher speeds demand still lighter engines. Incidentally, it will be noted that air condensation will not increase the work appreciably. The reason is that, although more work is expended, it goes into heating, which (upon expansion of the air) again yields the useful work of motion. Only slit compression heats the air between the floor and the roadbed; the air cools rapidly and returns only a small part of the work expended on heating.

16. This row gives the amount of work per kg-m per unit of distance covered and per ton of weight. It reaches a minimum at 100 m/sec, namely 1.8 kg-m per ton of lifting force.

17. The effectiveness of this mode of transportation is expressed in row 17. The maximum reaches 556 (at speeds of 70 to 100 m/sec), which means that the work of horizontal translation here is 556 times less than the work of vertical ascent or the work of lift-

ing. This mode of transportation is sufficiently economical for speeds between 10 and 500 or 600 m/sec.

18. Using formula (134) it is possible to calculate the ratio of actual work to the work of the resistance of the medium, or the reverse. The latter will correspond to the efficiency of the screw propeller of a steamship or the air screw of a dirigible. The 18th row gives this ratio for different speeds [see (135) et seq.].

19. The least radii of vertical curvature in metres [see close to (136)].

20. Radii of curvature for which variation of gravity amounts to one half the earth's gravity [see (139) above].

21. The magnitude of depression or convexity (height) for a length equal to the speed (row 1) in percentage of the distance covered (139).

22. The maximum radii of lateral curvature on condition of an increase in the lateral increment of (horizontal) gravity by 0.1 of the earth's gravity, in metres.

23. The appropriate magnitude of heights, provided $v_{tr} = l$ is expressed in percentage.

24-25. The work required to attain the initial speed is negligible only in the case of ordinary low speeds. But for high speeds, the amount of work required is tremendous. To get an idea of this work, let us suppose that the car is acted upon by a constant force P. Then, neglecting the air resistance, we find out the time (24) and the distance covered in that time (25) by the train (L). We have

$$a = g : \frac{Y}{P} ; \tag{146}$$

$$t = \frac{v}{a} ; \tag{147}$$

$$L = \frac{a}{2} t^2, \tag{148}$$

where a is the acceleration of the train in one second. Whence

$$L = \frac{v_{tr}^2 Y}{2gP} . \tag{149}$$

Here (150) let us put $Y = 79.65$ [see (12)], or 80 tons, let the thrust P be 1% of the lifting force, i.e., 0.8 ton, or 800 kg, which is close to the thrust for a speed of 800 m/sec [see Table 114, row 9]. Then, using the given formulae, we calculate the times (row 24) and the distances (row 25). The acceleration of the train will be 0.1 m/sec², or about 10 cm/sec². The time (24th row) is expressed in seconds. It will be seen that acquiring speed takes a rather long time—up to 2½ hours for a speed of 1,000 m/sec.

An ordinary speed of 10 to 20 m/sec is attained in a quarter of an hour. The distances covered during this time are still more terrifying. For ordinary speeds (10-20 m/sec), they are from 1.4 to 5.6 km. For acquiring a speed of 100 m/sec the train has to cover 140 km and for a speed of 1,000 m/sec — 1,400 km.

Speeds can be obtained by going down mountains. Row 4 indicates the mountain heights, row 1, the corresponding speeds. The highest terrestrial mountains cannot provide a speed greater than 400 m/sec. Row 4 also shows altitudes of mountains which can shed speed (row 1) acquired in ascent.

For a thrust of 10% of the lifting force, the times (for acquiring speed) and the appropriate distances are reduced by a factor of 10.

Explosion can yield an incomparably greater thrust. Taking the thrust equal to the weight of the train, the times and distances will be cut another 10-fold, making it a factor of one hundred as compared with rows 24 and 25. Then even at the top speed of 1,000 m/sec the time will be less than 2 minutes (100 sec), and the acceleration distance, 140 km. These distances are in agreement with the numbers of row five (5).

Any appraisal of the new mode of transportation is at present extremely difficult. On the one hand, we have the advantage of simplicity of a non-wheel train, great lifting force and high speeds, on the other, the high cost of an accurately made concrete roadway with iron or steel flanges. True, the pressure on it is very uniform, without jolts or vibrations, but still it would probably come out more expensive than a railway track, even without the flanges. However, the extra expense put into the concrete roadway might be compensated for by the smaller outlays on repair work. In the future we could even think of eliminating bridges across ravines and rivers and reducing earthwork. The future demands for high speeds may call for sacrifices in the way of expenditures in favour of this mode of transportation. At low speeds, up to 10 m/sec, the utilization of the roadway (see row 17) is low (not more than 122) and the speed itself is of little interest. Speeds of 20 to 300 m/sec (72 to 1,080 km/hr) are attractive because of high efficiencies (from 222 to 556) and the speed itself is substantial (half an hour to cover the distance between Moscow and Leningrad, 10 hours from pole to equator and less than two days around the earth following a meridian). The maximum utilization of energy (row 17) is 556 for speeds between 70 and 100 m/sec. But even for 150 m/sec, the efficiency is 453. In the latter case, a horizontal jump (row 5) reaches 3 km; in the distant future this may eliminate the necessity of bridges. But the vertical jump does not even reach 800 m. This is not enough for flying over all mountains. The efficiency is low at high velocities. For example at 400 m/sec, the efficiency is 147. But in this case the horizontal jump comes up to 24 km, and the vertical jump to 5.6 km, which is sufficient for all terrestrial cases. It will be noted that the efficiency may be increased on the basis of our formulae by elongating the train (λ), increasing its cross-sectional dimensions (D) and the pressure under the floor ($p_1 - p$) [see (110)]. This method of eliminating friction may be applied in the case of explosion engines for imparting a preliminary velocity to space rockets.

Incidentally, for speeds up to 100 m/sec (360 km/hr) it is simpler to employ an aeroplane propeller. This plus rudders would convert a train into a wingless aircraft sliding along the earth and only occasionally rising upwards to fly over a river or a mountain by means of the force of acceleration or inertia.

✳ BRIEF CAPTION TO TABLE 114

1. Speed in metres per second. 2. Speed in kilometres per hour. 3. Speed in kilometres per day. 4. Altitude of mountain climb following acceleration. 5. Horizontal jump. 6. Vertical jump. 7. f [formula (20)]. 8. The square of the speed per second. 9. Thrust in kilograms. 10. Jet pressure in atmospheres. 11. Volume of jet ejection per second. 12. Lifting force relative to thrust. 13. Slit work in metric horsepower per ton of lifting force. 14. Jet work per ton. 15. Total work in metric horsepower per ton of lifting force. 16. Work per unit of distance (metre) and per ton of weight, kg-m. 17. The efficiency of this work. 18. The ideal work of resistance of the medium relative to the actual work. 19. The least radii of vertical curvature. 20. The same radii doubled. 21. Depressions of roadway or their heights in percentage of the distance equal to the speed (row 1). 22. Maximum radii of lateral or horizontal curvature. 23. Maximum heights in percentage of the distance covered equal to the speed (row 1). 24. Time in seconds to attain speeds of row 1, assuming a thrust of 1% of the train's weight. 25. The corresponding acceleration distance in km.

Cosmic Rocket Trains

(1929)

✳ FROM THE AUTHOR

I am already 72 years of age. I have long since given up working with my hands and do not perform any experiments.

In the West, work on reactive vehicles has been in progress since the publication of my first paper in 1903.

At first, applications were sought in the military field (Unge in Sweden and Krupp in Germany).

Later, following the appearance of another one of my papers in 1911-12, the work performed was of a theoretical and experimental nature (Birkeland, Goddard). It was at that time also that Esnault-Pelterie expressed his views.

But from 1913 onwards many in Russia as well had become interested in problems of flight beyond the atmosphere, particularly when they saw the serious attitude towards this problem in the West. The pioneers were Ryumin, Perelman (scientific papers and articles of a popular nature), Shirinkin, B. Vorobyov, Manuilov, Ryabushinsky, Shmurlo and others.

Oberth became interested in astronautics after the publication of my work "Beyond the Earth" in the widely circulated magazine "Priroda i lyudi" (Nature and People), 1918 (the article was published separately in 1920). Oberth's article gave the German scientists and thinkers an appreciable impulse to the publication of fresh work by new people: Wolf, Valier, Heft, Hohmann, Ley,

Sander, Opel, Scherschevsky, Lademann. The last two (particularly Lademann) translated and circulated my works. In the USSR the same was done by Modestov, Bayat, Ivanovsky, Yegorov, Davydov, Lapirov-Skoblo, and others.

Rocket automobiles, hydroplanes, sleighs and even aeroplanes appeared (under the supervision of Stamer), they were all extremely imperfect but produced a lot of noise and were useful both experimentally and with regard to building up interest in the general public, and among scientists and designers.

These ideas became more widespread in the USSR as well. Very active were Vetchinkin (with lectures), Tsander and Rynin. Rynin did much to disseminate ideas of astronautics by means of his excellent works, extensive knowledge of the literature, and his impartiality. It may be said that our first specialist in this field was Prof. Rynin. The new idea was actively propounded by Chizhevsky, Rodnykh, Stroganov, Redin, Solovyov, and by other unknown investigators.

Not only abroad but here too, institutes are set up and societies formed whose members are successfully and ably disseminating the new ideas. Such are Lvov, Perelman, Vorobyov, Veigelin, Rodnykh, Vengerov, Kondratenko, Lutsenko, and other members of these societies. In particular, a large number of very serious articles have been written by Perelman and Lvov.

I greet the workers of astronautics both in the USSR and abroad. They will have to work many tens of years yet, for this is still a thankless, risky and immeasurably difficult undertaking. It will require not only an extraordinary concentration of strength and brilliant talent, but also much sacrifice.

Most people regard astronautics as a heretical idea and refuse to listen. Others are sceptical and view it as something absolutely impossible, while still others are all too trusting and believe that it will soon be accomplished. But the first unavoidable failures discourage and repulse the weak and undermine the trust of society.

Those at work here await great disappointments, for a favourable solution of the problem is much more difficult than even the most perspicacious minds realize. Their failures, exhaustion and loss of hope will compel them to leave this matter unfinished and in a sad state. New workers will again and again be needed to add fresh energy and selfless strength.

Astronautics cannot even be compared with flying in the air. The latter is a toy beside the former.

There have undoubtedly been advances, but when it will be accomplished is far from certain as far as I am concerned.

188

Any idea that the solution is easy is a passing delusion. True it is useful in that it is invigorating.

Many now working with enthusiasm would recoil with horror if they only knew the difficulties of the job.

But then how wonderful will the final achievement be. Conquest of the solar system will yield not only energy and life, which will be two thousand million times as abundant as terrestrial energy and life, but the expanse of space will be still greater. Man, in his mastery of the earth, is in possession, so to speak, of only two dimensions, the third is limited; that is, movement upwards and downwards is as yet impossible. But then man will have three dimensions... .

The absence of gravity, the virginal rays of the sun, and any desirable temperature obtained in structures by the sun's rays alone, and completely free motion in all six directions, and fresh knowledge of the universe... . We here are not able to appraise all the good and all the advantages of a conquest of the solar system. I have given some idea in my above-mentioned composition "Beyond the Earth".

✳ COSMIC ROCKET TRAINS

1. By rocket train I mean a combination of several identical reactive vehicles moving first along a roadway, then in the air then in empty space beyond the atmosphere, and finally between the planets or suns.

2. But only one part of this train reaches celestial space, the other parts, since they lack the necessary speed, return to the earth.

3. To reach cosmic velocity, a single rocket has to have a large supply of fuel. Thus, to attain the first cosmic velocity, which is 8 km/sec, the weight of the fuel has to be at least 4 times that of the rocket with all its contents.[1] This complicates the construction of reactive vehicles.

Now a train permits attaining high cosmic velocities or makes it possible to reduce the supply of components of explosion to relatively small amounts.

4. We shall first work on the problem in its most elementary form. We assume the design of all rockets to be absolutely iden-

---

[1] Using present-day propellants, it is possible for a single-stage rocket to achieve the first cosmic velocity (orbital velocity) with a fuel supply much less than four times the dry weight of the rocket (Editors).

tical. The fuel supply and the force of explosion as well. Actually, of course, there will be certain deviations. Thus, rockets moving along a roadway will be simpler; those for travel only in the atmosphere need not be equipped with devices for prolonged manned flight in ethereal space.

5. The explosion begins at the front rocket so that the whole train is subjected to tension and not compression, which is easier to combat.[2] Besides, it makes for stability of the train during explosion. In this procedure, it is possible to compose a longer train and, hence, obtain a higher velocity with the same fuel supply in each rocket car.

6. The shorter the cars, the greater must be their number for the same margin of safety; and the larger the number, the greater will be the ultimate speed of the rearmost car. This compels us to make the separate vehicles as short as possible. But the diameter of a rocket vehicle cannot be less than one metre. This means that the length of a rocket car cannot be less than 10 m. For a smaller elongation, the air resistance will be excessively great. For rockets returning to the earth, this may be sufficient, but a space car must be at least 3 metres in diameter and 30 metres in length. The conclusion therefore is that the rearmost space car will have to be made more spacious.[3]

7. The design of a space rocket is very complicated and will continue to become even more so. It is not our purpose for the present to go into details. The aim here is different: to show the advantages of a train relative to ultimate speed in comparison with a single reactive vehicle. Possibly, a small rocket will, upon reaching ethereal space, expand into a big one. But we will not take that up and will accept the rocket dimensions at 3 and 30 m.

8. The rocket has a diameter of 3 m and a length of 30 m, wall thickness being 2 mm (at the ends it is thicker). The material has a density of 8. The area of the median cross-section is 7 m², the surface area 180 m², the volume 105 m³. The rocket can hold 105 tons of water. A one-metre section of the shell weighs the same everywhere, namely 0.15 ton, since it is thicker at the ends. We assume the same weight for people, tanks, pipelines, machines and other accessories: a total of 0.3 ton per metre of length. Thus, the whole shell of the rocket will weigh $4^1/_2$ tons. The same

---

[2] In modern designs of multi-stage rockets, the rear engines and not the forward ones are fired first (Editors).

[3] According to modern data, the optimal rocket is a multi-stage one in which successive stages do not increase but diminish in size in a geometric progression (Editors).

for the internal contents, making 9 tons. Of this weight, it will be sufficient to allot one ton to people.

9. We apportion 0.9 ton of explosives per metre of shell length, or 27 tons for the whole rocket, which is three times the weight of the rocket with all its contents. (The appropriate speed of one rocket is equal to 5,520 m/sec in the case of petroleum.) In a single rocket, this supply will occupy (density being unity) 27 m^3, which is about one fourth of the whole volume of the rocket. This leaves 78 m^3 for people and machines. If we have 10 persons, that will mean 8 m^3 per person, or a cubic room with 2 m each dimension. At 2 atmospheres pressure, the oxygen for this volume will suffice for respiration of 160 people during 24 hours, or 10 persons in the course of 16 days, provided, of course, that the products of respiration are eliminated.

We want to demonstrate that even such a large supply of fuel is within the capabilities of a rocket.

10. Explosion produces a tension in the rocket, and for this reason the wall thickness in narrow places of the rocket is greater: the tensile strength in every cross-section of the rocket must be the same.

11. With a safety factor of 5, the shell of the rocket will be able to withstand a superpressure of 4 atmospheres. But since even in empty space it does not exceed 2 atmospheres, the safety factor will be 10.

12. Since all rockets may be called upon to glide — even the last one (the space rocket) upon its return to the earth, every rocket will have such a device.

A single inflated shell, which of necessity will have the shape of a body turned on a lathe (a solid of revolution), will be a poor glider. It is necessary, for instance, to combine three such surfaces. Inflated with air or oxygen to approximately 2 atmospheres they will form an extremely strong beam.

13. We cannot suggest wings because of their considerable weight.

14. Each rocket must have rudders: for direction, altitude, and to counteract rotation. They will have to be operative both in air and in empty space.

15. The rudders are located in the rear of each rocket. There are two pairs. Immediately behind them are the explosion pipes. Their direction is somewhat skewed, slightly to the side. Otherwise emerging gases will exert pressure on the rocket behind.

There are at least four explosion pipes. Their exit ends are arranged round the periphery of the rocket at equal distances from each other. Explosion occurs in the form of thrusts, like blank shots. These thrusts could harm the rocket. And so it is advisable to increase the number of pipes far above four. The firings will be more frequent and may be distributed so that the pressure on the rocket due to explosions will be rather uniform.

Each pair of rudders lies in a single plane (parallel to the longitudinal axis of the rocket), but they can deviate from it differently. Then the rocket will begin to rotate. From this it is seen that any pair may, in this case, serve to control the direction of the vehicle in the given plane. Generally speaking, we obtain the desired direction in space and avoid rotation. The flow of exiting gases is directed onto these rudders. It is thus obvious that they serve both in air and in empty space as well.

16. Small quartz windows let through several sun beams into the rocket; these are needed for control. The other (large) windows are closed from without by shutters. Later, they are opened in the rarefied atmosphere or in empty space.

17. The forward section is occupied by the passengers. Then comes the machine section (pumps and pump engines), and, finally, the rear section with the explosion pipes and the oil tanks around them. The tanks containing the oil are surrounded by tanks containing freely evaporating cold liquid oxygen.

18. Here is roughly what happens. A train of say five rockets glides along a roadway several hundred versts long, rising to a height of 4 to 8 versts above sea level. When the forward rocket has almost burnt up its fuel, it disengages itself from the other four behind. These four continue to move after acceleration (by inertia), the front one going out ahead of the rear ones due to the continuing, though weakened, explosion. The operator directs it to the side and it gradually drops back to earth, thus not interfering with the motion of the four remaining coupled rockets.

When the way is clear, the second rocket (now the front one) begins to fire. The same process occurs again: it is disengaged from the rear three and at first overtakes them, but later—due to insufficient speed—returns to the earth.

The same happens to the other rockets, except the last one, which not only gets out beyond the limits of the atmosphere but also acquires a cosmic speed. As a result it begins to circle the earth like a satellite, or it flies onward to the planets and even to other suns.

19. For a single rocket we have the formula (see my "Investigation of World Spaces, 1926. Formula 38):

$$\frac{V}{W} = \ln\left(1 + \frac{M_2}{M_1}\right),$$

where we give the ratio of the ultimate velocity of the rocket V to the ejection speed W as a function of the ratio of the total mass of ejected products M_2 or the fuel to the mass of the rocket with all its contents, with the exception of the components of the explosion. The sign ln stands for natural logarithm.

20. This formula may be applied to a composite rocket too, that is, a train made up of reactive vehicles. V will signify the additional speed of each train due to the explosion of material in a single rocket. The relative speed of ejection W is always the same. The mass of ejected materials M_2 will likewise remain the same. The mass of the rocket M_1 is not the mass of a single rocket, but of a whole train, minus the mass of the explosives M_2 of the forward rocket which acts on the entire train with all the untouched fuel it still contains.

21. Therefore we have to substitute, in formula (19), the mass of the train M_1' for the mass of the rocket M_1 in accordance with the formula

$$M_1' = (M_1 + M_2) n - M_2,$$

where n is the number of rockets. This expression obviously refers not only to a complete train consisting of a definite number of rockets n_1, but also to any other partial train (after the dropping of several forward rockets) consisting of a smaller number of them, n_1'.

22. Now in place of formula (19) we get

$$\frac{V}{W} = \ln \left[1 + \frac{M_2}{(M_1 + M_2) n - M_2} \right].$$

23. For the first train consisting of the largest number (n_1) of rockets, we obtain

$$\frac{V_1}{W} = \ln \left[1 + \frac{1}{\left(\frac{M_1}{M_2} + 1 \right) n_1 - 1} \right].$$

24. For the second train, which has one rocket less, we find

$$\frac{V_2}{W} = \ln \left[1 + \frac{1}{\left(\frac{M_1}{M_2} + 1 \right) (n_1 - 1) - 1} \right].$$

25. The same goes for the others as well. Generally, for a train of the order x, we have

$$\frac{V_x}{W} = \ln \left[1 + \frac{1}{\left(\frac{M_1}{M_2} + 1 \right) (n_1 - x + 1) - 1} \right].$$

26. For example, for the last train $x = n_1$. Putting this in, we get formula (19) for a single rocket.

27. The speed of the first train is expressed by formula (23), the total velocity of the second, by the sum of the velocity of the first train and the additional velocity of the second. Generally, the total velocity of a train of order x is expressed as the sum of the additional velocities (25) of the first x trains. The total velocity of the last, rear, rocket will be equal to the sum of the additional velocities of all trains from the most complex to the last one, consisting of a single rocket (of order n_1).

28. From the general formula (25) we see that the additional velocities of the trains increase with decreasing number of rockets. A complete train has the smallest additional velocity; the maximum is obtained when $x = n_1$, i.e., when there is only one rocket left. Additional velocities increase very slowly and for this reason a very large number of rockets has only a slight advantage; that is to say, it increases the total speed of the final rocket just a little.

Still, the increase in cosmic velocity would be limitless if there were no restriction to the strength of materials of which the rocket is constructed.

29. The calculations may be simplified if we count the trains from the rear, in the reverse order, i.e., by considering the last train of a single rocket as the first, the second from the last as the second, and so forth. Then the serial number will be y and we get

$$y + x = n_1 + 1.$$

30. Using this equation to eliminate x from equation (25), we get

$$\frac{V_y}{W} = \ln \left[1 + \frac{1}{\left(\frac{M_1}{M_2} + 1\right) y - 1} \right].$$

We have thus proved that in counting the trains from the end, the additional velocity does not depend on the total number of rockets (n_1) in the train but only on their reverse order (y).

31. Now let us compile a table that will readily show the total velocity of each partial train and the maximum total velocity of the last train consisting of a single rocket.

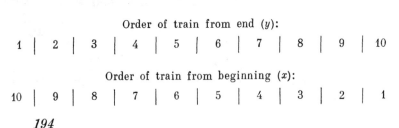

Order of train from end (y):

1	2	3	4	5	6	7	8	9	10

Order of train from beginning (x):

10	9	8	7	6	5	4	3	2	1

Relative additional velocity if $M_1 : M_2 = 1/3$:

1.386 | 0.470 | 0.262 | 0.207 | 0.166 | 0.131 | 0.113 | 0.100 | 0.09 | 0.08

Relative ultimate velocity of last train (composed of one rocket)
consisting of several rockets at the start of motion:

1.386 | 1.856 | 2.118 | 2.325 | 2.491 | 2.622 | 2.735 | 2.835 | 2.925 | 3.005

32. If, for instance, we have a train of four rockets, the last ultimate relative velocity will be 2.325, i.e. it will be the same number of times the ejection velocity.

The velocities of partial trains (for four rockets) in the normal order x may be found from the third row. As to time, they will be (beginning with the most composite one):

$$0.207; \quad 0.207 + 0.262 = 0.469; \quad 0.469 + 0.470 = 0.939;$$
$$0.939 + 1.386 = 2.325.$$

For a train made up of ten rockets the total velocity of the last rocket will be equal to 3.005. The velocities of the partial trains of this train, following order x, will also be found from the third row by combining the numbers starting from the right.

33. We can determine the true velocities, if we know the exhaust velocity (W), i.e., the speed of the combustion products emerging from the explosion pipe. We get a table like the following:

Number of rockets in the train:

1	2	3	4	5	6	7	8	9	10

The ultimate speed of last train in km/sec if $M_1 : M_2 = 1/3$ and $W = 3$ km/sec:

4.17 | 5.58 | 6.36 | 6.96 | 7.47 | 7.86 | 8.19 | 8.49 | 8.76 | 9.00

The same but for $W = 4$ km/sec:

5.56 | 7.49 | 8.49 | 9.28 | 9.96 | 10.48 | 10.92 | 11.32 | 11.68 | 12.00

The same but for $W = 5$ km/sec:

6.95 | 9.30 | 10.60 | 11.60 | 12.45 | 13.10 | 13.65 | 14.15 | 14.60 | 15.00

Even when petroleum is used and the utilization of combustion energy is 50% ($W = 3$), given 7-8 trains, the speed obtained is cosmic. For greater utilization, it is obtained for three and even two trains. A ten-rocket train may be sufficient to leave the earth and reach the planets and asteroids.

34. If in formula (30) the mass of the rocket M_1 is great compared with the mass of ejection M_2, or the partial train contains a large number of rockets, that is, y is great, then the second term in formula (30) will be a small regular fraction Z.

Then, approximately, we can put

$$\ln(1+Z) = Z - \frac{Z^2}{2} + \frac{Z^3}{3} - \frac{Z^4}{4} \cdots .$$

The smaller the fraction Z, the fewer terms we can take.

35. For example, suppose, as before: $M_1 : M_2 = 1/3$ and $y = 6$.

The first approximation by (34) yields $1/7 = 0.143$. This is slightly more than from Table 31 (0.131). The second approximation will be 0.133, which is still closer to the truth. If we take a nine-rocket train, then $Z = 1/11$ and the first approximation will yield $Z = 0.091$, which is almost in agreement with the table.

36. And so, beginning with the 11th train, we can boldly put

$$\frac{V_y}{W} = Z = \frac{1}{\left(\dfrac{M_1}{M_2}+1\right) y - 1} .$$

37. The sum of the additional velocities of the trains beyond the 11th from the end may be found, approximately, by integrating expression 36. We then get

$$\frac{M_2}{M_1+M_2} \cdot \ln\left[\left(\frac{M_1}{M_2}+1\right) y - 1\right] + \text{const.}$$

If const $= 10$, the sum of the additional velocities is equal to zero. Consequently,

$$\text{const} = -\frac{M_2}{M_1+M_2} \ln\left[\left(\frac{M_1}{M_2}+1\right) \cdot 10 - 1\right] .$$

Hence, for the sum of the additional velocities we get

$$\frac{M_2}{M_1+M_2} \cdot \ln\left[\frac{\left(\dfrac{M_1}{M_2}+1\right) \cdot y - 1}{\left(\dfrac{M_1}{M_2}+1\right) \cdot 10 - 1}\right] .$$

38. Putting $y = 11$ here (the eleventh train, i.e., an addition of one rocket to ten), we find the relative additional velocity as 0.077 (see Table 31).

If we add 10 trains, then $y = 20$ and the combined additional velocity of ten trains will be 0.55. For an ejection velocity of 4 km/sec the absolute addition will come to 2.2 km/sec.

We add 90 rockets, $y = 100$ and the additional velocity will be 1.78. The absolute addition ($W = 4$ km/sec) is 7.12 km/sec. From Table 33, ten trains, under the same conditions, yield 12 km/sec. Thus, one hundred trains will give a speed of 19.12 km/sec. This is more than enough to travel to other suns.

For 50% utilization of fuel (Table 33) we find that the velocity from 100 trains will be $9 + 5.34 = 14.34$ km/sec.

39. For over a hundred rockets in a train we can express the combined additional velocity by the formula (from 37)

$$\frac{M_2}{M_1 + M_2} \cdot \ln \frac{y}{10} .$$

40. For example, for a thousand trains the maximum relative velocity will be 3.454. If $W = 4$, then the absolute addition from 990 rockets $= 13.82$, and from a total of one thousand rockets we get 25.82 km/sec.

41. Let us first imagine all trains to be moving horizontally. The last rocket will have the greatest acceleration (an addition of velocity per second). For practical purposes it is convenient for the force of explosion to be constant. If that is so, then the acceleration of a single rocket will at first be weaker because the mass will be great, since the fuel has not yet been consumed. Then, as the fuel burns, the acceleration will become greater. For instance, given our triple supply, acceleration at first will be 4 times less than at the end, when the entire explosive supply will have been expended.

42. In the case of explosion normal to the direction of gravity, it is not profitable to employ large accelerations (on a solid roadway, in the air or in empty space). Firstly, special protective facilities would be needed to save the passenger from enhanced gravity, secondly, the rocket itself would have to be stronger, and hence, more massive, thirdly, the explosion pipes and other machines would have to be stronger and more massive.

43. Let us take the maximum acceleration of the train at 10 m/sec^2. This is the acceleration that the earth imparts to freely falling bodies in one second. It is the acceleration that will clearly be found in the last train made up of a single rocket and, moreover, at the end of uniform explosion. We assume that the force of the explosion diminishes in proportion to the diminishing total mass of the rocket so that the acceleration is all the time constant and equal to 10 m/sec^2.

44. The mass of trains consisting of two or more rockets changes but slightly and so there the explosive force may be taken to be constant. There the acceleration may be considered con-

stant and will be the less, the greater the number of rockets in the train, so that a certain unevenness will do no harm.

45. Acceleration of the second train (from the end) will be one half, since the mass will be doubled. Acceleration of the tenth will be one tenth, since it will contain 10 rockets of identical mass, and so forth.

It follows then that the tension of a horizontal train or its relative weight does not depend on the number of rockets. Indeed, even if there are 1,000 rockets, its tension will be 1,000 times greater due to the mass and 1,000 times less due to the small acceleration. Obviously, a train made up of an arbitrary number of rockets will have the same tension as one consisting of a single rocket.

46. If the tension of a long train is greater, then this is due solely to the friction and air resistance. For the time being we disregard these factors.

47. The inclination of the roadway to the horizon likewise increases the tension of a train in proportion to its length. But if we take a curved roadway that gradually rises, the inclination (the tangent or sine of the inclination) being very small and proportional to the acceleration of the train, then this too may be neglected.

48. Bearing all this in mind, let us calculate the time, velocities, routes and ascents of trains (see Table 49).

It is very convenient to presume that the explosion section in each rocket is of identical design and operates in the same way. Then the duration of an explosion that consumes the whole supply of fuel will be identical in all rockets.

If we acquire the first cosmic velocity of 8,000 m/sec, then when we are outside the atmosphere, the light pressure or some other thing will readily allow us to leave the vicinity of the earth and travel within the limits of the solar system and even beyond (see "The Investigation", 1926).

49. A train made up of five rockets (Table 49).

50. From the sixth row we see that a fivefold train yields a velocity sufficient to leave the earth and even the earth's orbit. The next to the last train consisting of two rockets almost gains the first cosmic velocity (8,000 m/sec), so that it just lacks a bit to be able to circle the earth beyond the atmosphere together with the final rocket whose explosive material is still intact. Naturally, it may be replaced by some other load. From this it is clear that we can make whole loaded trains into earth satellites if the total number of component parts of a train (i.e., rockets) is sufficient.

TABLE 49

Numbers of trains in serial order:

(1)	1	2	3	4	5

Number of rockets in each train:

(2)	5	4	3	2	1

Mean acceleration, m/sec^2:

(3)	2	2.5	3.33	5	10

Relative additional speed of each train
(Duration of explosion is constant):

(4)	0.2	0.25	0.333	0.5	1.0

Ultimate relative velocity of each train:

(5)	0.2	0.45	0.783	1.283	2.283

Absolute speed of each train if additional speed of last rocket is taken
at 5,520 m/sec (see "The Investigation", 1926):

(6)	1,104	2,484	4,322	7,082	12,602

(7)   Duration of explosion in seconds $= 1,104 : 2 = 5,520 : 10 = 552$.
It is the same for all rockets.

Mean velocity of each train, m/sec:

(8)	552	1,242	2,161	3,541	6,301

Distance covered by each train, km (during explosion):

(9)	288.14	685.58	1,192.87	1,954.63	3,478.15

Tangent of inclination:

(10)	0.02	0.025	0.033...	0.05	0.1

Total vertical ascent of each train, km:

(11)	5.76	17.1	39.6	97.7	347.8

Same if the incline is half of the preceding one:

(12)	2.88	8.5	19.8	48.8	173.9

Ultimate speeds for 50% utilization of explosives
when speed of single rocket $= 3,900$ m/sec:

(13)	780	1,755	3,054	4,992	8,892

Length of trains, m:

(14)	150	120	90	60	30

51. From the seventh row it is seen that the duration of explosion in each train is equal to 552 seconds, or 9.2 minutes. Five trains will take 46 minutes of time. Hence, in less than an hour everything will be over and the last rocket will become a wandering body.

The supply of explosives here is three times the weight of the rocket with all its contents and therefore comes out to 2^7 tons. Consequently, 48.9 kilograms of explosive should be exploded every second. To ensure uniformity will require a large number of explosion pipes. If each rocket has 40 and if the motor is running at 30 revolutions per second, or 30 injections (portions) per second, then each portion will amount to 0.041 kg, or 41 grams. With what can we compare this cannonade? 1,200 blank shots per second with 41 grams of high-explosive substance in each. And this continues in succession and without interruption in all rockets during 46 minutes.

52. For the rocket diameter we gave 3 metres. At first we can confine ourselves to 1 metre. Then all this terrifying picture will be reduced 27 times (three cubed). We have said that in that case the last space rocket can open up in a special way and become a spacious room for human beings. We shall take this up elsewhere.

53. From the ninth row it is seen that the distances covered by trains do not exceed the dimensions of the globe. But vertical ascent of each train (row 11) is much less. Thus, only the first train, after covering 288 km on the earth, rises to a height of 5 to 6 km. The second train will soon have to leave solid ground and fly in the air. The last rocket flies out beyond the limits of the atmosphere without having completed the explosion process. This occurs when the maximum tangent of the angle of acsent (of the last train) is 0.1, and the appropriate angle with the horizon is 6°. For the first train it is slightly over 1°, for the second, 2°, and so forth.

54. For an inclination half that (row 12), two trains can fire while still on solid ground. The heights of the earth's mountains permit this. Then the ground pathway will come out to about 600-700 km.

55. In row 13 we presumed 50% energy utilization of explosives. Then the last train acquires a velocity greatly exceeding the first cosmic velocity of 8 km/sec. This will of course make rocket routes much shorter.

56. The longest initial train has a length of 150 m. If we confine ourselves at the beginning to dimensions three times smaller, we get a total of 50 m for a five-rocket train.

200

57. We have already said that the tensile strength of a train is not dependent on the number of rockets on the horizontal pathway. However, is the strength of a single rocket sufficient?

The cross-sectional area of the rocket shell is everywhere the same and is equal to 18,000 mm² (for a wall thickness of 2 mm). The breaking strength, in the case of a sixfold safety factor, will be at least 180 tons. A rocket with all its contents (including the fuel) will have a mass of 36 tons. In connection with ordinary gravity, an acceleration of 10 m/sec² will create a relative gravity 1.4 times the earth's gravity. But the horizontal component will only be equal to the earth's gravity. Thus, the rocket will be subject to a tension equal to 36 tons. This destructive force is 5 times smaller than the strength of the material. And if we take rockets with 3 times smaller diameter and length, the destructive force will be less than the strength of the material by a factor of 15.

58. Inclined motion increases this destructive effect. But it is the same for all trains. Thus, for a single rocket the incline is greatest and increases the tension only by 0.1. For example, the incline of a fivefold rocket is 5 times less, so that despite the great mass, the tension will increase (totally) by 0.1 as well.

59. It is thus evident that rockets could be made less massive, if it weren't for the excess gas pressure, which is unavoidable in empty space. Still it may be reduced by a factor of four, so that in place of 4 atmospheres of excess pressure, we can confine ourselves to one. However, for small rockets the shell will turn out impracticably thin.

60. In view of the excessive tensile strength of the train, we propose additional tables for trains made up of 1, 2, 3, 4 and 5 rockets. But here we assume that the force and rate of explosion of one and the same mass of explosive material are proportional to the mass of the train. Thus, the first train, say of 5 rockets, is drawn by a force five times that of one rocket and therefore both trains have one and the same acceleration. Just like all the partial trains of one and the same convoy. The result is that despite the difference in the number of rockets of the different trains, we have what would seem to be a single body moving with a constant acceleration (per second). But of course the times of explosion are the reciprocals of the masses of the partial trains (because the stronger the explosion, the sooner it is over).

61. In all the tables (see 62 and 63) we take the final overall velocity of the last rocket as equal to the first cosmic velocity of 8 km/sec. Incidentally, the tables answer the question: What additional speed is needed in this case for a single rocket? From the sixth row of the tables we see that these maximum additional

speeds will be the following for different trains:

Number of rockets in train:

1 | 2 | 3 | 4 | 5

Required additional speed of single rocket, km/sec:

8 | 5.3 | 4.4 | 3.8 | 3.5

We see that the greater the number of rockets in a train, the less the additional speed. Thus, for a five-rocket train it is only 3.5 km/sec, which is achieved with a relative fuel supply of 1 or 1.5.

From rows 10 and 16 we see that the lengths of the runs on solid ground are much smaller. The entire take-off process is shorter too—only 800 seconds or 13.3 minutes—since the acceleration (10 m/sec) does not diminish while the explosion is taking place.

62. Length of rocket, 30 m (see Table 62).

TABLE 62

	One rocket	Two rockets		Three rockets		
	Numbers of the trains:					
(1)	1	1	2	1	2	3
	Number of rockets and relative force of explosion:					
(2)	1	2	1	3	2	1
	Relative duration of explosion:					
(3)	1	1	2	1	1.5	3
	Relative time of accelerated motion of each train:					
(4)	1	1	3	1	2.5	5.5
	Terminal velocity of each train, m/sec:					
(5)	8,000	2,667	8,000	1,454	3,636	8,000
	Increment in velocity of each train, m/sec:					
(6)	8,000	2,667	5,333	1,454	2,182	4,364

TABLE 62 *(continued)*

	One rocket	Two rockets			Three rockets		
Time of motion of each train with preceding one, sec:							
(7)	800	266.7	800	145.4	363.6	800.0	
Time of motion of one train, sec:							
(8)	800	266.7	533.3	145.4	218.2	436.4	
Mean velocity of each train, m/sec:							
(9)	4,000	1,333.3	4,000	727.2	1,818.2	4,000.0	
Distance covered by each train with preceding ones, km:							
(10)	3,200	355.5	3,200	105.7	661.1	3,200	
Distance covered by each train separately, km:							
(11)	3,200	355.5	2,844.5	105.7	555.4	2,538.9	
Height of ascent. Sine of angle = 0.30:							
(12)	960	106.7	960	31.7	198.3	960	
Same. Sine of angle = 0.25:							
(13)	800	88.9	800	26.4	166.3	800.0	
Same. Sine of angle = 0.20:							
(14)	640	77.1	640	21.1	132.2	640.0	
Same. Sine of angle = 0.15:							
(15)	480	53.3	480	15.8	99.2	480.0	
Same. Sine of angle = 0.10:							
(16)	320	35.5	320	10.6	66.1	320.0	
Length of entire train, m:							
(17)	30	60	30	90	60	30	

63. Length of rocket, 30 m (see Table 63).

TABLE 63

	Four rockets				Five rockets				

Numbers of the trains:

(1)	1	2	3	4	1	2	3	4	5

Number of rockets in each, and the relative force of explosion:

(2)	4	3	2	1	5	4	3	2	1

Relative duration of explosion for each train:

(3)	1	1.33	2	4	1	1.25	1.67	2.5	5

Relative time of accelerated motion of each train:

(4)	1	2.33	4.33	8.33	1	2.25	3.92	6.42	11.42

Terminal velocity of each train, m/sec:

(5)	960.4	2,237.7	4,158.5	8,000	700.6	1,576.3	2,746	4,497.8	8,000

Increment in velocity of each train, m/sec:

(6)	960.4	1,277.3	1,920.8	3,841.5	701	876	1,170	1,752	3,502

Time of motion of each train with preceding one, sec:

(7)	96.0	223.8	415.8	800	70	158	275	450	800

Time of accelerated motion of one train, sec:

(8)	96.0	127.8	192.0	384.2	70	88	117	175	350

Mean velocity of each train, m/sec:

(9)	480.2	1,118.8	2,079.2	4,000.0	350	788	1,373	2,249	4,000

Distance covered by each train with preceding ones, km:

(10)	46.08	250.43	864.45	3,200	24.50	124.50	377.57	1,012.05	3,200

Distance covered by each train separately, km:

(11)	46.1	204.3	614.0	2,335.6	24.5	100.0	253.1	634.4	2,188.0

TABLE 63 *(continued)*

	Four rockets				Five rockets			

Height of ascent. Sine of angle = 0.3:

| (12) | 13.8 | 75.1 | 259.3 | 960.0 | 7.35 | 37.35 | 112.28 | 303.61 | 960 |

Same. Sine of angle = 0.25:

| (13) | 11.5 | 62.6 | 216.1 | 800.0 | 6.1 | 31.1 | 94.4 | 253.0 | 800 |

Same. Sine of angle = 0.20:

| (14) | 9.6 | 50.1 | 172.9 | 640.0 | 4.9 | 24.9 | 75.5 | 204.4 | 640 |

Same. Sine of angle = 0.15:

| (15) | 6.9 | 37.5 | 129.7 | 480.0 | 3.67 | 18.6 | 56.7 | 151.8 | 480 |

Same. Sine of angle = 0.1:

| (16) | 4.6 | 25.0 | 86.4 | 320.0 | 2.45 | 12.4 | 37.8 | 101.2 | 320 |

Length of entire train, m:

| (17) | 120 | 90 | 60 | 30 | 150 | 120 | 90 | 60 | 30 |

64. The incline of the hard roadway to the horizon must here too be taken as very small but constant, for example 6 degrees, the sine of the angle being 0.1. The roadway will come out straight but not concave, as in the case of variable acceleration (per second) of the partial trains.

65. For trains made up of 2, 3 and 4 rockets, one can assume the acceleration constant and also the duration of explosion just as invariable. But to achieve this, the fuel supply in each leading rocket must be proportional to the force of the explosion or to the mass of each train. This means that the first rockets (or trains) do not only fire (explode) faster but also for a longer time, than as follows from Tables 62 and 63, due to the larger supply of fuel. Here too, all partial trains move as a single body with constant acceleration. On this basis we compile the following table (see Table 66).

66. Length of rocket, 30 m.

TABLE 66

	Two rockets		Three rockets			Four rockets			

Numbers of the trains:

(1)	1	2	1	2	3	1	2	3	4

Number of rockets in partial train, relative explosive power and fuel supply:

(2)	2	1	3	2	1	4	3	2	1

Relative time of accelerated motion of each train:

(3)	1	1	1	1	1	1	1	1	1

Relative total time of explosion for each train:

(4)	1	2	1	2	3	1	2	3	4

Terminal velocity of each train, km/sec:

(5)	4	8	2.7	5.3	8	2	4	6	8

Additional speed of each train, km/sec:

(6)	4	4	2.7	2.7	2.7	2	2	2	2

Total time of motion of each train if acceleration is always 10 m/sec^2:

(7)	400	800	267	533	800	200	400	600	800

Time of motion of one train, sec:

(8)	400	400	267	267	267	200	200	200	200

Mean velocity of each train, km/sec:

(9)	2	4	1.33	2.67	4.00	1	2	3	4

Total distance covered by each train (with preceding ones), km:

(10)	800	3,200	355.5	1,422	3,200	200	800	1,800	3,200

Distance covered by each train separately:

(11)	800	2,400	355.5	1,066.5	1,778	200	600	1,000	2,200

Total height of ascent, km. Sine of angle = 0.1. Angle = 6°:

(12)	80	320	35	142	320	20	80	180	320

Length of train, m:

(13)	60	30	90	60	30	120	90	60	30

67. Incline of hard roadway to the horizon may be constant here as well. For example, the tangent of the angle (6°) of incline is 0.1.

Even the first partial train here can travel over solid ground part of the way only. The other, greater, part is through the atmosphere.

From the sixth row it is evident that the additional speeds are the same for partial trains of one convoy, and the greater the number of rockets in a convoy, the lower the additional speeds. For a four-rocket train the increment in velocity is only 2 km/sec, which corresponds to a relative fuel supply of 0.5-0.7 (relative to the mass of the rocket minus the explosives).

The forward terrestrial trains can have a greater mass of fuel, since there may be fewer people aboard and the equipment may be simpler, for they return directly to the earth.

68. Still, the most practical and feasible trains are those made up of identically constructed rockets with an invariable supply of fuel and a constant explosive force (see Item 4). They can also consist of an enormous number of elements (separate rockets), which increases the ultimate speed and allows for a small fuel supply in each separate rocket (or its incomplete utilization). In a word, then, cosmic velocities may be attained even in imperfect reactive vehicles.

69. Table 69 gives data on a ten-rocket train. The duration of explosion (row 3) in each partial train is the same; this follows from the identical construction of the elements of the train. If we denote this time by x and demand that the last rocket (of the train) attain the first cosmic speed, then on the basis of the fourth row we have

70. $1x + 1.1x \ldots + 1.25x \ldots + 2x \ldots + 5x + 10x =$

$$= 29.29x = 8,000, \text{ whence } x = 273.1 \text{ sec.}$$

TABLE 69

Length of one rocket = 30 m. Rockets have same design and fuel supply

Numbers of the partial trains:

(1)	1	2	3	4	5	6	7	8	9	10

Number of rockets in each partial train:

(2)	10	9	8	7	6	5	4	3	2	1

(3)   The duration of explosion is the same.

TABLE **69** *(continued)*

Acceleration of each train, m/sec²:

(4) | 1 | 1.111 | 1.250 | 1.429 | 1.667 | 2 | 2.5 | 3.333 | 5 | 10

(5) If we desire to achieve the first cosmic velocity of 8 km/sec, the explosion time will be 8,000 m/sec : 29.29 m/sec² = 273.1 sec.

Additional speed of each train, m/sec:

(6) | 273 | 301 | 343 | 391 | 456 | 546 | 682 | 1,009 | 1,365 | 2,734

Terminal speed of each train, m/sec:

(7) | 273 | 574 | 917 | 1,308 | 1,764 | 2,310 | 2,992 | 3,901 | 5,266 | 8,000

Average speed of each train, m/sec:

(8) | 136 | 287 | 458 | 654 | 882 | 1,155 | 1,496 | 1,950 | 2,633 | 4,000

Distance covered by each train, km (see rows 3 and 5):

(9) | 37.1 | 78.3 | 125.0 | 178.5 | 240.8 | 315.3 | 408.4 | 532.3 | 718.8 | 1,092.4

Total distance covered by each train with preceding ones, km:

(10) | 37.1 | 115.4 | 240.4 | 418.9 | 659.7 | 975.0 | 1,383.0 | 1,915.7 | 2,634.5 | 3,726.9

Incline of path of each partial train. Tangent of angle (6°) of last train taken at 0.1. Inclines of others are proportional to the acceleration:

(11) | 0.01 | 0.0111 | 0.0125 | 0.0143 | 0.0167 | 0.02 | 0.025 | 0.0333 | 0.05 | 0.1

Total height of ascent of each train, km:

(12) | 0.731 | 0.870 | 1.562 | 2.553 | 4.021 | 6.306 | 10.21 | 17.72 | 35.94 | 109.24

Total height, km:

(13) | 0.371 | 1.241 | 2.803 | 5.356 | 9.377 | 15.683 | 25.89 | 43.61 | 79.55 | 188.79

Height relative to route (12 and 10):

(14) | 0.01 | 0.01090 | 0.01179 | 0.01278 | 0.0140 | 0.0161 | 0.0187 | 0.0227 | 0.0302 | 0.0508

Total time of explosion for each train, sec:

(15) | 273 | 546 | 819 | 1,092 | 1,365 | 1,638 | 1,911 | 2,184 | 2,457 | 2,730

71. The greatest additional speed demanded of the last single rocket will be only 2.7 km/sec (at 6°), which corresponds to a relative fuel supply of 0.8 to 1. But if the supply is greater, the final speed will be greater. For the time being, however, that is not needed.

72. The first 4 trains can move over the hard roadway, the rise being 6 km and distance covered 419 km (see rows 13 and 10). This is permissible for the earth. The fifth train completes its path in the atmosphere, and the remaining 5 even begin their paths in the atmosphere. In view of the sphericity of the earth, the last trains reach much greater heights than is evident from row 12.

The overall distance covered during explosion comes out to as much as 3,000 versts.

73. The hard roadway is curved: concave (see row 14). Exact calculations relative to this curvature yield formulae that are much too involved (with second derivatives) and we do not give them here so as not to obscure the main thing. But let us suppose the curvature of the pathway is constant for each train. From a familiar elementary theorem we have: $r = L^2 : 2h$, where r is the radius of curvature, L the distance covered, and h the vertical ascent. Rows 10 and 13 permit determining the radius of curvature for each portion of the pathway. Thus, for the first, fifth and last, that is, the tenth, we find, in km: $r = 1,850, 23,220,$ and $36,770,$ respectively. It is thus clear that the radii of curvature increase. And for this reason the centrifugal force falls off. Yet at the same time it increases with increasing train speed (the true radii are greater and therefore the true centrifugal force is less).

74. For these three cases we calculate the centrifugal force in terms of acceleration (m/sec²). As we know, it is $F_{cen} = V^2 : r$, where F is the centrifugal force, V the speed, and r the radius of curvature of the pathway. This formula, row 7 and paragraph 73 yield: $F_{cen} = 0.04, 1.34,$ and 1.74. Relative to the force of the earth's gravity (the acceleration of gravity is 10 m/sec²), this is from 0.004 to 0.17. But let us not forget that only the fourth train can move on solid ground and develop a centrifugal force. The others move in the atmosphere where there may be no centrifugal force at all: generally speaking, it will depend upon us, i.e., on control (on the inclination of the rudders). For the fourth train, $r = 16,360$ and $F_{cen} = 1.05$, that is to say, the force pressing the train to the pathway does not exceed one tenth the weight of the train (actually even less).

75. Let us examine the relative force of gravity generated in a train during its motion. The centrifugal force presses the train to the roadway, at first imperceptibly, then more strongly, but

the maximum does not reach 0.1 of the earth's gravity. We shall neglect this force. The second force (normal to the first) depends on the accelerated motion of the train. Its greatest magnitude is equal to the earth's acceleration (10 m/sec^2). We cannot ignore this quantity. When combined with the earth's attraction, the two forces yield an acceleration roughly equal to 14 m/sec^2, which is 1.4 times the acceleration of the earth. In the train a person with a usual weight of 75 kg will not weigh more than 105 kg. It is easy to withstand such an increase in gravity during a few minutes even in the standing position, to say nothing of young healthy people and a more restful position. Gravity will increase little by little, varying between 1 and 1.4 relative to ordinary. The inclination of this relative gravity to the vertical likewise increases gradually from zero to 45°. As acceleration builds up, the horizontal surface of the earth inclines, as it were, more and more and finally at the end of accelerated motion the train appears to the passenger to be climbing up hill at an angle of 45°. At the beginning of motion this mountain is almost horizontal, then it becomes steeper and steeper, and finally at the end the roadway appears to be almost vertical. This is a startling and terrifying spectacle. Friction and air resistance somewhat reduce the accelerated motion and thus also retard the build-up of gravity.

76. When the train takes off the hard roadway and hurtles through the air, the phenomenon becomes more complicated.

In the atmosphere we have the same thing if the resultant of the explosive forces is directed along the longitudinal, and slightly inclined axis of the rocket. Then, as the rocket falls it will experience air resistance equal to its weight. The air will press on it like a solid roadway.

However, the rocket, flying in the inclined position, nose upwards, will not fall to the earth because it will be rising faster than it falls.

77. Fall due to the earth's gravity will at first be slow and accelerated, then it will attain a speed such that the air pressure will become equal to the weight of the rocket. Then the vertical speed of fall will be constant and not very substantial in comparison with the constantly increasing speed of ascent of the rocket.

78. A rocket, tripled or quadrupled in parallel, will, as we have seen, yield about 0.9 ton of gravity on 3 m^2 of its horizontal projection at the start of explosion. (This is 9 times less for a rocket 1 metre in diameter.) That will be 0.3 ton per square metre (see 8). Such also will be the air pressure per square metre of horizontal projection of the vehicle. This circumstance can serve us for forming an equation. It will also give us the necessary conclusions.

79. We take the direction of the resultant of explosion to be horizontal. Then the head-on flow will be directed onto the rocket (assuming the base of the rocket to be flat) at an angle whose tangent is equal to $(V_h : V)$, where V_h is the constant rate of fall of the rocket due to gravity, and V is the variable translational speed of the rocket.

80. The pressure of the air flow on a surface of one square metre normal to it will be at least $(d : 2g) \cdot V^2$, where the notations are air density, acceleration of the earth's gravity and rate of flow, respectively.

Now a current of air acting on a plate in an inclined position exerts a greater pressure (double the tangent of the angle). Consequently, the pressure on each square metre of the base of the rocket is expressed by

$$(d : g) \cdot V \cdot V_h.$$

81. We must equate the value of this pressure to the weight (G_1) of the rocket per square metre of its base (0.3 ton, or 300 kg). Consequently

$$G_1 = (d : g) \cdot V \cdot V_h.$$

Hence we have

$$\frac{V_h}{V} = (g \cdot G_1) : (d \cdot V^2).$$

From this we see that the relative rate of fall, or the angle of fall (tangent), diminishes rapidly with increasing translational speed of the rocket. But it increases with diminishing air density, i.e., with increasing altitude of the rocket.

82. Let us calculate the tangent of the angle for different rocket velocities and different air densities.

If, for example, $d = 0.0012$, $G_1 = 0.3$ ton, $g = 10$ m/sec², and $V = 1,000$ m/sec, then the inclination will be 0.0025. Even at altitudes of 8 to 10 km, where the air is four times more rarefied, the inclination will be 0.01. With rocket velocity one half (500 m/sec), the inclination will be 0.04. This inclination too is 2.5 times less than that which we take (0.1 for the longitudinal axis of the rocket to the horizon when the vehicle takes off from the ground). This means that even under such conditions the rocket not only will not fall but will rise rapidly away from the earth's surface (this is also because of the sphericity of the earth).

83. But in time the air becomes more rarefied at a rate far in advance of the square of the translational speed of the rocket. For this reason, a time will come when the weight of the rocket will not be balanced by the air resistance, the relative vertical component of gravity will be diminishing until it disappears

in the empty space beyond the limits of the atmosphere. Then all that will remain will be the gravity due to the accelerated translational motion of the rocket, equal to 10 m/sec². It will generate an apparent gravity equal to that of the earth and nearly perpendicular to the earth's gravity. Then the earth will appear to be a vertical wall, parallel to which we are in motion (rising).

But this too lasts for only a few minutes: as soon as the explosion process comes to an end, all traces of gravity vanish, as it were.

84. If in the last equation we put the tangent of the angle of inclination at 0.1 and $V = 1,000$ m/sec, we then calculate: $d = 0.00003$, i.e., it is possible to climb to a height where the air density is very low (0.00003. It will be 40 times less than at sea level) and still not fall, having a velocity of 1,000 m/sec. This speed does not yet develop a centrifugal force equal to the earth's gravity, and for this reason does not make the path circular without approach to, or recession from, the earth. Only when the velocity has reached a value of 8 km/sec, or about that, does the flight path become circular and eternal (only if it is outside the atmosphere).

85. Let us give a description of different systems of trains. There may be four cases.

A. The rockets are almost of the same design. The supply of explosives is the same in all of them, but the explosion is the stronger, the greater the mass of the train. Because of this the acceleration is the same for all partial trains, but the duration of explosion is inversely proportional to the mass of the train (62 and 63).

B. The supply of explosives and the explosive force is the greater, the greater the mass of the partial train. As a result, acceleration (per second) and the duration of explosion are the same for all trains (see 66).

C. The supply of explosives is proportional to the mass of the partial train, but the force of explosion is constant. In this case the time of explosion in each train increases with the mass. But acceleration is inversely proportional to the mass of a partial train. We did not examine this case.

D. All rockets are absolutely identical as to fuel supply and explosion machine. The greater the mass of a partial train, the smaller the acceleration. The duration of explosion for all trains is the same (see 49).

86. System A is inconvenient in that it requires intense and rapid explosion in the first rockets and consequently a more complicated and heavier explosive mechanism. As a result, the

tension in the first long trains will be enormous. The whole system will be threatened with rupture and for this reason it will be impossible to employ multiple-rocket trains. The additional velocity of each train is the same as in system D. The advantage lies in reducing the length of the ground pathway and the duration of explosion, but this is not at all important (62 and 63).

87. System B, like system A, requires increasing the mass and volume of the rocket as the number of elements in the leading train increases. This is because space is required for fuel and more complicated and stronger machines. Then one cannot employ a large number of rockets in the train: it will break because of the highly accelerated motion. The advantage lies in the rapid build-up of speed, since the additional speed is the same for all trains. This means that the final velocity is proportional to the number of rockets in the train. If, for example, the additional velocity of a single rocket is 8 km/sec, then a train of system B consisting of two rockets attains a speed of 16 km/sec, which is almost enough for travelling to other suns. If from a single rocket we can extract a velocity of 2 km/sec, then a four-rocket train will impart to the last rocket a velocity of 8 km/sec, which is the first cosmic velocity (see 66).

88. System C is more practicable because for long trains the acceleration is lower than in system D, and so a large number of rockets may be employed. The explosive mechanisms and the rockets themselves are nearly the same. But since the quantity of fuel is proportional to the mass of the partial train, the forward rockets will have to be larger to accommodate the greater mass of fuel. That is their drawback. But we have seen that there is enough room in our rockets and so a train made up of 2 or 3 rockets is feasible even without altering the volume of the vehicles. There is also an advantage in the fact that additional velocities do not diminish with increase in the number of rockets, as in system B. Indeed, although the acceleration in a long and massive train is less, the duration of explosion (in virtue of the larger supply of fuel) is just as many times greater. Therefore, the ultimate additional velocities of all partial trains are the same, which is a great advantage. The extended times and ground routes (compared to systems A and D) are insignificant.

89. Though we have not examined this case, Table 66 can serve to indicate the relative values of additional speeds. System C deserves the closest attention. If, for example, we could obtain a velocity of only 1 km/sec for a single rocket (the speed of a cannon-ball may be greater), which, according to the table in my article "The Investigation" of 1926, requires a relative supply

of from 0.2 to 0.3, even then 17 trains would be enough to attain a maximum cosmic velocity sufficient to reach all our planets (but not for descent onto them) and for travel out into the Milky Way. The fuel supply in the rockets, starting with the forward one, will not exceed:

$$5.1 \quad 4.8 \quad 4.5 \quad 4.2 \ldots \quad 1.2 \quad 0.9 \quad 0.6 \quad 0.3$$

Such supplies are quite permissible. The last space rocket will be nearly empty, that is, free of fuel.

That is the promise which trains hold out to us and that is how they facilitate the attainment of cosmic velocities!

90. We have spoken enough about system D (see 49). Its advantage lies in the complete uniformity of the elements of the train (with the exception of the last space rocket).

Generally speaking, having accomplished its mission, that is, having sent the last rocket into outer space, all the other rockets, no matter what the system, will fly a more or less long distance in the atmosphere and will then glide down to the ground or water and will be ready to serve again in the future in the same capacity. One and the same train on one and the same route can send off a million vehicles on celestial missions. The only thing that is needed is an uninterrupted expenditure of fuel composed of the cheap products of petroleum and endogenous compounds of oxygen.

A drawback of system D is the small additional speed. But if row 89 is replaced by identical elements, say 5.1, then system C turns into system D and the terminal velocity will be substantially increased.

91. The problem of combustion materials, the design of the explosion pipes, shells and other components of the rocket cannot at present be solved. I therefore meanwhile presume petroleum products and liquid oxygen or its endogenous compounds for the explosive components and a variety of familiar grades of steel, such as chromium and beryllium steels and other kinds for the rocket itself.

Of course, it is more advantageous to employ monatomic hydrogen and ozone as explosive components. But are such materials sufficiently stable and can they be conveniently had in the liquid form? These are problems for chemists who deal specially with such substances.

If good results with oxygen, petroleum and steel are possible, then all the better will be the results in the case of other more suitable materials.

The problem of a solid roadway is elaborated in my paper "The Resistance of the Air and High-Speed Trains", 1927.

Even among scientists there are contradictory and unclear conceptions concerning the temperature of bodies in the ether, for instance the temperature of a rocket.

One hears talk of the temperature of celestial space. But one cannot speak about that because it has no meaning, we do not have a clear idea of the ether. One can only speak about the temperature of gases, liquids and solids located in celestial space.

If we can assume that round about some body in the ether of celestial space there are no other bodies, as for example suns, planets, comets and small bodies, then such a body will only lose heat and will not receive any heat from other bodies. It is highly probable that the temperature of such a body will reach absolute zero, i.e., will be 273° C below zero: molecules will cease to move, but that does not mean that the movement of parts of molecules and, all the more so, of protons and electrons will come to a halt. Even the motion of molecules and atoms will hardly cease completely.

But we shall not go deep into this question. All we need is an idea of the temperature of bodies in celestial space. It is very probable that the temperature is close to 273°C below zero. That is the temperature at great distances from suns, when they appear as stars, for in that case the heat received from them may be neglected. It is difficult to have any doubts about this (although in this matter the conclusions of scientists are contradictory). Indeed, it has now actually been confirmed that the planets which are far away from the sun have very low temperatures, yet they are heated by the sun's rays. If they were at greater distances still, so that all suns appeared as stars, then the temperature would undoubtedly reach absolute zero (273°C below zero).

Planets have a certain amount of their own heat, however, and they strive to delay the cooling process; they still have a great supply of heat and sources of heat.

Now as to small bodies—and these can include not only the terrestrial objects that surround man here on earth, but also the asteroids (if they are far removed from hot or incandescent bodies)—they rapidly take on the temperature of absolute cold.

For this reason, a space rocket far from the sun, amid the faintly twinkling stars, is apparently in a critical position. Its temperature would soon fall to 273°C below zero.

But first of all, it can have its own source of heat, and secondly it may be protected from loss of heat by a number of shells to such an extent that these losses will readily be made good artificially even over the course of thousands of years.

But for the time being we shall leave this question. Let us examine a vehicle which is at the same distance from the sun as the earth. This will not in the least prevent it from being outside the earth, in the earth's orbit, hundreds of millions of kilometres from the earth, so that our planet will be like a tiny star, something like Venus as we see it.

Our rocket will lose heat only by radiation, for there is no air or other material medium about it. But it will also be receiving heat from the sun, and therefore the temperature will fall until the loss of heat (due to radiation) becomes equal to the gain (from the rays of the sun).

Thus, we have to think about the quantities of gain and loss and then deal with the question of the established constant temperature of the body.

The income of heat depends of course on the energy of the sun's rays. We will take that to be constant. But our body will not take up any energy at all if it is shielded from the sun by one or several shiny shells that completely reflect the heat. Thus, no matter how great the energy of the sunlight, it need not be absorbed by our rocket, given proper design and appropriate surface properties.

On the contrary, there are black surfaces that almost completely absorb the heat of the sunlight impinging on them.

To summarize, then, the gain in heat may fluctuate from zero to some maximum value dependent on the energy of the incident rays.

If there were no loss of heat due to radiation, then our rocket would heat up to the temperature of the sun.

Let us examine loss of heat.

All bodies lose heat from their surfaces, but some more and some less. Now this loss increases rapidly (to the fourth power) with increasing absolute temperature of the body. True, losses also increase with increased surface area (of the vehicle, for example).

All these arguments lead us to the following conclusions.

A structure, which on one side faces the sun and on this side has a dark heat-absorbing surface and on the opposite (shaded) side is shielded from loss of radiant energy by several brilliant surfaces, may have a temperature with a top limit of at least 150°C.

Here is a practical case. We have a closed spherical vessel containing a gas. A third of the surface area facing the sun is covered with glass that transmits radiant energy. The latter falls on the dark surface inside the sphere which readily absorbs the sun's rays. The other two thirds of the surface are protected from loss of heat by one or several brilliant surfaces. The temperature of the gas inside the sphere rises to 150°C.

The same hollow sphere facing the sun with the bright surface has an inside temperature close to 273°C below zero. The temperature range exceeds 400°C.

The same sphere turned sideways to the sun so that only part of the transparent surface faces the sun's rays, has a temperature somewhere between the minus 273° and the plus 150°.

By turning the sphere in various ways we can get any temperature we desire between these two extremes: for example, the temperatures of all the climates, all the altitudes, and all the seasons of the year on the earth.

If our vehicle is in sufficiently rapid rotation, with the transparent side periodically facing the sun, a mean temperature close (according to calculations) to 27°C is set up. This is nearly twice the mean temperature of our rotating planet, the earth.

However, the earth does not absorb but reflects back into celestial space the greater part of the sunlight. This is because 50% of the terrestrial atmosphere is permanently covered with clouds, the bright surface of which is an excellent reflector of sunlight. That is why the mean temperature of the earth is close to 15°C.

Generally speaking, the temperatures of the planets are a very complicated matter and largely rather relative; we shall not investigate this question here. In my manuscripts there are a good many arguments and calculations concerning the temperatures of planets. The published works confine themselves only to the results.....

The question of the temperature of space rockets would now seem to have been sufficiently explained....

However, it is also possible to design celestial vehicles so that their temperature will be expressed in thousands instead of hundreds of degrees. To achieve this, it is necessary to reduce loss of heat still more, without cutting down the gain from the sun.

If in our sphere we reduced the area of the windows and increased the area of the bright surface, then there would be a cut in loss of heat and also a decrease in the amount of heat absorbed. Still we can break out of this vicious circle. We can leave a very small transparent orifice open in the sphere and let through any desired quantity of solar energy with the aid of a lens or spherical mirror. The opening in the sphere should in that case coincide with the focal image of the sun. That will cut loss of heat to a minimum without reducing the influx of solar energy in the least.

What will be the outcome? The quantity of heat in the sphere will increase until the influx per second becomes equal to the loss per second. This will unavoidably occur because loss of heat increases with increasing temperature. The temperature inside the sphere can reach 1,000°C and more.

Even if our vehicle receded to the very limits of the solar system, to the orbit of Saturn with its rings and to Uranus and Neptune—even there the space rocket would be able to absorb from the sun sufficient heat for life (in the manner described).

On the other hand, there are opportunities for generating low temperatures despite the very hot rays of the sun. This will enable our rocket vehicle to explore the vicinity of the sun. Not only in the region where the planet Mercury circles and steams in the heat of the sun, but even closer.

We wrote about that a long time ago (1920) and are now only repeating what was said at that time.

A New Aeroplane

(1929)

1. Imagine a surface of revolution in the form of a spindle that is inflated to a high degree with air or oxygen. It has a cross-sectional diameter of at least 2 m and is not less than 20 m in length.

A number of such spindles are joined side by side (in parallel) and form a wavy square surface (plate) with teeth at the rear and on the ends (see drawings, which show: top view, side view, front view, cross-section and a diagram of take-off from a water surface).

The area of the plate is at least 400 m² (20 × 20). Both in the front and in the rear, on each sharp end, is an air screw of diameter at least 1 m (the total number of air screws being at least 10 to 20).

On the sides, to the rear, are two large rudders of altitude, which also serve as rudders of lateral stability. One or several direction rudders are mounted on the top of the vehicle (also at the rear).

The engines drive propellers (air screws, for example).

2. For take-off from a water surface, the aeroplane must be mounted on special pontoons in a slightly inclined position. When a sufficient speed has been reached and the vehicle takes off, the pontoons are jettisoned and the aeroplane flies without them. Descent onto water is possible without the pontoons because the ship is made watertight. Take-off from an aerodrome may be effected in the same way, only in place of pontoons the wheel gear will be left on the ground after the aeroplane has taken to

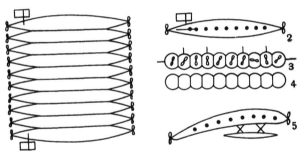

Fig. 1

the air. In this case, too, descent will require a broad expanse of water surface. It is also possible to land on an even field or on a flat surface of snow. It is not advantageous to carry along a heavy wheel carriage or pontoons, and they will soon be given up.

3. Such are the main features of the new non-fuselage aeroplane. What advantages has it, one may ask. They become evident only in the calculations. However, we shall first simply give a list of the most obvious ones.

4. Thanks to the airtightness of the craft, there is a permanent pressure inside the aeroplane, which consequently ensures safe flight in the rarefied layers of the atmosphere. It is then necessary to pump air into the chambers to feed the engines. But pumping is necessary also in ordinary aeroplanes during high-altitude flights.

5. High strength of the whole vehicle due to the internal super-pressure and, hence, its minimum weight.

6. Least weight and maximum strength are also due to the possibility of a uniform distribution of people and cargo.

7. Low air resistance since the hull, wheel gear, pontoons, wings, rods, and so forth have been dispensed with, and this results in a higher speed.

7_1. An economy in weight stems therefrom.

8. Simple design and hence low cost of the whole vehicle.

9. The possibility of constructing large cargo-carrying aircraft accommodating one hundred and more passengers.[1]

10. Convenient layout of many air screws and motors, thus ensuring complete safety. Even if up to five motors go out of action and stop, safety is not impaired and the flight will hardly be slowed up. From this stems the possibility of using air screws

---

[1] Modern planes can carry several hundred passengers (Editors).

of small diameter and of obtaining a large number of revolutions of the motor with the concomitant increase in power.

11. The vehicle may be extended in length and broadened without increasing its height. Its work diminishes upon expansion (the elongation of the wing is transverse) and increases upon becoming narrow (elongation is longitudinal). The subsequent calculations have to do with a square wing.

12. Low power output of a single motor and hence minimum weight, uniformity, cheapness and simplicity.

13. Considerable spaciousness and comfort.

14. The possibility of flying at high altitudes where the air is tenuous, and for this reason to have high translational velocities.

15. A gradual transition to a reactive spaceship. Other merits will emerge from calculations, which will confirm the merits we have already stated.

16. It is not convenient to keep up a constant pumping of air into the aeroplane but generally it is unavoidable when the engines perform worse in rarefied air; it is at present employed if the aircraft is designed for high-altitude flights.

17. Let us begin the calculations. I want to warn the reader that they are all approximate.

The basic units, where not indicated, are the second, metre, and its derivatives: ton, ton-metre, and so forth.

Imagine a section between two parallel cross-sections of a single spindle, at a distance of one metre. We will take it to be a circular cylindrical section with a diameter D (middle section).

18. The circumference u of this section and also the surface F will be $u = F = \pi D$, where π is the ratio of the circumference to the diameter.

19. The weight of the shell (G_1) will be expressed as $G_1 = \pi D \delta \rho$, where δ and ρ are the thickness of the shell and the density of its material.

20. The area of its horizontal projection is $F_h = D$.

21. The load (q_1) of one shell per unit area of projection is found from (19) and (20):

$$q_1 = G_1 : F_h = \pi \delta \rho.$$

22. But this is not a full load. It is only the load due to the weight of the shell (q_1). It increases with the weight of the motors, control gear (q_2), fuel and fuel tanks (q_3), people and cargo (q_4) and the reserve load (q_5), so that the total load (q) will be

$$q = q_1 + q_2 + q_3 + q_4 + q_5.$$

23. If, for simplicity, we put all loads equal, then from (21) and (22) we have

$$q = 5q_1 = 5\pi\delta\rho.$$

24. The breaking strength of the shell (S_h) must be equal to the super-pressure (P) of the gas inside the shell. We therefore write

$$S_h = \delta \cdot 2K_z : n = P \cdot F_h = P \cdot D.$$

K_z is the tensile strength, n is the safety factor and P is the super-pressure of the gas per unit area.

25. Formula (24) enables us to find the thickness of the shell and, hence, its weight and load. Then we will know the total load. Thus, from (23) and (24) we have

$$\delta = PDn : 2K_z \quad \text{and} \quad q = 5q_1 = 5\pi\rho PDn : 2K_z.$$

The partial loads per square metre of projection were taken to be one fifth of the total load (22).

26. In general, the surface of the whole aeroplane is, as it were, in the form of one single flat wing. We take the most unfavourable conditions. Thus, we could slightly bend the wing and the lifting force (due to the oncoming air flow) would increase by a factor of two.[2] But we do the calculations for a flat wing.

27. Likewise, we take the pressure on the plane (P_n) of normal air flow from the formula $P_n = (c^2 : 2g)\,\gamma$, where c is the rate of the air flow, g is the acceleration of gravity, and γ is the air density. This formula yields a pressure that is one and a half times less than the actual value. Neither is this to our advantage.

28. As for the pressure on a plane inclined to the air flow, I take Langley's formula, since it is close to my own and is quite justified by my experiments. According to Langley, the pressure on an inclined plane may be found by multiplying the magnitude of pressure of a normal flow by

$$2 \sin y : (1 + \sin^2 y).$$

But in favourable flight conditions, the angle of inclination to the horizon is very small and for this reason we can simply take the normal pressure and multiply it by twice the sine of the angle. The error will not be appreciable. From now on the sine of the angle will be denoted as $\sin y$.

29. Then, from 26, we get pressure, which is actually much greater, particularly if our craft is made with a slight curvature. Namely, the lifting force (P_v) of 1 m^2 somewhat inclined to the

---

[2] This is not exact. See, for example, Zhukovsky's formula for an arc plate (Editors).

horizon will be (26 and 28)

$$P_v = (c^2 : g) \cdot \gamma \cdot \sin y.$$

The error will be slight. For instance, at an angle of 10° it does not exceed 3%. What is that in comparison to the fact that we reduced the lifting force of the air by the conditions of (26) and (27).

30. Uniform horizontal flight of an aeroplane requires that the total load (q) should be equal to the lifting force (P_v). We therefore get, from (25) and (29),

$$c = \sqrt{5\pi g \rho P n D : 2\gamma \sin y K_z}.$$

Here the velocity is expressed irrespective of the weight of the shell and, generally, the weight of the aeroplane and its parts. It is assumed, however, that the weight must be equal to the total lifting force resulting from the pressure of the air flow on the wing. The lifting force may be very small and then the weight of the aeroplane will also have to be small, which is not feasible; and conversely, it may be very great, and this likewise is not feasible. The velocity is therefore of little interest to us. From the formula it is seen that the velocity should increase with increasing super-pressure, desirable strength and dimensions (D) and should decrease with increasing density of the air, angle of inclination of the wing and strength of material.

31. We now have to examine the value of energy (or engine power) and the air resistance due to friction and inertia.

Imagine our aeroplane of length l, width b and height D. We have to determine the total air resistance and the specific resistance, i.e., per square metre of the horizontal projection.

I make use of my paper "Resistance of the Air and High-Speed Trains", 1927. There, formulae (20) and (23) determine the total resistance of the surface of an ellipsoid of revolution. We cannot investigate the values of the constants in these formulae, and will only substitute numbers for them. Besides, we will divide the total resistance by the value of the horizontal projection. We can put its area equal to $l \cdot D \cdot 0.75$, where the notations are the diameter and the length of the ellipsoid, respectively.

32. Then, in place of formula (23) which yields the total resistance, we get the specific resistance, i.e., per square metre of projection:

$$P_{h_1} = \gamma f c^2 \cdot (A : X^3 + B : XD),$$

33... where $A = 0.0212$; $B = 0.00134$; X is the elongation of shape, or the ratio of the length to the height, and f is a special friction factor [formula(20), "Resistance", 1927] which depends on the ratio $l : c$. It is found from (20) or in the tables of work.

34. Determining A and B, we put $\pi = 3.14$, $g = 9.8$, $K_{sp} = 0.4$; $K_{sh} = 1$; $K_{pl} = 1$; $K_\eta = 0.75$; $\delta_1 = 0.0084$. The values of these constants were explained in my paper "Resistance", 1927.[3]

35. For convenience in calculations, in formula (32) we put $A : X^3 + B : X \cdot D = C$. Then $P_{h_1} = \gamma f c^2 C$.

36. This is the specific resistance due to friction and inertia when the aeroplane is flying in a perfectly horizontal path. An inclination is needed to obtain lifting force. For this reason, a horizontal resistance (P_{h_2}) appears because of the inclination of the aeroplane. This is the horizontal component of the lifting force (P_v) or of the normal air pressure on the wing. It is (see 29) equal to

$$P_{h_2} = P_v \cdot \sin y = (c^2 : g)\, \gamma \cdot \sin^2 y.$$

37. Now we could find the required work to be obtained from the aeroplane by multiplying the sum of all the horizontal resistances (34 and 35) by the velocity of the aircraft. But the use of a propeller (air screw or other means) increases the work of the aeroplane over the ideal work by a certain factor a.

38. To summarize, we get the work of the aeroplane per second (from 35, 36 and 37):

$$(P_{h_1} + P_{h_2})\, ac = a\gamma c^3\, (fC + \sin^2 y : g) = N_1.$$

The last letter designates the value of the specific power of the motor, that is, the work per second per square metre of the horizontal projection of the aeroplane.

39. On the other hand, the power (N_1) depends on the value of lifting force: the greater the lifting force, the more mass can be allocated for the engines and, hence, the greater will be their power. In paragraph 23 we assumed that the masses allocated for 5 components of aerial flight are the same and are equal to the mass of the shell. Thus, the weight of the motors will be expressed by the weight of the shell or a fifth of the total load (see 25). Knowing the weight of the motors, their energy (E), or the work of unit mass per second (specific work), it is also easy to express their power. Thus, by means of (25) we find

$$N_1 = 0.5\pi E P \rho D n : K_z.$$

[3] The full title is "Resistance of the Air and High-Speed Trains" (1927). The constants are K_{sp}, the coefficient of resistance of a sphere; K_{sh}, coefficient of shape; K_{pl}, coefficient of resistance of a flat plate; K_η is the coefficient of constriction, and δ_1 is the thickness of the surface layer (Editors).

40. The basic equations are the following. Formula (25) expresses the total load per square metre of projection as a function of the weight of the shell. Formula (29) expresses the same, but the lifting force as being dependent on the translational velocity. Formula (38) gives the specific power as a function of the horizontal velocity and the angle of inclination. Formula (39) also gives the power per square metre of projection as a function of the weight of the motors, which weight is taken equal to the weight of the shell, or 0.2 of the total lifting force. Equations (32), (33) and (36) are auxiliary. All seven formulae refer to one square metre of the horizontal projection of the aeroplane. We cannot get along without equation (25) since the shell, because of high altitude flight and for added strength, has to be rather massive.

For horizontal flight, the total load (q) must be equal to the specific lifting force (P_v). This permits us to eliminate from equations (25) and (29) the specific load or the specific lifting force.

Also, the specific power (N_1), as a function of the resistance of the medium (38), and it again—only this time as a function of the specific weight of the motors (39)—are equal; this enables us to eliminate the specific power (N_1) as well.

We thus get

41.
$$2.5\pi\rho PD \cdot \frac{n}{K_z} = \frac{c^2}{g} \cdot \gamma \cdot \sin y$$

and

42.
$$a\gamma c^3 \left(fC + \frac{\sin^2 y}{g} \right) = 0.5\pi E\rho PD \cdot \frac{n}{K_z} .$$

Eliminating from equation 42 the air density (γ) by means of 41, we get

43.
$$c = E \cdot \sin y : \left\{ 5ag : \left(fC + \frac{\sin^2 y}{g} \right) \right\} .$$

From this we see that the aeroplane speed is proportional to the specific energy of its engines. Thus, if their weight were (for the same power) diminished by a factor of 10, the independent horizontal speed would be increased just as many times.

44. But let us not forget that the density of the medium is not just any kind in this process: it obeys equation 41, from which we obtain

$$\gamma = 2.5\pi\rho PDng : (K_z \sin yc^2).$$

Consequently, this density must decrease with increasing square of the speed. If, for example, the speed increases 10 times, the aeroplane should rise to an altitude where the density of the medium is 100 times less than down below where it had flown with one-tenth motor power. But at high altitudes it is hard to extract energy from motors if the rarefied air is not condensed first or if liquid oxygen is not employed. It is a remarkable fact that the speed is not dependent on the weight of the shell or on its properties.

45. Let us recall that f itself is dependent on the ratio of speed c to the length of the aeroplane [formula (20) in "Resistance"]. We therefore give an approximate expression for the speed. Incidentally, f does not change appreciably. Thus, from formula (20) or from the tables of "Resistance" we find (assuming the length, l, of the aeroplane at 20 metres):

Speed	100	200	300	400
f	2.5	3.4	3.7	4.2

Consequently, the corrections are slight.

Note C. Formula (35) expresses the dependence of C on the dimensions (D) and the elongation (X) of the aeroplane. Consequently, the magnitude of speed depends also on the elongation.

But let us determine the speed c itself. Assume that $l = 20$, $D = 2$, $\pi = 3.14$, $E = 100$ (metric horsepower per kilogram of motor weight), $a = 1.5$, $\sin y = 0.1$ ($6°$ inclination to the horizon); $g = 10$, $X = 10$. From these figures we find $f = 2.5$ (see 45, we assume a speed of 100 m/sec), $C = 0.000088$ and $c = 109$ m/sec (393 km/hr).

This is the first approximation to the solution. But we presupposed a speed of 100 m/sec, whereas it came out to about 109. Therefore, f will not be 2.5 but somewhat more, which will quite imperceptibly increase the speed.

46. We calculate the appropriate air density from formula 44. Let us put $\rho = 8$, $P = 10$ (super-pressure of one atmosphere), $D = 2$, $n = 10$, $g = 10$, $K_2 = 10^5$ (100 kg/mm^2 cross-section) and $c = 109$. Then for the density of the medium we find a quantity somewhat less than 0.0011. This means that we cannot go above two versts.

47. On the basis of formula 44 we compile the following table:

Speed, m/sec	109	545	1,090	2,180
Ratio of densities of medium	1	1 : 25	1 : 100	1 : 400

48. The dependence of speed on the inclination of the aeroplane ($\sin y$) is not quite clear. But the function: $\sin y : (f \cdot C + \sin^2 y : g)$ has a maximum, therefore a maximum velocity is attained. Taking the derivative, equating it to zero and deter-

mining from the equation obtained the inclination. (sin y), which corresponds to its maximum, we get sin $y = \sqrt{f \cdot C \cdot g}$.

49. Substituting this inclination (sin y) into formula 43, we find

$$c = \frac{E}{10a \sqrt{f \cdot C \cdot g}} = \frac{E}{10a \sin y}.$$

50. Put $C = 0.000088$, $f = 2.5$, $g = 10$. Now, from 48, we get sin $y = 0.047$ (angle $= 2°40'$).

51. Also, assuming $E = 100$ (ordinary aviation motor) and $a = 1.5$, we calculate $c = 141.8$ m/sec, or 511 km/hr. This is the maximum velocity obtained at an angle of inclination of the aeroplane nearly 3° to the horizon. Neither a greater nor a smaller inclination yields a higher velocity.

52. If we always maintain the optimum inclination, then from 44 and 49 we get the density of the medium:

$$\gamma = 250\pi\rho PD \cdot \frac{a^2}{E^2} \cdot \frac{n}{K_z} \sqrt{fGg^3}.$$

It is evident from this that if maximum power is to be extracted from the motors, flights would have to be in the most tenuous layers of the atmosphere, because the formula states that the density of the medium must fall off with increasing motor power.

53. We determine sin y from equation 41 and find

$$\sin y = A \cdot D : (c^2 \cdot \gamma),$$

where $A = 2.5\pi\rho Pg$ $(n : K_z)$.

54. Eliminating sin y from equation 42 and solving for the relative density of the medium (γ), we get

$$\gamma = \frac{AED}{10gfCac^3} \cdot \left\{ 1 \pm \sqrt{1 - \frac{100g \cdot fCa^2c^2}{E^2}} \right\}.$$

55. Obviously, therefore,

$$c \leqslant E : \left(10a \sqrt{fCg} \right),$$

which means that the velocity cannot be greater than a definite magnitude. Taking the earlier conditions, we calculate $c \leqslant 141.8$. We get the same maximum velocity that we found earlier (49).

55_1. Thus, the velocity of conventional aeroplanes cannot be increased in the rarefied layers of air without increasing the specific motor power. For this reason, ordinary aircraft engines, apparently, are not suitable for attaining high speeds.

55_2. For this maximum speed, the necessary rarefaction of air is expressed by formula (54) as follows:

$$\gamma = AFD : (10gfCac^3).$$

If we eliminate the velocity c and A by means of equations (54) and (55), we get formula (52).

56. What is the work of the aeroplane? The specific work is expressed by formula (38) or (39). Under conditions (45) and (46) we calculate $N_1 = 2.5$ ton-metres, or 24 metric horsepower per square metre of the horizontal projection. The complete projection (20 × 20) gives 10,000 metric horsepower.

57. The total load is given by formula (25), namely:

$$q = 5q_1 = 0.125 \text{ ton} = 125 \text{ kg.}$$

Each type of load (0.2) will comprise 0.025 ton, or 25 kg.

58. A man weighing 75 kg requires 3 m² of projection area, i.e., 75 metric horsepower. And since the entire projection is about 400 m², the aeroplane can take aboard 133 persons.

59. The volume that corresponds to 1 m² of projection will come out to about $0.75 \cdot 2 = 1.5$ m³. Hence, one person will have about 4.5 m³. The floor area of 3 m² will even be more than needed.

61. The specific motor work that we obtained per person— 75 metric horsepower—is much too great and therefore the motor is operating at a loss (though the speed of 511 km/hr fully covers the expenses for energy). Can it be reduced? To do this it is first necessary to express the work of the motor not per unit area of the horizontal projection but per unit of lifting force and per unit of translational speed. Indeed, if we are moving 10 times faster and are lifting a cargo 10 times heavier, why shouldn't 100 times more work be expended? Cutting the time by increasing the speed is a new advantage, which we shall not take into account here (because of its indeterminacy).

62. From formulae (39), (55) and (25) we obtain

$$N_1 : (c \cdot q) = 2a \cdot \sqrt{f \cdot Cg}.$$

Here we divide the power (39) by the maximum velocity (55) and the total load (25).

63. From the foregoing it is clear that the power required per unit of distance of unit cargo does not depend either on the motor power or on the speed, but only on the shape and size of the aeroplane. It is almost constant.

64. Formula (62) gives the work per second (in ton-metres) in carrying one ton of the aeroplane over a distance of one metre.

But the passengers account for only one fifth (0.2), or 200 kg. This means that we will obtain work for carrying two persons (with luggage) over a distance of one metre.

65. Let us assume the conditions of (46). Then from (62) we find 0.047 ton-metre, or 47 kg-m per ton of aeroplane and one metre of distance. This is for two persons, for one (100 kg) we

would get 24. A very ordinary aeroplane expends 40 metric horsepower per person at a speed of 40 m/sec (144 km/hr). That is one metric horsepower per metre. In our case, it is one fourth this. But then take the extra saving in time.

66. What distance can our aeroplane cover without landing, given the conditions of (46)? We have seen that the speed is then 551 km/hr. The total load is 125 kg, partial load (motors, for instance), 25 kg (per square metre of horizontal projection). The corresponding power will be 25 metric horsepower (56). Twenty-five metric horsepower requires $0.2 \times 25 = 5$ kg of fuel. This means that our petrol will last for 5 hours, in the course of which our aeroplane will cover a distance of 2,555 km. But we have demonstrated that the lifting force of our aeroplane will actually be twice as much, which will add another 75 kg of fuel. This will enable it to fly non-stop for 30 hours and cover a distance of 15,338 km, or over 15,000 km, which is sufficient to cross the ocean.

67. The speed of an aeroplane depends on the peripheral speed of the air screw (and not on the number of revolutions per second, which is the greater, the smaller the size of the air screw). The latter does not at all depend on the size of the screw (its diameter), but only on the strength of the material and its distribution in the shape of the screw. For example, it is more advantageous to make the root of the screw more massive. At any rate, the peripheral speed should not exceed 500 m/sec, otherwise no material will be able to stand up to the centrifugal force and the screw will fly to pieces. In actual practice, the speed of an aeroplane in the case of least inclination (45°) of the blades of the screw to the air flow will not exceed 250 m/sec, or 900 km/hr, which is very far away from cosmic velocities.

68. Consequently, if we wish to obtain cosmic speeds flying in the rarefied layers of the atmosphere, the air screw is not suitable (aside from the ordinary low power of the motors).

There is yet another obstacle no less serious than these. It has to do with oxygen. It is possible to compress the air, i.e., pump it into the chamber of the aeroplane. But when the air is compressed 6 times, its absolute temperature is doubled. Here is a table:

Number of times rarefied air is compressed:

1	6	36	216	1,296	7,776

Absolute temperature of compressed air, °K:

200	400	800	1,600	3,200	6,400

Temperature, °C:

−73	127	527	1,327	2,927	6,127

69. The temperature of the compressed air will reach 6,000°C. An enormous amount of work is expended, some of which is regained if, without reducing this fantastic temperature, we drive the compressed air into the motors. Compression 36 times is permissible (if the compression is greater, the chemical reaction and liberation of heat will be retarded). Here the temperature will be about 527°C.

70. For an aeroplane, this is already good; in other words, we get 1,019 km/hr. Such a high compression has not yet been achieved, but perhaps it will be in the future.

71. But what more can be done? How will it be possible to get higher speeds for which neither the air screw nor air compression in motors is applicable any longer? We will have to give up conventional motors and the air screw.

We can take along supplies of oxygen in the liquid form, explode fuel with its aid, and eject the products of the explosion through an outlet pipe (as I described in 1927; see "The Space Rocket") and use the recoil for propulsion.

But on the other hand, it is extremely uneconomical to burden the aeroplane with the weight of oxygen, which previously had always been taken from the atmosphere. However, the speed of the aeroplane is not so considerable that recoil need be employed.

If we count per unit weight of fuel consisting of pure carbon, we have to take 2.7 (32 : 12) times as much oxygen. And so the mass of the energy supply is increased by a factor of 3.7. If utilization of the fuel were that many times as great, then we might reconcile ourselves to this unpleasantness, all the more so since we gain much in speed.

72. In tenuous air, utilization of heat may be raised to 50-100% (in the motion of the gaseous exhaust). Rockets moving at 1 to 2 km/sec will hardly be more efficient than ordinary aviation motors.

For rocket utilization to be complete, the exhaust velocity (at every instant) must be equal to the speed of motion of the aeroplane ("The Investigation", 1926).

73. All this suggests a very intricate design of a high-speed flying vehicle. First the ordinary motors and air screw are started. Then the screw is stopped or rotates idly and the motors pump air into an isolated rear compartment, out of which it races with a speed equal to that of the aeroplane. Since at first this speed increases, that of the air escaping from behind should also grow. When it reaches 1 km/sec or more, the motors pump into the explosion pipes explosive components that emerge into the rarefied air with a speed of 3 to 5 km/sec.

74. At this point the centrifugal force of aeroplane motion round the earth has already become very appreciable and has greatly reduced the weight and the work of translational motion. It falls to zero when the aeroplane attains the first cosmic velocity and gets out beyond the limits of the atmosphere.

75. An air screw is capable of producing more aeroplane speed than some think. Of course, its peripheral speed cannot be more than 500 m/sec, but the blades of the air screw may be set almost parallel to the oncoming air flow or to the motion of the aircraft (with a deviation of 20° to 40°). At first the work will be almost useless. But when the aeroplane acquires a high speed, the air screw (given a certain ratio) can function more economically. No matter what air screw you have, the work at the beginning of motion, when the aeroplane has not yet acquired its final and appropriate constant velocity, is uneconomical. It would be good if the blades of the air screw could be controlled automatically or manually to change and gradually reduce their inclination to the oncoming air flow as the speed of the aircraft builds up.

Though operation is extremely uneconomical in the case of a small inclination of the blades to the air flow, there is nothing else we can do when employing an air screw. However, we do not recommend this design or the small inclination of blades to the air flow.

76. It is simpler to give the aeroplane a high speed in some way and then start up the air pumps. Driven by ordinary motors, they compress the air and pump it into a special rear chamber. From this chamber the air exits through special pipes at the rear of the ship. It is easy to regulate gas ejection to bring it into agreement with the aeroplane speed obtained and with economy.

77. The speed of the gas emerging from the opening into the rarefied air is rather uniform and depends but slightly on the compression ratio. But this is true only of a constant temperature of the gas. Generally, however, the temperature is not constant and may reach many thousands of degrees (no matter how rarefied and cold the gas undergoing compression was at first). If a low ejection speed (for small vehicle speeds) is needed, we compress the air and pump it in at a moderate rate. Then, at exit, it may have a speed even less than 500 m/sec. But if higher ejection speeds of air are needed, the pumping is accelerated and the air is compressed still more; the air then heats up and its speed increases. When highly compressed and heated to many thousands of degrees, air is capable of speeds up to 2 km/sec and more (in proportion to the square root of the elasticity of the gas, or of its absolute temperature).

Let us not forget that the air being compressed is highly rarefied, 1,000 times for example, that its compression will yield a pressure of only, say, one atmosphere, that it is first cold, but that compression heats it up terrifically, and that the higher the temperature, the faster the air flow at exit. The density of the compressed air is immaterial if the air round about is rarefied.

78. Motors can also function with a constant power output. Then the rate of ejection of compressed air may be controlled by chokes. The smaller the exit opening, the more air will accumulate in the reservoir and the more highly compressed it will be, and the higher will be the temperature and the greater its exit speed from the pipes.

79. It is necessary, however, to protect the air chamber from heat losses. If the compressed air is cooled, it is hard to boost the rate of ejection and, besides, we will be expending energy fruitlessly (the energy will turn into heat and escape into celestial space).

80. At still higher aeroplane speeds it will be profitable to burn the fuel directly in the stored oxygen.

81. Every heat engine is at the same time a reactive device if the exhaust gases are directed into conical pipes and if they emerge in a direction opposite that of the carriage or ship. But since only a little bit escapes, the speed of the ship is low, and utilization of this additional energy will be very slight. That is why it is not used, say, in automobiles and conventional aeroplanes, and the gases are ejected in all directions without any devices.

We should not neglect this factor in our high-speed aeroplane at high altitudes. But of course the force of this reaction will not be sufficient due to the small quantities of material exploded in the motors.

The engines can pump air and generate an aerial reaction. But the exhaust gases will also produce a gaseous reaction.

In aerial reaction, approximately 20% of the heat of combustion will be utilized. The remaining 80% will be lost as exhaust. But because of the low speed of the aeroplane, only about 10 to 20 per cent of this exhaust energy will add to the speed of the vehicle.

Still, it turns out that use of the exhaust gases in rarefied space can double the work output of the motors.

82. Incidentally, it will be noted that the air for pumping will have to be extracted from the surrounding space (by pumps mounted in the forward section of the ship) and ejected from the rear. Then the air in front of the vehicle will become rarefied,

while at the rear it will be compressed. That will add thrust to the aeroplane.

83. The complicated design of the aeroplane motors increases the weight of the ship making it too heavy and unpracticable. We therefore propose several types. They all envisage heavy loads: at least 133 passengers and at least 20 metres in length and width and no less than 2 metres in height. The motors will develop at least 10,000 metric horsepower. (Incidentally, it is possible to make the aeroplane twice as narrow and then the specific work will increase 1.4 times.)

Do not forget, however, that the total actual lifting force of the aeroplane or the load per square metre is at least twice what we calculated — (26) and (27).

This excess lifting force may be utilized in various ways: it may be used to increase the number of passengers by a factor of 6, it may be employed to build up fuel supplies that will enable non-stop flights over distances one quarter of the circumference of the earth. A portion of the excess lifting force may be sacrificed for strengthening the aircraft (25). There may be other uses as well.

84. However, let us return to types of aeroplanes.

A. An aircraft for flying in the lower layers of the atmosphere no higher than 3 to 4 km. The super-pressure of one half an atmosphere is needed solely for adding strength and rigidity to the shell. The engines and air screws are conventional, speed: 500 km/hr; a transatlantic flight from Europe to America would take no more than 12 to 15 hours. The number of passengers for smallest size (20 × 20): from 133 to 798. That will mean between 75 and 12 metric horsepower per passenger.

85. B. An aeroplane for high-altitude flights where human beings suffer from the tenuous atmosphere and where the plane speed may be much higher. The engines are conventional but the blades of the air screw are only slightly inclined to the direction of flight. Part of the work of the motor goes to compress the air for the motors, the other part is spent on the aerial reaction. Here, the work of air screws is not economical, but the aeroplane speed is increased twofold.

86. C. The air screw is eliminated. The engines are engaged solely in compressing the air to promote an aerial reaction. Exhaust gases are likewise utilized. The speed and altitude are higher than in the preceding type.

87. D. The speed and altitude are still greater. The engines are low-power types used for the sole purpose of pumping oil and oxygen compounds into conical explosion pipes.

88. E. The speed is still higher. At high altitudes there is no air resistance, and the speed and centrifugal force eliminate

the effect of the earth's gravity. Both together make the motion of the vehicle eternal, without any expenditure of energy.

89. The last three types require a considerable initial velocity, which may be generated by auxiliary trains that climb mountains (see my article "Rocket Trains").[4]

90. For new engine systems it will be possible to attain still greater altitudes, rarefied layers of the atmosphere and high speeds. Travelling will be expensive, but there will be an enormous saving in time. Those are the advantages of such aeroplanes. Then, too, they serve as a smooth transition to astronautics.

91. There is no need to make the horizontal projection of the aeroplane square. It may be narrow, consisting of three to five inflated surfaces of revolution. But then the specific work of the engines will be greater due to the elongated structure. Thus, for such a reversed elongation equal to two, the work will increase by something like 30% (see my article "Air Resistance and Aeronautics", 1903).

92. For an aeroplane moving at a speed of 300 to 400 m/sec along the equator in the direction of the earth's rotation, the centrifugal force reduces the weight of the aeroplane by about 1%. I have at hand formulae and calculations of the motion of a new aeroplane at high altitudes in the tenuous air where the centrifugal force is also taken into account (my manuscript of 1926)[5].

※ PRINCIPAL CONCLUSIONS FROM MY PAPER "A NEW AEROPLANE"[6]

The idea of this aeroplane is not new at all. It is the flying wing: a long since designed vehicle. Its pneumatic strength is no novelty either.

The formulae and conclusions drawn from them, however, are quite new.

It has generally been thought that the speed of aeroplanes in rarefied layers of the air may be very great due to the low air resistance if of course the motor, equipped with a compressor, does not falter.

But this is utterly wrong. At high altitudes, the speed is greater only when the motor power (per unit of mass in one second) is

---

[4] See this volume, p. 187—218 (Editors).

[5] The manuscript is entitled "Rocket Aeroplane (A New Aircraft for High Altitudes and Speeds)", Archives, USSR Academy of Sciences (Editors).

[6] The manuscript "Principal Conclusions from My Paper 'The New Aeroplane'", dated December, 1929, was first published in the Selected Works of K. E. Tsiolkovsky in 1962 (Editors).

proportional to the square root of the rarefaction of the medium, i.e., when the thrust is constant. In that case, the velocity is proportional to the motor power.

On this basis we get the following table.

Rarefaction of the air:

1	4	9	16	25	36	49

Number of times the speed and required specific motor power increase (per second per unit of motor mass):

1	2	3	4	5	6	7

This conclusion refers to conventional air-screw aeroplanes. But, firstly. we do not have motors more powerful than the ones we know, secondly, if we did, the conventional air-screw propeller would be torn to pieces at that high speed.

We therefore have to give up the air screw and take advantage of the reaction of combustion products ejected backwards. Indeed, the thrust or reaction in this case will be the same, irrespective of the speed of the vehicle, and the work will be proportional to the speed, just as required. Only in ordinary fuel consumption will the reaction be insufficient. From 5 to 10 times more will have to be burnt. Now the motors are called upon to perform only a small amount of work: solely for compression of the air needed for explosions in the working cylinders. For this reason, such a motor of 100 to 200 horsepower may be somewhat heavier than usual. A reactive aeroplane of this kind will be very uneconomical when it flies in the dense layers of the air.

The correctness of the conclusion about the relationship between the speed of a rocket plane and the density of the medium may be confirmed by very simple reasoning.

Suppose that the aircraft has unit speed for unit air density and unit propeller thrust. Now, if it flies where the atmosphere is 1/9 as dense and the horizontal speed is three times as great, its equilibrium will not be upset for the same thrust of the air screw, i.e., it will neither fall nor rise.

Indeed, familiar laws state that through a reduction in the density of the medium, the pressure of the medium on the wings of the aeroplane will diminish ninefold, whereas the pressure stemming from a threefold increase in speed will increase ninefold. The result, therefore, is that the pressure will remain the same and be equal to the weight of the vehicle, which for this reason will not fall.

On the other hand, the thrust of the air screw, being one of the components of pressure on the wings (the angle of attack of which has not changed) remains constant. But the motor work per second still increases three times because the speed has increased threefold. The thrust of the air screw remains unchanged because its rotative speed has increased threefold, which causes the pressure on its blades to increase 9 times. But the density of the medium has diminished just as many times, so that the thrust of the propeller does not change. Unfortunately, it is impossible to increase the rotative speed of the air screw because the centrifugal force can tear it to pieces.

If, generally, the medium has become rarefied by a factor n^2, the speed and work of the motor will increase n times.

Quite obviously, when using rocket engines, the thrust of which is independent of the speed of the vehicle, the latter's velocity can increase in a rarefied medium.

But the supply of explosives (see my articles on the space rocket) is limited; and for this reason, the greater the velocity of the rocket plane, the shorter the time of flight, yet the maximum distance covered remains the same. The sole gain is in speed and time.

Here we have in view horizontal and uniform motion and do not take into account the work of ascent to a high altitude, which is necessary to attain the desired velocity, or the initial speed itself, which requires expenditure of energy and hence fuel consumption. Both these additional items of expenditure are the greater, the more considerable the desired speed. Thus the major portion of the fuel energy is absorbed by the initial velocity and in ascent. Both reduce the distance covered by the vehicle. But the speed and the altitude enable us (when shedding them in descent) to cover a certain additional distance.

There is a velocity at which all the fuel is absorbed in gaining the desired speed and in raising the vehicle into the tenuous upper layers of the atmosphere.

Then the entire trip will consist solely of accelerated ascent to the required altitude and the same inclined decelerated descent.

We shall not take that question up here because we have in view low speeds (up to 500 m/sec, or 1,800 km/hr) and low altitudes that consume relatively small quantities of fuel.

Reactive Aeroplane

(Taken from the Large Manuscript, 1930)

2. This aeroplane differs from an ordinary one in that it has no air screw at all.

Its action is replaced by the recoil of the products of combustion in ordinary aircraft motors.

But these motors will require a certain transformation and modification. For instance, a great deal of fuel is burnt that yields a relatively small amount of work, for example, 10 times less than is to be expected from the quantity of fuel. The engines have large numbers of revolutions and, for this reason, wide valve openings. The combustion products are directed in conical pipes rearwards through the aeroplane.

Besides, the combustion of even the very cold air at high altitudes is accompanied by extreme heating.

Here is a table.

The number of times a stable gas or mixture of gases (air) is compressed:

1	6	36	216	1,296	7,800

Ratio of absolute temperatures:

1	2	4	8	16	32

Absolute temperature:					
+273	546	1,092	2,184	4,368	8.736

Temperature, °C:					
0	273	819	1,911	4,095	8,463

Absolute temperature:					
+200	400	800	1,600	3,200	6,400

Temperature, °C:					
−73	+127	+527	1,327	2,927	6,127

From the last row it is seen that even for the icy (−73°C) air of high altitudes, a 36-fold compression will already require compulsory cooling.

For this purpose we make use of the intense expansion of combustion products in the tenuous atmosphere and their extreme cooling that follows therefrom. And so this air heated greatly by compression is first fed to a special jacket surrounding the rear ends of the pipes containing expanding combustion products. This compressed and cooled air will serve to cool the working cylinders and then will be burnt in them.

3. My theory of the aeroplane [1895 and 1929 ("Aeroplane")][1] has demonstrated that at high altitudes the aircraft will acquire high speeds in the rarefied layers of the atmosphere only when the work of the motor is proportional to the speed of the plane. The following table will serve to explain this:

Relative air density at high altitudes:				
1	1 : 4	1 : 9	1 : 16	1 : 25

Approximate height of flight above sea level, km (at 0°C):				
0	11.1	17.6	22.1	25.7

Relative forward speed of aeroplane:				
1	2	3	4	5

Required relative power of motors:				
1	2	3	4	5

This ability (to perform work in proportion to the speed of the vehicle) is inherent only in the reactive engine; it is into this

[1] The works referred to are "The Aeroplane or Bird-like (Aviation) Flying Machine", Mockow, 1895, and "The New Aeroplane", Kaluga, 1929. See this volume, p. 219-236 (Editors).

engine that we want to transform the conventional aircraft motor for the purpose of increasing the speed of the aeroplane in the rarefied layers of the air. There is no other way out. That is the conclusion we come to if we disregard the work of stopping the oncoming air flow needed to burn the fuel.

But at high altitudes one has to compress the rarefied air so as to be able to utilize it in the motors. That, in the main, is what the ordinary mechanical work of the engines will be used for. Therefore we cannot do away with them entirely.

An engine doing a great number of revolutions operates almost uselessly and performs a relatively small amount of work: it is not economical. But we do not need a large amount of work, since the work of compressing the cold rarefied atmospheric air is relatively slight, the power output of the motors will definitely suffice, and there will be a lot to spare too. The main purpose of the engine is the reactive (jet) action of exhausting the combustion products, the propeller has already been removed.

We shall show what the magnitude of this work is. Since the air undergoing compression is cooled by the rearward parts of the reaction pipes, its temperature is assumed to be constant. Then, to determine the work of its compression, we take advantage of formula (14_1) (see my article "Pressure",[2] page 9):

$$A = P_1 \cdot V_1 \cdot \ln \left(\frac{V_1}{V} \right) .$$

Here, P_1 and V_1 are the initial pressure and volume, and V is the final smallest volume (after compression). Suppose the air is rarefied 1,000-fold. The pressure will then also be 1,000 times less. Our purpose is to compress this enormous volume 1,000 times so as to reduce it to the original small volume; work will be performed in the process. It will then be seen that the product $P_1 V_1$ remains constant no matter how rarefied the air is. Hence, the work of compression depends solely on the logarithm of compression ($V_1 : V$). At 0°C the product $P_1 V_1$ is equal to 10.3 ton-metres. Now from formula (14_1) it is easy to compile a table of work values to obtain 1 m³ of compressed air of normal density. Namely:

Rarefaction of the air or the required compression:

1	6	36	216	1,296	7,800

Work required to obtain a cubic metre of air of normal density (0.00129) at zero temperature, ton-metres (approx.):

0	18	36	54	90	108

[2] Here and henceforth the reference is to the paper "Pressure on a Plane in Normal Motion in the Air", Kaluga. 1930 (Editors).

Later (8) we shall see that for unit mass (1 kg) of fuel (in the case of benzene) we require about 11 m³ of normal air.[3] It will require 108 ton-metres to obtain it from air rarefied to the extent of 7,800 times. But a kilogram of benzene is capable of yielding at least 4 horsepower in one hour. This amounts to the work of $(75 \cdot 3,600 \cdot 4)$ 1,080,000 kg-m, or 1,080 ton-metres. This work is thus 10 times greater than that needed for compression.

Less work is needed for a smaller compression, as may be seen from the table. But without cooling the air, more work will be needed. Here we can take advantage of formula (39), namely,

$$A = B \cdot P_1 \cdot V_1 \{1 - (V_1 : V)\}^{1:(B+1)}. \tag{32}$$

From (44) we know that $B = 2.48$ and $1 : (B + 1) = 0.287$. Suppose $V : V_1 = 780$. Then we calculate the work $A = P_1 \cdot V_1 \cdot 34.7 = 358$ ton-metres, which means that it will be some three times more than the preceding one (108 ton-metres). Still it is three times less than that performed by the motors. For practical purposes, one should take the mean work, which will be some 5 times less than that performed by the motors. The computed work refers to compression in empty space. Air pressure helps compression, and so the actual work is less, particularly in the lower layers of the atmosphere and in the case of a slight compression.

The aeroplane does not stay long in the lower layers of the atmosphere. But the work performed by the motors is useful there too and will serve to cool the working cylinders with air and even to compress the air in order to accelerate combustion of petrol, increase motor power and the thrust of the exploding gases.

Indeed, the formulae and tables may also be used for compression of normal air (near the sea level) to boost motor power (the walls of the motors, however, have to be made stronger). From (14_1) and (39) it is seen that the work of compression will then proportionally increase, since P_1 increases. But then the work of the motors increases the same number of times as well. And since the working cylinders are always designed for an excessively great safety factor (so as not to make the walls very thin), it is extremely advantageous to compress air even in the lower layers of the atmosphere.

4. In elaborating the theory of such aeroplanes we have to deal with compression and expansion of gases, with their calorific values, i.e., their heat of combustion, with their exhaust speeds, their reaction, the air resistance, with compressors and their operation and with other different things.

[3] The calculation is based on 1 m³ of compressed air (Editors).

Therefore we must again refer to our published work entitled "Pressure on a Plane" (1930).

5. In the investigation of fuel, we examine, for the sake of definiteness, the following three types of fuel: hydrogen, carbon, benzene. For combustion we take pure oxygen, ordinary air or nitric anhydride (N_2O_5).

This does not mean that we consider such materials the best ones for engines or the most profitable; simply no other materials have as yet been tested and so there is no proof that they are practicable.

For example, monatomic hydrogen (H) releases in the formation of diatomic hydrogen (H_2) 16 times more energy than the same mass of detonating gas. (See my article "Space Rocket", 1927, p. 15.)[4] But we cannot suggest a fuel that has not been tested practically. For instance, I do not know whether monatomic hydrogen (H) can be converted into a liquid and whether that liquid is safe relative to explosiveness. The same may be said of other materials proposed as fuel by different authors, for example ozone (O_3) and light metals (for instance, aluminium, lithium, calcium, and so forth). Likewise impracticable, so far, is the idea of jettisoning parts of the aeroplane or converting them into fuel.

6. The following is a table that indicates relative weights of materials participating in combustion:

Fuel	Hydrogen	Carbon	Benzene
Formula of fuel	H_2	C	C_6H_6
Relative weight of particle (molecule) . . .	2	12	78
Combustion products . .	Water	Carbon dioxide	Water and carbon dioxide
Formula of combustion products	H_2O	CO_2	H_2O and CO_2
Relative weight of oxygen (O_2) required for combustion	16	32	240
Same, but for nitric anhydride (N_2O_5) . .	21.6	43.2	324
Relative weight of products of combustion in oxygen	18	44	318
Same, but in N_2O_5 . .	23.6	55.2	402
Weight of fuel taken as unity	1	1	1

[4] The full title is "The Space Rocket. Experimental Preparation", Kaluga, 1927 (Editors).

Then weight of oxygen will be	8	2.67	3.33
Then weight of combustion products will be, using oxygen	9	3.67	4.33
Then weight of N_2O_5 will be	10.8	3.6	4.5
Then weight of combustion products using N_2O_5 will be	11.8	4.6	5.5

7. If we burn air in our aeroplane, we must indicate the quantitative ratios of its components.

For this purpose we give the following table:

Name	Air	Oxygen*	Rest
Composition of air by weight . .	100	23.6	76.4
Same by volume	100	21.3	78.7

* More precisely, oxygen comprises 23.15% of air by weight and 20.93% by volume (Editors).

From here we find the following weight ratios of the component parts of the air: $N_2 : O_2 = 3.24$, $O_2 : N_2 = 0.309$, $O_2 : \text{air} = 0.236$; air $: O_2 = 4.24$. For instance, this means that oxygen comprises 0.31 of the weight of nitrogen and 0.236 of the weight of all the air.

For volume relations we get: $N_2 : O_2 = 3.69$; $O_2 : N_2 = 0.271$; $O_2 : \text{air} = 0.213$; air $: O_2 = 4.70$.

8. Now we can give the quantity of air by weight and volume per unit of mass (1 kg) of fuel.

Formula of fuel	H_2	C	C_6H_6
Quantity by weight	1	1	1
Needed quantity of oxygen . . .	8	2.67	3.33
Weight of combustion products using oxygen	9	3.67	4.33
Required quantity of air	33.9	11.3	14.13
Weight of combustion products using air	34.9	12.3	15.13
Required quantity of air as to volume (density $= 0.0013$), m^3	26.1	8.7	10.9

9. But it is also important to know the required amount of oxygen of the air and of nitric anhydride per metric horsepower (100 kg-m). We therefore propose the following table:

242

	H_2	C	C_6H_6
1. Formula of fuel			
2. Quantity of heat per unit mass of fuel . . .	34,180	8,080	11,500
3. Thermal ratio	2.97	0.709	1
4. Amount of fuel per metric horsepower per hour, kg	0.0842	0.353	0.25
5. Amount of oxygen per horsepower (100 kg-m) per hour	0.674	0.942	0.833
6. Amount of air per hour per horsepower, kg	2.498	3.994	3.532
6_1. Amount of N_2O_5	0.910	1.272	1.125
7. Weight of ejected products per hour (combustion in oxygen)	0.758	1.295	1.083
8. Same for combustion in air, kg	2.584	4.347	3.782
8_1. Same for N_2O_5	0.994	1.625	1.375
9. Weight of ejected products using oxygen for 1,000 horsepower per hour	758	1,295	1,083
10. Same per second	0.21	0.36	0.30
11. Same for combustion in air, kg	0.72	1.21	1.05
11_1. Same for use of N_2O_5	0.275	0.450	0.380
12. Hourly supply of fuel per 1,000 horsepower, kg	84	353	250
13. Ejection rate (per second) using oxygen ("Rocket", 1926)*, metres	5,650	4,290	4,450
14. Same for combustion in air	2,743	2,082	2,160
14_1. Same for nitric anhydride N_2O_5	4,900	3,840	3,900
15. Acceleration of one-ton rocket using oxygen, m/sec²	1.19	1.54	1.33
16. Same, using air, m/sec²	1.97	2.52	2.27
16_1. Same, using N_2O_5	1.35	1.75	1.48
17. Pressure (recoil) on rocket in case of oxygen, kg	119	154	133
18. Same in the case of air, kg	197	252	227
18_1. Same in the case of N_2O_5	135	175	148
19. Rocket speed, after one hour using oxygen, in empty space, m/sec	4,284	5,544	4,788
20. Same but for air (see 15, 16)	7,092	9,072	8,172
21. Number of seconds to reach speed of 8,000 m/sec with oxygen	6,720	5,200	6,010
22. Same, hr	1.87	1.44	1.67
23. Corresponding amount of fuel, kg (see 12) . .	154	508	418
24. Number of seconds to reach 8,000 m/sec with air (see 18)	4,061	3,175	3,524
25. Same, hr	1.13	0.88	0.98
26. Corresponding amount of fuel	94.9	310.6	245.0
[27]. Volume of air required for 1,000 horsepower per hour, m³. Air density = 0.0013	1,921	3,079	2,717
[28]. Same, per sec	0.53	0.35	0.75

* Tsiolkovsky has in mind his work "Investigation of World Spaces by Reactive Vehicles", Kaluga, 1926 (Editors).

10. Let us give some explanations and draw some conclusions from this table. When using atmospheric oxygen it is very profitable to have a reserve of hydrogen. The weight of this fuel, for the same work, will be three times less than that of the petrol (rows 3 and 12). The only unfortunate thing is that liquid hydrogen is as yet hard to obtain. It is also a good thing to use liquefied marsh gas, or methane (CH_4).

Now in the case of stored liquid oxygen the difference in supplies or explosive components is not great (row 7). There is no particular advantage in replacing petrol with hydrogen. And that goes for the use of N_2O_5 almost to the same extent.

For the full weight of an aeroplane of one ton even an hour's supply of fuel does not appear to be excessive (12). But for hydrogen it is very small.

Rows 13 and 14 give the speed, in seconds, of ejection for the most favourable conditions: in the case of complete combustion, without loss of heat, for long conical pipes and expansion of the combustion products in empty space. When we use air, it is clear that the mass of the explosion products will be nearly 4 times greater (7 and 8) than in the case of pure oxygen. Therefore the ejection rate here will be one half. But on the other hand we are relieved of burdensome supplies of oxygen. However, oxygen will be needed in empty space or in the very rarefied layers of the atmosphere. Supplies of N_2O_5 yield a slight advantage compared with oxygen.

Rows 15 and 16 give the acceleration of a 1-ton rocket (mass), air resistance being neglected. It appears that it is more profitable to use the air, since it produces a greater acceleration, to say nothing of the extra burden of liquid oxygen. We obtained these figures in the following manner. We found out how many times the weight of the rocket (1,000 kg) was greater than the ejection mass per second. Then the figure obtained is divided by the ejection rate per second. (A well-known law states that due to the action of a force between two masses, the greater mass receives a smaller speed the same number of times that the greater mass exceeds the smaller one.) Of course, there will be an increase in vehicle acceleration as the fuel burns up. We gave the smallest.

Rows 17 and 18 express the recoil or thrust in kilograms.

Rows 19 and 20 give the rocket speed after one hour, the resistance of the medium being neglected. When air is used, this speed will reach the first cosmic velocity.

But the question arises: Is a motor of 1,000 horsepower feasible with total mass 1,000 kg? The petrol alone will take up 250 kg (row 12). Under the present state of motor engineering, an engine of 1,000 horsepower will weigh at least 500 kg. But the

244

point is that our motor can generate only 100 to 200 horsepower (see 3) so long as it consumes as much as does a motor of 1,000 horsepower. The main thing here is not the work but the combustion and reaction. A motor of this kind may weigh much less, say 100 or 200 kg. Then enough will remain for the other components and equipment.

Row 23 indicates the amount of fuel alone for use with oxygen in order to obtain a velocity of 8 km/sec (in empty space). Even without oxygen supplies it turns out to be great, and with oxygen it is impossible for a rocket weight of one ton. On the contrary, that supply of fuel for use with air for the same purpose is possible.

But can an ordinary aeroplane, of mass 1,000 kg, take off with the reactive thrust we have found (17th and 18th rows)? Assuming an ordinary aeroplane of 100 horsepower per ton of weight and with a speed of 40 m/sec, we find the thrust to be 125 kg. We take the efficiency of the air screw at 0.67. With oxygen, the thrust is close to 125 kg (17) in the case of a jet (reactive) aeroplane, so that here too the aircraft will rise and fly without a propeller (with a velocity of 40 m/sec). But when air is used (18), the recoil is nearly doubled. According to my theory ("Aeroplane", 1895 and 1929), an aeroplane with a thrust of 125 kg can fly with a velocity twice as great—at an altitude of 12 km where the air is rarefied by a factor of four.

11. We have in view a uniform and horizontal motion of the vehicle. We do not take into account the work of ascent to the required altitude and the work of acquiring a constant speed. These can be neglected only at velocities that do not exceed 500 m/sec and for ascents that do not go above 30 km. For these conditions, the natural compression of air in the forward pipe is insufficient, and so we cannot, generally speaking, avoid employing some kind of compressor.

12. Suppose that at sea level we have a speed of 100 m/sec. This is attained when using our jet engine. At an altitude of about 12 km, where the air is rarefied fourfold, the speed of the vehicle with the same motor will already be doubled. How does this occur? Particularly since the motor is the same. The point is that the power developed by a reactive motor is proportional to the speed of the vehicle. Indeed, its thrust, or reaction, does not change, no matter what the velocity. For example, if the reaction is 250 kg, then what will change it for a greater or smaller speed of the aeroplane? If that is the situation, then the work performed in one second will be proportional to the speed of the aircraft. If its speed is increased fivefold, then—for the same thrust— the work will also increase five times. For zero speed, the motor

power, despite the enormous reaction, will also be zero. We of course have in view the utilized work: the higher the speed, the better the energy of combustion is utilized.

13. The work necessary for covering unit distance at different altitudes remains constant (see "The New Aeroplane"). It does not depend on vehicle speeds at different altitudes. This signifies that the power, or work per unit time, is proportional to the velocity of the aircraft. But this is only for ordinary propellers. Now for a reactive (jet) motor, the power (or more precisely, the fuel consumption) is the same. Consequently, fuel consumption per unit distance is the less, the higher the speed.

14. Let us take an example. We found that an aircraft weighing one ton should burn at least as much fuel as is required for 1,000 metric horsepower. At sea level, it will have a velocity of 100 metres a second. And in flight it will burn 5 times as much fuel as is required for an ordinary aircraft with an air screw. Therefore, an ordinary plane is five times more profitable than our jet plane. But the jet plane flies twice as fast—where the density of the atmosphere is 1/4. Here, it will be at a disadvantage of only 2.5 times. Still higher, where the air is 25 times more rarefied, it will fly 5 times as fast and will now utilize the energy just as successfully as an air-screw plane. At altitudes where the medium is 100 times more rarefied, its speed will be 10 times greater and it will be more profitable than an ordinary aeroplane by a factor of two.

At very high velocities the phenomenon becomes so complicated that our conclusions no longer hold so closely (for we disregard the fact that the oxygen needed for combustion is taken from the atmosphere. See my article "Resistance of the Air and High-Speed Trains", 1927).

15. Then what are we after if the economy in work is not particularly pronounced? The point is that we obtain a speed of motion that is beyond the capabilities of an aircraft with an air-screw propeller.

At considerable speeds we will definitely reach high altitudes. Besides, there will be a noticeable centrifugal force which reduces the work and raises us higher with increasing speed. At a speed of about 8 km/sec, the work is reduced to zero and we get beyond the limits of the atmosphere.

16. The high speed of the vehicle will find applications in terrestrial transport even if no economy of fuel is effected.

We have seen that flight under these conditions cannot last more than an hour. The following are the distances which a vehicle can fly at different altitudes for different velocities of forward motion.

Relative density of rarefied layers of the atmosphere:

1	1:4	1:9	1:16	1:25	1:100

Altitude of flight, km (approximate):

0	11.1	17.6	22.1	25.7	36.8

Speed, m/sec:

100	200	300	400	500	1,000

Speed, km/hr:

360	720	1,080	1,440	1,800	3,600

The last row indicates the distance covered in one hour as well. It is obviously insufficient for practical purposes. But firstly, the altitude and velocity can be made still greater, secondly, the weight and energy of fuel may be increased. Then trans oceanic flights will be possible.

17. Here, we have hardly at all touched on calculations relating to the accelerated motion of the vehicle during ascent and the reaching of cosmic velocities that relieve it of the resistance of the atmosphere. We speak only of terrestrial transport and hint at celestial travel; we point to the transitional stage between them. The era of air-screw aeroplanes will be followed by the era of jet aeroplanes or aeroplanes of the stratosphere.

To Astronauts

(1930)

People of a more practical bent strive to apply the force (or the principle) of recoil (reaction) to the designs of: (1) powerful jet engines, and to the developing of high speeds in (2) automobiles, (3) hydroplanes and (4) sleighs.

Let us examine all these items.

An explosion motor, like a hydraulic turbine, cannot yield high efficiencies in utilizing the energy of explosion, since the peripheral speed of a wheel with blades (i.e., a turbine) cannot exceed 200 to 400 m/sec. Yet profitable utilization requires blade speeds 1.4 times less than the speed of the emerging products of explosion, which is capable of attaining 5,000 m/sec. Hence, the speed of the blades will be about 3,500 m/sec; this is impossible relative to the strength of the very best materials.

Now if we confine ourselves to blade speeds of 100 m/sec, we will be utilizing only 3% of the given chemical energy. This is not economical.

What is needed here is a complicated wheel and, in general, the techniques employed in the construction of modern steam turbines. Then it would be possible to achieve a very high percentage of utilization of the given energy.

Now here is yet another condition. The explosion products have to be exhausted into empty space, otherwise they will not have sufficient speed. From this alone it follows that such motors cannot be very lightweight. Besides we shall encounter a great many difficulties of a practical nature, about which this is not the place to speak. There can be no doubt, however, of the great future of these motors.

Automobiles cannot gain high speeds by the rocket method (or any other method) because of the great resistance of the air in the lower layers of the atmosphere. Also, their wheels, even without rubber tyres, are torn to pieces by the centrifugal force when the peripheral velocity gets beyond 200 to 400 m/sec. To obtain a speed exceeding 100 m/sec, we must get rid of the wheels and devise a special roadway for our vehicles (see my article "High-Speed Train")[1]; moreover, they must be made more elongated and their shape must be improved. But even then we will not achieve a speed exceeding 1,000 m/sec. And what is the sense if so much effort is expended? Enormous work is gobbled up by the resistance of the air.

Compressed gases (for example, carbon dioxide, CO_2) are not profitable here because their internal energy of motion (kinetic energy) is extremely small. What is more, they demand vessels weighing ten times the weight of the compressed gases. Cold liquefied gases that freely evaporate do not require strong and massive vessels, but their kinetic energy is still less than that of compressed gases. In releasing their energy, they borrow heat from surrounding bodies and the air, and this takes more time than can be allowed for.

Explosives (like powder, dynamite, etc.) in the ready-to-use form are also inapplicable. Aside from the hazard of explosion (detonation), they require heavy guns or vessels due to the fact that an explosion in one place transmits pressure to the entire mass. The extreme probability of an explosion was recently confirmed by the tragic death of Valier and in other cases as well.

The same may be said about hydroplanes and sleighs. Their advantage is that they have no wheels. But to the resistance of the air is added the resistance and friction of the water or snow. I am speaking, of course, about automobiles and hydroplanes propelled by recoil (rocket vehicles). Other types of vehicles are doomed to smaller speeds because of revolving propellers or wheels.

Two principal approaches to astronautics emerge at present: (1) the gradual transition from aeroplane to astroplane; and (2) a purely reactive (rocket) device.

At first the aircraft does not go beyond the limits of the atmosphere, rises to small altitudes and flies short horizontal distances. Then it goes higher and higher and covers longer and longer distances. Finally, it gets out beyond the atmosphere and flies by inertia like a celestial body.

[1] This volume, pp. 164—186.

Both the modified aeroplane and the rocket vehicle will continue on their way thanks to the pressure of light. To be frank, I myself don't believe very much in this pressure, even despite corroborative experiments. But their results can be explained in another way, much more simply, and light pressure need not play any role whatsoever in this explanation. In my opinion, the experiments even refute the pressure of light.

But since most scientists believe in light pressure, we too can accept it without encountering any objections. My calculations have been checked many times and cannot give rise to doubts.

Thus, I have shown ("Rocket", 1926) that 1 kg of substance with a surface area of 1 m² receives from the sun's light during one year an increment in speed amounting to over 200 m/sec.

In the absence of gravity it is easy to set up vast surface areas of just the slightest weight. For example, a 0.01-mm-thick surface of water density and with an area of 100 m² weighs only 1 kg. Rotation of this square (10 metres on a side) will impart a certain tautness, smoothness and strength. In the course of a year, the light pressure will give it an additional speed of 20 km/sec. This is more than sufficient for travelling throughout the solar system and even for leaving the sun and journeying about in the Milky Way. Indeed, the vehicle already had a speed of 30 km/sec (upon escape from the earth). With the additional speed, we now have 50 km/sec. To escape from the sun completely, one needs 42 km/sec (30 × 1.4). There is still an extra speed of 8 km/sec for the Milky Way.

Suppose the vehicle weighs one ton and the surface area just as much again. Then in two years the vehicle will obtain the same increment of speed, i.e., 20 km/sec.

It would indeed be nice with light pressure ensuring space travel throughout the universe: if not 2 years, then a number of years would produce a velocity sufficient for this purpose.

Only out beyond the atmosphere can we solve the problem of the existence of light pressure....

Let us first take up the problem of the transition from aeroplane to astroplane; after that we can examine the rocket vehicle.

In my works ("Aeroplane", 1895 and "The New Aeroplane", 1929) I demonstrated that an aircraft can fly twice as fast in a medium that is four times more rarefied (at an altitude of 10 km), and the motor power required will be doubled for the same weight. In general, the speed of an aircraft increases n times if the medium is rarefied n^2 times; but the motor energy must then definitely be n times more.

On the one hand, the power output of an ordinary motor cannot be increased in a tenuous medium; on the contrary, it falls drastically. This means that an air compressor is needed, and this again means power consumption and added weight for the vehicle. Moreover, when gas is compressed, it heats up terrifically. Consequently, a cooling means is required.

On the other hand, accelerated rotation of the propeller will tear it to pieces because of the centrifugal force.

For the present, let us aim at increasing the aeroplane speed by a factor of only two. To double the motor power we can double the revolutions. But then it will be necessary to enlarge the valve openings and use fuels that mix rapidly with the air. Such are the best grades of petrol, or liquid hydrogen, or some combustible gas.

The tangent of inclination of the blades of the air screw to its plane will also have to be doubled: roughly from 0.3 to 0.6. The corresponding angles will be 17° and 31°. These angles are quite permissible without any great disruption of economy. Then the speed of the aeroplane can be increased twofold for the very same number of revolutions. But the number of revolutions of the machine has doubled. What is to be done? Either employ a transmission of 0.5 or reduce the diameter of the air screw by a factor of two. The first method is more economical (chain transmission).

It is also necessary to compress the fourfold rarefied air. Here its absolute temperature will increase 1.75 times (see my paper "Pressure", page 4).[2] If at an altitude of 10 km the temperature is 43°C below zero, or 230° of absolute temperature, compression will raise it to 403°, i.e., the air will heat up to 130°C (403 − 273). This is tolerable and we can even dispense with cooling. But the compressor is still needed.

This is not all. The combustion products emerge from the motor with a great force. No damping device will be used, and we shall take advantage of their recoil. The higher the velocity of the aeroplane, the more profitable this is. Also, the more rarefied the medium, the less of a barrier there will be to the expansion of the combustion products and the greater will be their exhaust velocities and their recoil.

Naturally, the combustion products are directed into special conical pipes located along the aeroplane with their wide open muzzles pointing rearwards, to the tail of the aircraft. As my unpublished calculations show, the recoil can as much as double the power output of the aircraft.

It is even possible to triple the speed at an altitude where the air is 9 times more rarefied. The angle of inclination of the blades

    [2] "Pressure on a Plane in Normal Motion in the Air", Kaluga, 1930 (Editors).

of the air screw to the plane of its rotation will change from 17°
to 42°, which is quite tolerable. The transmission will be 1 to
3 (or the diameter of the air screw will be reduced threefold),
and this will reduce the number of revolutions of the air screw
by a factor of three, thus restoring the former speed of revolution.
(Let us not forget the tripled speed of the motor shaft and the unavoidable enlargement of the valve openings.) The absolute temperature will increase by 2.4. Thus, at 73°C below zero, or 200° of
absolute temperature, we get 480°, or 207°C (480 − 273). This is
still tolerable and does not require cooling.

But still and all, doubled and tripled aircraft speeds are very
far away from cosmic velocities. What more can be done? The
angle of the blades cannot be increased further. Heating will
require cooling. And where do we get the cold? There is a good deal
of it at high altitudes, but it is still not enough because the air is
too rarefied and its temperature is not below 70°C.

Thus, all further increase in speed comes to a halt because of:
(1) the air screw, (2) the necessity of compression, (3) intense
heating, and (4) the necessity of cooling. The air screw may be
replaced by moving wings (like those of a bird). Though this is
very advantageous since it increases the lifting force of the aircraft, it is complicated structurally.

It is simpler to give up the propeller altogether. This is possible
at high aircraft velocities and for flights in a rarefied medium,
since the recoil of combustion products is the more productive,
the higher the speed of the craft and the more rarefied the medium.
A rarefied medium enables the gases to expand more readily, as
a result of which they attain higher exit speeds from the pipes
and a lower temperature, which in the limit (in a vacuum) reaches
273°C below zero.

This is what may serve as a source of cooling of the air heated by
compression. For this purpose we compel the air that has been
heated and compressed by the motor to flow round the rear ends
of the pipes with the combustion products that have been greatly
cooled through expansion. Then the compressed air, which has
now been cooled, is directed into the working cylinders of the
motor.

Here, we kill three birds at once: in the pipes we heat the combustion products that have cooled through expansion and thus
boost their speed and recoil, at the same time we cool the air
heated by compression and designated for the working cylinders,
and, finally, we obtain an enhanced reactive effect, for an engine
without a propeller can execute a greater number of revolutions.
And its mechanical work will be slight, since it will be employed
mainly for compressing the air.

Using these methods, it is not known to what limits one can go in increasing aeroplane speed. It is a question whether it is possible thus to build up to cosmic velocity and get out beyond the limits of the atmosphere. And to this question we have no answer (even more so, nothing affirmative). At any rate, the construction of high-altitude aircraft will teach us much and bring us closer to the astroplane. Detailed mathematical calculations on aircraft recoil for the foregoing design have long since been done by me and were even sent to an institution. I, of course, have copies of these studies.

※ ※ ※

Let us now turn to the purely rocket machine. Here, we cannot do without a motor, for it is necessary to inject or pump explosive components into the mix-and-combustion chamber. Here again there are no propellers because of the rapid attainment of considerable speeds that propellers would not be able to withstand. But there is nothing to prevent us from taking advantage of the recoil of combustion products in engines as has just been described.

We thus revert to the earlier design with the addition of a purely rocket device. It is described in my article "The Space Rocket" (1927).

But here is a question. When the vehicle reaches the very tenuous atmosphere high up, the air will no longer serve to feed the engine. How are we to supply it with oxygen? But a rocket motor has its own supply in the vehicle itself, and therefore part of this supply will go to feed the engine when the tenuous upper layers of air are reached.

We now point to those conditions of design of a rocket vehicle that practical workers, generally speaking, refrain from observing (as a result, the hero Valier paid with his life).

1. Ready-prepared explosive material is not suitable. For example, various powders, nitroglycerin, lyddite, dynamite, and others.

2. The explosive components (say, oxygen and hydrogen) must not be mixed prior to their union in the pipes.

3. They are held separately and kept in different vessels or compartments.

4. They must be liquid at ordinary temperatures, for example, like petrol and nitric anhydride.

5. They must be as dense as possible so as not to occupy a large volume.

6. Their vapours must not exert a substantial pressure on the walls of the vessels so that the latter need not be made massive.

253

7. They must not have a very low temperature, like liquefied and freely evaporating gases, so as to retain as much energy as possible.

8. The pumps are piston-type and pump liquids that have not yet been heated.

9. These should not produce any chemical action on the walls of the pumps, on pipelines leading to the combustion chamber and on the explosion pipes themselves. They are therefore made of suitable material or such material is used to coat the inside surfaces.

10. The explosive components have to be mixed as thoroughly as possible in the explosion chamber and as quickly as possible so as to produce an instantaneous explosion like that of gun powder or a shot.

11. The explosion chamber must be cooled by cold borrowed from the expanded explosion products whose temperature at exit should reach 273°C below zero. For this purpose, the explosion chambers and their continuation, i.e., the pipes for exhausting combustion products, have to be surrounded by a jacket that contains an artificially circulating thin layer of light liquid (for example, oil, gas, etc.), which transfers heat from the explosion chamber and intensely heated parts of the exit pipes to their cold parts. The advantage will be a dual one, as I have explained. The pipes themselves may be utilized to some extent for the same purpose if they are good conductors of heat.

12. Explosion must be fast, just like the build-up of pressure in the chambers and pipes. The result is an instantaneous explosion, pressure several hundreds of atmospheres and then a release of the pipes and chambers from the great pressure. After that, pumps inject a new portion of explosives, producing a second explosion, a thrust and release of the gases that have formed.

13. There should be as many injections per second as possible, say 30 or 50. That will produce the same number of shots per second.

14. The work of pumping will be slight due to the fact that it will be done at the moment of the least pressure in the combustion chamber and pipes.

15. The pipes that lead from the chambers and convey the explosive products must be flared at the ends (like musical instruments, megaphones, ear trumpets, etc.). This reduces their length and enhances recoil.

16. There should be several such pipes, and explosions should occur at different times so that the chambers fire in succession at equal intervals of time, then the 30 to 50 thrusts per second in one pipe merge into a single one, and ten pipes, for instance,

yield 300 to 500 shots a second, and all the more merge into a single whole. In this way we protect the vehicle from destructive vibrations. Also, the greater number of explosion pipes and chambers serve to economize on material. From artillery we know that the weight of a gun increases much faster than the pressure in it for the same volume of barrel.

The experiments of Prof. Oberth were the most scientific but they did not satisfy the majority of these conditions. There is nothing whatsoever to say about the other astronauts. That is why the results so far obtained are so very miserable. Such is the practical aspect of all great undertakings. Still, they are valuable and should not upset anyone.

The first attempts at flying, aeronautics, the use of steam, electricity and all other inventions likewise pushed ordinary people and even inventors to dispair. But we, having learned the lesson of history, must be brave and not give up our work because of failures. We must seek their causes and eliminate them.

Semi-Reactive

Stratoplane

(1932)

✳ BRIEF DESCRIPTION OF DRAWINGS

1. We first give the plan or horizontal projection (Fig. 1). We see three nearly identical hulls of good shape. One houses the pilots. It is tightly closed against loss of air, so at high altitudes it will be just as easy to breathe as down below. Another one contains the fuel. The middle one carries the air screw (propeller), the engine, compressor, refrigerator, etc. (The middle hull will be described further on along with the drawings [see Figs. 2-3].) Passing across the top of the hulls is a large wing, which also serves to join them. To the rear are two smaller wings that can turn. When turned in unison, they serve as a rudder for altitude, when not in agreement, the wings give lateral stability. Finally, there is a direction rudder mounted rearwards on top of the middle hull.

2. Fig. 2 depicts the longitudinal section of the middle hull. The front part (*1*) can open up to a greater or lesser degree (also see Fig. 3). It is never completely closed. The rear part of the hull (*9*) is of the same design. When the aircraft is in motion, the oncoming air flow always passes through it; this is aided by the air screw (*2*) driven by an oil or petrol engine (*3*), which is cooled by the general air flow in the middle hull (casing). Currents of pure air are designated on this drawing by single arrows. The

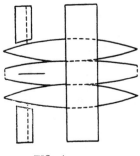

FIG. 1

combustion products of the engine flow through a multitude of pipes (*3*) and are collected in an annular-like space (between two cylinders) that gradually broadens out.

Here the products expand intensely, their heat is converted into motion, and they thus acquire high speeds; their temperature falls, reaching 250°C below zero. The result is an effective refrigerator (*5*). The pipes with the combustion products are shown cross-hatched in the drawing. Double arrows indicate the direction of flow of the combustion products.

The aircraft is propelled by the air screw and also by the recoil of the combustion products. All this mass of gases exits with a great speed through the rear flared opening of the middle hull.

Contiguous with the annular space (*5*) of the refrigerator is another similar space which also lies between two cylinders. Currents of pure air enter through the annular opening (*7*) and turn back. Cooled intensely by the refrigerator (*5*), they pass through a number of pipes (*8*) into a gas compressor (*10*), which is driven swiftly by motor (*3*) via gear wheels and a Hooke's joint (*11*). From the compressor, the pure, compressed and already

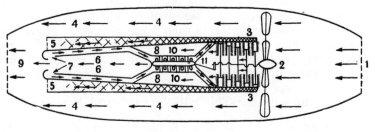

FIG. 2

FIG. 3

heated (by means of compression) air is directed along several pipelines to the motor, where together with petrol it is fed to the working cylinders.

The higher the speed of the aeroplane, the narrower the openings in front and in the rear of the middle hull are made. The design of these variable openings is seen in Fig. 3, which shows the opening from the front or from the rear. The end surface of the hull consists of rectangular plates, which at the opening are formed into folds or into a corrugated star. Any other similar device may be employed.

Let us now enumerate the things that this machine is capable of doing.

3. The closed pilot-and-passenger hull permits flying in the most rarefied layers of the atmosphere.

4. The air screw is always in revolution with a definite safe speed (150-300 m/sec at periphery), despite the tremendous speed of the aircraft. The point is that the area of the opening in front and back diminishes the same number of times as the speed increases. By way of an example, for a complete opening of the muzzle (cylinder) let the speed of the aeroplane be 100 m/sec. If the velocity of the vehicle is increased 9 times (900 m/sec), then the area of the openings will be reduced ninefold, and their diameter, thus, three times. Consequently, in such cases the amount of air entering the middle hull will always be the same, and this is what ensures invariable speed of the air flow in the broad section of the hull and the same invariable speed of the air screw, despite the great diversity of speeds of the aeroplane and the speeds of the air entering the muzzle.[1] This will be explained later on (34).

---

[1] The actual phenomena of air flow and the operation of air intakes are much more complicated (Editors).

5. The thrust of the aircraft is generated not only in the ordinary way by the air screw, but also by the recoil of the combustion products.

6. The higher the stratoplane flies and the more rarefied the atmosphere, the more the gaseous combustion products expand, the lower their temperature, the more intense is the cooling of the air fed to the motor, and the more intense the action of the compressor. So that the latter operates smoothly both in the dense and in the tenuous atmosphere.

The theory of the gas compressor has been described in one of my published works, which may be obtained from me.[2]

7. At first the stratoplane moves along rails, on the snow or water (it is also a stable hydroplane). After attaining a speed of 100 m/sec, it rises into the air and flies upwards higher and higher at an angle. Flying in the lower layers of air, it would soon reach a limiting speed of approximately 200 m/sec. But as it rises steeply, it enters more tenuous layers of air, and this enables the speed to build up, at first gradually, and then faster at higher altitudes where the air is very tenuous.

8. We bear in mind that the work of the motor, far from falling off, even becomes more intensified due to the low temperature of the refrigerator and the intense cooling (perhaps even liquefaction) of the air entering the compressor.

9. All the drawings are of a schematic nature. All secondary details have been eliminated in order to bring out more clearly the design and operation of the vehicle. For example, the connections and the mechanism for changing the cross-section of the input and output (for air) openings are not indicated.

If the speed of the stratoplane is to exceed a certain number of times that which an ordinary air screw without a casing can withstand, then it will be more practicable to make this casing smooth and of good shape, but with equal apertures both in front and in the rear.

For example, if the maximum speed of the vehicle is to exceed conventional speeds by a factor of 9, then the openings should, in area, be 9 times less, and 1/3 in diameter.

In this way, we can construct stratoplanes with double, triple, and so forth speeds.

In order not to spend extra work on motion at the beginning of a flight, at low speed, the casing may have special longitudinal and gradually closing openings: on top, at the front of the casing, and at the bottom, towards the rear. The lifting force will only be increased thereby.

[2] The article in view is "Gas Ccmpressor and Its Design Calculations", Kaluga, 1931 (Editors).

10. It is of interest in itself and may have numerous applications. Such devices are probably in existence and have even been patented. But I have mastered their operation, significance and theory only just recently. That is what the whole matter is about. Let us explain.

The Chinese had rockets all of 3,000 years before our era. A hundred and fifty years ago, a rocket was even able to raise a ram into the air. It may be that people too were carried aloft by the force of rockets, although this must have been very risky.

What could be more simple than the idea of applying rockets to moving over land, water and in the air. However, only theory pointed out the true value of reactive devices. Up until 1903 the rocket was only a toy or a thing with but few real down-to-earth applications. Its cosmic significance was not perceived by anyone, at least it was not defined scientifically. The same may be said of my compressor.

11. The ordinary air screw is not applicable in the case of fast motions of a high-altitude aeroplane, for it is torn to pieces, no matter what the size, when the peripheral speed reaches a definite value. Likewise, the blades of a fan cannot have a peripheral speed greater than some limiting value. The number of revolutions can be made the greater, the smaller the diameter of the screw, but the peripheral speed does not exceed a specific limit that depends on the strength of the material of which it is made.

12. A fan-type compressor is portrayed in Fig. 2 (*10*). However, a conical surface tapering off to the vertex must be added at the rear, at the exit of the flow. The opening at the vertex can be made to expand and contract as desired by the operator. From the barely perceptible aperture of the cone, the surface can be converted into a cylinder.

13. The fan-type compressor (Figs. 2 and 3) consists of a circular cylindrical pipe, inside of which is another rotating closed cylinder with air screws mounted round it (they are similar to aeroplane screws or have the form of an Archimedean screw). Between every two screw circles is a flat stationary blade located lengthwise, parallel to the axis of the cylinders. It can be extended eccentrically in the large cylinder and attached to it. The purpose of these blades is to prevent, as far as possible, any rotation of air in the compressor. The diameter of the inner rotating cylinder is roughly one half that of the outer stationary one.

14. When the axle revolves as the terminal cone is completely open and becomes a cylinder, the air hardly encounters any

resistance at all and moves almost without compression, as if by the action of the air screw alone. But the more the exit opening (Fig. 3) is narrowed, the more the gas passing through the exit is compressed.

This action is best comprehended if we imagine that the exit opening is completely closed. There will be no flow, but the closer the air is to the end of the pipe, the more compressed it will be.

15. Here each pair of blades compresses it by a certain amount. Let us suppose that the first screw increases the pressure and the compression of the air by 1.1. Then the second screw, together with the first, will increase this pressure by $(1.1)^2$, the third, with the first and second, by $(1.1)^3$, the tenth, by $(1.1)^{10}$, and so forth.

We see that the limiting pressure (and compression) in the pipe increases with the number of air screws. In one and the same pipe it is not the same and is expressed by a series of numbers: (1.1), $(1.1)^2$, $(1.1)^3$ ... $(1.1)^{10}$ ... The last figure expresses the pressure in the pipe behind the tenth air screw.

Besides, there is an increase in the temperature due to compression; this distorts the conclusions by showing lower pressure, since the air density diminishes with heating.

16. If we open the aperture a little, there will be a flow, but the indicated pressure will immediately fall off. The broader the opening in the cone (Fig. 3), the faster the flow but the lower the pressure and compression (actually this is a much more complicated phenomenon).

There is a mean outer resistance for which the action of the flow is most advantageous.

18. Let us suppose that the axle is surrounded by a cylinder whose diameter is one half that of the pipe. The air-screw blades are situated round the smaller cylinder, and the air flows in the annular space between the two cylinders. This passage is 0.75 the area of the cross-section of the large cylinder. The small cylinder ends with smooth surfaces that close it at both ends.

19. The drawing (Fig. 2) shows a longitudinal section *10*. We see partitions in it. They are attached to the large cylinder but do not come in contact with the smaller one. The partitions are designed to prevent the development in the pipe of any rotative currents that might destroy or weaken the gas tension and its translational motion.

20. It is an advantage that the partitions have least weight for least resistance. To achieve this, both ends of each one are attached to the large cylinder.

21. We determine the highest peripheral speed (u) of a rotating body. Let this body be a cylindrical stick, or, generally, a cylinder located perpendicular to the axis of revolution (like the spoke of a wheel).

The highest peripheral speed is obtained when, under the action of the centrifugal forces the greatest tension of the cylinder (at the axis) is equal to the resistance of the material. On this basis we form an equation:

$$\frac{u^2 \cdot l}{l \cdot g} \cdot \gamma \cdot 0.5 = \frac{K_z}{S} ,$$

where we see the length of the cylinder, l, the expression for terrestrial gravitation, g, the density of the material, γ, the tensile strength of the material, K_z and the safety factor, S. The coefficient 0.5 is found by simple integration. Whence,

$$u = \sqrt{\frac{2g \cdot K_z}{\gamma \cdot S}} .$$

From this we see that the maximum peripheral speed of a cylinder does not in the least depend on its thickness or length. It is clear that the number of revolutions of the stick per second is the greater, the less its length l. But the speed u is proportional to the square root of the strength of the material and is inversely proportional to the safety factor S and the density of the material γ (see formula).

22. The rod can be tapered, like a cone, a wedge, or a body of everywhere equal resistance. This will increase the peripheral speed. But we have in view the blades of an air screw and it is hardly convenient to reduce the cross-sectional area towards the end. Because of flattening of the cylinder, the blade is thinner towards the end anyway.

23. To what degree will the blade of the fan compress the air?

The shape of the blade is that of part of an Archimedean screw. We only make use of the upper half of the rod.

If the inclination of the upper element of a blade to the plane of its rotation is designated by tan α, then the inclination of its lower element will be $2 \cdot \tan \alpha$. In the cylindrical pipe the greatest velocity of an air flow normal to a circle will be $v = u \cdot \tan \alpha$. Thanks to the properties of the Archimedean screw, this speed will be the same throughout the blade or for a specific cross-section of the pipe.

24. This current of air through the pipe can exert a maximum pressure P not less than as follows:

$$P = \frac{(u \cdot \tan \alpha)^2}{2g} \cdot d.$$

25. Here, u can be eliminated by means of formula (21). Then we get $P = \tan^2 \alpha \{K_z : (\gamma S)\} \cdot d$.

We are particularly interested in this greatest pressure. It increases with the specific strength of the material $(K_z : S)$, the density of the medium (d) and the tangent of the blade inclination (squared).

It is not an advantage to have a large safety factor (S).

26. The tangent of the angle of the upper part cannot be taken more than 1. Then the blade will make an angle of 45° with the circumference (and the lower part of the blade, 64.5°). Further, in formula (25) we put $K_z = 2 \cdot 10^6$ kg/cm² of cross-section (this may be taken only for the best grades of chromium steel and other such steels); $\gamma = 8$, $S = 4$ (at least), $d = 0.0012$ kg/dm³.

Then we compute from formula (25): $P = 75$ kg/dm², or 0.75 metric atmosphere. Formula (21) also yields an appropriate peripheral speed of blades, namely, $u = 353.5$ m/sec.

27. It will be more practicable to put $\tan \alpha = 0.5$. Then $P = 19$ kg/dm², or 0.19 atmosphere, and $u = 353.5$ (same).

28. A cylindrical pipe having several air screws on a single axle will give the following maximum pressures for different numbers of screws.

For pressure increase, we can take the number 1.2, assuming constant temperature, or an artificial cooling of pipes and air.

Number of air screws:							
1	2	3	4	5	6	7	8
Compression, atmospheres:							
1.2	1.44	1.73	2.07	2.48	2.99	3.59	4.28

Number of air screws:							
10	12	14	16	18	20	22	24
Compression, atmospheres (approximate):							
6.75	8.94	12.9	18.3	26.3	37.8	54.4	79.9

29. In formula (25) we suppose—to be more practicable— $\tan \alpha = 0.5$; $K_z = 10^6$; $\gamma = 8$; $S = 5$; $d = 0.0012$.

Then $P = 7.5$ kg/dm² or 0.075 atmosphere. From formula (21), $u = 223.6$ m/sec.

30. From this we get the following table:

Number of screws:

2	4	6	8	10	14	18	20

Pressure, atmospheres (approximately):

1.15	1.32	1.52	1.74	2.00	2.64	3.48	4

Number of screws:

30	40	50	60	70	80	90	100

Pressure:

8	16	32	64	128	256	512	1,024

31. For a stratoplane flying at high altitudes in highly tenuous layers of the atmosphere, high compression, a small number of screws and an enormous volume of compressed air are needed for combustion.

Let us take the conditions of (26), namely: $u = 353.5$, compression 1.75 (for one screw).

Number of screws:

1	2	3	4	5	6	7	8	9

Compression:

1.7	2.9	4.9	8.4	14.3	24.0	40.8	70.5	117.6

Number of screws:

10	12	14	16	18	20	22	24	26

Compression:

204.5	591	1,714	4,960	14,380	41,470	120,000	$348 \cdot 10^3$	10^6

In all these tables we of course obtain the maximum limiting pressure. The high compression is applicable only for appropriate rarefaction of the air in the upper layers of the atmosphere.

❋ USE OF COMPRESSOR

32. This compressor can produce any desirable pressure (up to liquefaction of the gases or to a very high temperature) and any desirable quantity of air. The efficiency of motor operation

depends on the design of the compressor, the pressure and the rate of flow.

The low efficiency is compensated for by simplicity of design, compactness, the possibility of obtaining high temperature, light weight and cheapness of the compressor, and the lack of any need for lubrication. It finds application in fans, various furnaces and devices where there is a demand for large amounts of air at high pressures and temperatures. The same goes for stratoplanes, reactive ships, carriages, and high-speed trains (for example, "Zeppelin on Rails" and my non-wheel train). It converts mechanical work into heat and vice versa. It can also serve for lifting liquids, or, conversely, as a turbine.

✳ PROPELLER

33. We shall now describe the propeller. It differs from the above-described compressor in only one way: in the front as well it has a cone similar to the rear one. The number of its air screws is not fixed and may be limited to a single screw (Fig. 2).

When the propeller with fully open apertures (in the form of a cylinder) races along with the vehicle, the relative (to the pipe) flow rate in it will be $c + W$, i.e., the velocity (c) of the vehicle plus the relative (to the screw) ejection speed (W) caused by the action of the air screw. But since the speed of the vehicle (c) may be very high, so the relative speed of the flow in the pipe of the propeller will also be high. Yet the latter one cannot exceed a limit determined by formulae (21) and (23), which yield

$$c + W = \sqrt{\frac{2g \cdot K_z}{\gamma S}} \cdot \tan \alpha.$$

This speed is quite definite. We determined its maximum at 353 m/sec. Hence, the vehicle cannot have a high speed, otherwise the air screws (that is, the blades in the pipe) would fly to pieces because of the centrifugal force.

34. What are we to do? Is there no way to impart a high speed to the vehicle? Yes, there is a way out of this impasse.

We begin with an experiment (see Fig. 4). I designed the external part (casing) of my propeller without blades (without a screw).

In this pipe (which is greatly widened in the middle) are suspended plates (pendulums) at four points: in the middle, at the intake opening, at the exit, and laterally at the intake, outside the pipe. Both openings are of the same size, the pendulums are identical.

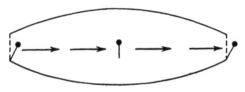

FIG. 4

I took this device and moved uniformly or stood still near the half-opened door of a warm room. In the latter case, there was a very regular flow of air over the doorway from the warm room into the cold room.

All wind vanes were absolutely identical. For this reason, the observed identical deviation of the extreme ones indicated identical force or rate of air flow. But deviation of the middle plate (or wind vane) was hardly noticeable. This indicated a low speed of air current in the wide portion of the pipe.

35. What do we see? Suppose a pipe like this is moving together with a vehicle in the direction of its longitudinal axis. The oncoming air current enters the forward opening with the velocity of the vehicle, is then greatly retarded in the broad section of the pipe, but is ejected from the rear opening with the same speed as it entered. This is what our experiment corroborates.[3]

36. If we reduce the area of the end openings in proportion to the increase in aeroplane speed, then the relative speed in the broad portion of the pipe will remain constant despite the increase in velocity of the vehicle. Indeed, if, say, the speed of the aircraft is increased by a factor of 10, and the end openings are reduced (in area) the same number of times, the volume of air taken into the propeller will remain constant. And since the mean cross-sectional area of the pipe has not changed either, the rate of flow in this cross-section will likewise not change.

37. Thus, air screws will operate safely at any aeroplane speed, since the speed of the medium surrounding them does not increase, despite any increase in the speed of the aircraft.

In the absence of air screws, the relative speed of the medium at the intake and exit of the propeller will be approximately equal to the speed of the aeroplane (only friction and temperature variations due to compression and expansion of the air will reduce it somewhat). However, thanks to the action of the propeller, this speed is increased by some quantity, depending on the power output of the motor.

[3] When the speed of the flow approaches the speed of sound, phenomena at the air-intake entrance differ radically from the conditions of Tsiolkovsky's experiment because of the appearance of shock waves (Editors).

This means that at exit the air flow acquires a certain excess speed above the speed of the stratoplane.

38. In flight, the openings should become narrower as the speed increases. Thus, if the speed of the vehicle is increased 25 times, the area of both openings must be reduced 25 times, and the diameter has to fall off by a factor of five.

39. In this work, we should be guided by the acceleration indicator of the vehicle: the openings have to undergo change up to the point where the acceleration of the vehicle reaches its maximum value. Now acceleration of motion of any body is indicated exactly by a special instrument called the accelerometer.

To summarize, then, our device makes it possible to employ an air screw at any aeroplane velocity, since our air screw is always in rotation at a constant speed, despite the changing speed of the vehicle.

We determined the maximum speed of air flow in the middle portion of the pipe at 353 m/sec. A safer speed would be less, say, 210. At first we do not get this speed. But gradually, the velocity of the vehicle is increased and reaches, say, 200 m/sec. The rate of ejection (relative to the screw) is taken at 10 metres. Then, if the pipe is cylindrical in shape, i.e., the apertures of the propeller pipe are wide open, the rate of flow and the rotation of the blades should not increase. Therefore, as the speed of the vehicle increases, we reduce the area of the end openings in proportion to the increase in speed of motion of the vehicle.

This may be shown in tabular form:

Speed of vehicle, m/sec	100	400	900	1,600	2,500
Relative area of extreme cross-sections of the pipe	1	0.25	0.11	0.067	0.04
Relative diameter of openings	1	0.5	0.33	0.25	0.2

The rate of the air flow in the broad section of the pipe will always be 210 m/sec, but the speeds of the incoming and exiting flows are approximately the same and will be

110   420   630   840 1,050

Of course, it is possible to narrow the apertures still more (it is disadvantageous, however), but it is not possible to expand them beyond what is normal, for then the air screw would be torn to pieces.

And so with wide-open apertures of the propeller pipe, we can move at speeds up to 100 m/sec. After that the apertures will have to be narrowed. If this is done more than required, the air screw will remain intact, if less than indicated in the table and than follows from the law, the air screw will be torn apart.

I shall attempt to publish a continuation of this study.

Meanwhile I can report that this stratoplane must have at least 1,000 metric horsepower to reach even moderate altitudes with a total weight of one ton. Consequently, the motor must be lighter than an ordinary aviation motor. Roughly speaking, at least 2 to 4 metric horsepower are needed per kilogram of weight. Practical attainments are moving in that direction and there are already motors which generate up to 2 horsepower per kilogram of weight. (This article was written at the end of 1930.)

Reaching the

Stratosphere

(1932)[1]

✳ I. EXPLOSIVE SUBSTANCES AND FUEL

Actually, there is no sharp borderline between the process of explosion and simple combustion. Indeed, both are a more or less rapid chemical combining. Combustion proceeds slowly: say, one gram of substance combines in one second; and explosion is fast combustion: one ton of substance may combine in one second—this is 1,000,000 times more.

The same may be said of smoldering, rusting and slow oxidation or, generally, any slow chemical reaction. In a word, then, the difference in all these phenomena is purely quantitative.

It will be noted that the energy of explosive substances per unit mass is even much smaller than the energy released by unit mass of fuel.

Thus, 1 kg of black powder yields 783 calories (338,000 kg-m),[2] dynamite, from 1,291 to 1,900 calories, oximide mixtures, from 2,000 to 2,500 calories, detonating gas, 3,200 calories, and a mixture of pulverized carbon and liquid oxygen, 2,200 calories.

Now combustion of 1 kg of carbon yields 8,000 calories, 1 kg of petroleum products, from 10,000 to 12,000 calories, and 1 kg of hydrogen, 29,000 calories. The chief reason for the difference

---

[1] Manuscript dated 1932, first published in 1936 (Editors).
[2] A more precise value is 334,340 kg-m (Editors).

lies in the fact that in combustion, the oxygen of the air is not regarded as something of no importance or something that is not stored.

To summarize, fuel is more profitable than explosives, particularly since the latter are more expensive and entail more difficulties when employed. So far it has not been possible to make this process economical. All these experiments with reactive automobiles, hydroplanes, sleighs, and gliders are of importance only as study aids and as preparation for the stratoplane and the astroplane.

Then what are the advantages of explosive substances? The advantages are great, but they are not of an economical nature. Indeed, explosive substances release tremendous energies in a brief space of time, since the chemical union of the mixed components of combustion takes place almost instantaneously.

Let us suppose that carbon is burning at the rate of one kilogram per second; now an explosive substance of several tons can burn up in that very same second. And if in the process, as is usually the case, we obtain volatile products, these can acquire speeds up to several kilometres a second. Their energy of motion may be utilized in a turbine, although as yet no practical solution of this problem has sufficiently matured. However, we believe that the future of reactive motors will be brilliant. We proceed from the fact that the volatile products of an explosion expand in an artificial or natural void (outside the atmosphere) and convert all their energy into motion. And so the percentage of utilization may be exceptionally high. Besides, the speed of combustion and, hence, the liberation of energy are of great importance.

The advantages of explosives are already being utilized for firearms and for the destruction of solid masses (granite rock, for example). In the same way, they can impart high speeds in a fraction of a second to a cannon-ball, releasing (on the average) several million horsepower in one second. In the same small fraction of a second they perform large quantities of work in the breaking up of masses of rock.

Rocket devices of direct action (rockets) can yield huge power outputs for vehicles and carriages, provided speeds of several kilometres a second are attained. But such speeds are impossible in the lower layers of the atmosphere because of the resistance of the dense air. Only in the extremely tenuous upper atmosphere are such speeds possible and decent efficiencies attainable.

Incidentally, we shall refute straight off the extremely widespread delusion that cosmic velocities are attainable in the upper tenuous atmosphere with the aid of the ordinary energy of engines.

As early as 1895, I stated in my published works[3] that the required motor power in the most favourable tenuous layer is proportional to the speed of the aircraft.

For example,

Rarefaction ..	1	4	9	16	25	36	49	64
Speed	1	2	3	4	5	6	7	8
Required power output for same weight of motor ..	1	2	3	4	5	6	7	8

(This was corroborated 35 years later by the American scientist Corvin-Krukovsky.) This is good, too, since for an invariable air density, the power is proportional to the cube of the speed, i.e., the power increases in the ratio of the numbers: 1, 8, 27, 64, 125, 216, 343, 512, etc.

The difficulties of stratospheric flight are great, but they can be overcome by utilizing this fantastic power produced by explosive substances.

✳ II. ENGINES AND EXPLOSION

1. Strictly speaking, in any furnace, explosions are constantly occurring; this is particularly evident where spray burners are used. However, in the ordinary steam engine or turbine, explosions are not used directly. Only the heat is utilized: the heat raises the temperature of the water and steam and this yields the work. The power output of these motors is the least, i.e., the power output per second per kilogram of engine weight is low. When we have cheap fuel, like peat or coal with unusable admixtures, and we are not embarrassed by the weight of the machine, this is very economical. But in a locomotive the fuel is cleaner and more expensive and the economy is often questionable. There is an apparent trend to go over to explosion motors (petrol and diesel) or electric motors.

2. Another case is internal-combustion engines. Here, the explosive force is employed, and therefore these motors should more properly be called explosive. Their advantages are: enormous energy, economical utilization of fuel and therefore small storage

---

[3] Tsiolkovsky has in view a reprint, put out in 1895, of his paper "The Aeroplane or Bird-like (Aviation) Flying Machine" (Editors).

capacity. A disadvantage is that the fuel has to be more refined and is therefore more expensive. Incidentally, diesel motors operating on cheap petroleum residues are devoid of this defect. But lightweight types of diesels are still not common.

In both cases, use is made of the oxygen of the air, which costs nothing.

3. Reactive automobiles, hydroplanes, sleighs, aeroplanes, stratoplanes and astroplanes utilize stored oxygen or other element necessary for combustion. The aim is to obtain monstrous quantities of energy in a short time.

Two approaches are possible here.

A. The oxygen component (or its substitute) can be mixed with the combustible portion (powder, say) beforehand. Up till now, only ready-made explosive substances have been employed for manned flight.

The advantages of this technique are: an arbitrarily fast release of energy and simplicity of engine design. The disadvantages are many more, namely: danger of a general explosion of the entire supply (the wounds and death of Valier and others); the extra burden of the oxygen compound (liquid oxygen or its liquid nitric compounds); the added weight of pipelines filled with the explosive substance and withstanding enormous pressures of the emerging compressed products of combustion (the pipes therefore have to be strong and heavy); for the low speeds accessible in the lower atmosphere, a low percentage of utilization of chemical energy; the high cost of explosives.

B. In the second approach, the oxygen compound is separated from the fuel. The components are combined gradually, like in an aircraft engine, only the oxygen is not taken directly from the air. There is no danger of a general explosion, heavy pipelines are likewise dispensed with. But the other disadvantages remain.

What compels us to resort to stored oxygen? At very high altitudes in the extremely tenuous air, or still higher, beyond the atmosphere, in empty space, we need a supply of the oxygen compound, for it is then impossible to extract oxygen from the atmosphere, and of course there is no oxygen in outer space. In this way it is possible to attain high speeds and the utilization of the chemical energy may be very substantial indeed. There remain the disadvantages: the extra weight and high cost of oxygen or its compounds. But for explosive components we can take: cheap petroleum (fuel) and liquid oxygen or its compounds, for example liquid nitrogen peroxide. This is not so expensive.

Separation of the explosive components has already been achieved in a practical way in small flying vehicles (unmanned). The idea is obviously being advanced. But these vehicles have other shortcomings that I have mentioned in the magazine "Samolyot" in 1932.[4] That is why they yield such poor results.

✳ III. CHOICE OF EXPLOSIVE COMPONENTS FOR STRATOPLANE

We have in view the attainment of the very tenuous layers of air where oxygen can be extracted from the air only with difficulty.

The explosive components for this machine must possess the following properties.

1. They must release maximum work per unit mass in combustion.

2. When they combine they must produce gases or volatile liquids which, upon heating, yield vapours.

3. In combustion they must develop as low a temperature as possible, i.e., have a low temperature of dissociation so as not to spoil the barrel (nozzle).

4. They must occupy a small volume, i.e., have as high a density as possible.

5. They must be liquid and mix readily. It is complicated to employ them in the form of powder.

6. They may be gaseous but have a high critical temperature and a low critical pressure so as to be convenient for use in the liquid form. Generally, liquefied gases are not advantageous due to their low temperature, for they absorb heat in raising their temperature. Therefore, their use entails losses due to evaporation and there is the danger of explosion. Also unsuitable are expensive products that are chemically unstable or difficult to obtain.

Here are some examples. Hydrogen and oxygen satisfy all conditions with the exception of 4 and 6. Indeed, liquid hydrogen is 14 times lighter than water (its density is 0.07) and is therefore inconvenient since it occupies a large volume. Also, the critical temperature of hydrogen is 234°C below zero, of oxygen, 119°C below zero. Separately, carbon is not suitable because of its solid state. Silicon, aluminium, calcium, and other substances are disqualified not only because of their solid state, but also because with oxygen they yield non-volatile products. Ozone will not

---

[4] The full title of this article is "Reactive Motion and Its Successes". It was published in the journal "Samolyot" (Aeroplane), 1932, No. 6 (Editors).

do because it is expensive and chemically unstable. It has a boiling temperature of 106°C below zero.[5] The majority of simple and complex substances are unsuitable because in combining they liberate very little energy per unit of product.

So what are the suitable substances?

The following.

1. Simple or complex, but which are liquid at ordinary or at not very low temperatures and have densities not much different from the density of water. This means we can permit the use of liquefied gases, but only those with a high critical boiling temperature in a vacuum.

2. Those that liberate maximum work per unit of products obtained. Such are certain weakly exogenous and particularly endogenous compounds (the latter disintegrate with the release, and not absorption, of heat and are therefore particularly profitable.)

3. Inexpensive and chemically stable substances.

4. Substances which yield volatile products in combustion: gases or vapours.

The most energetic explosive components that yield volatile products are hydrogen and oxygen. In the formation of one gram of water vapour, 3,233 calories is released. The same combustion of light metals (lithium, aluminium, magnesium, and boron) produce from 3,400 to 5,100 calories, which is a great deal more. But these materials fail due to the non-volatile products they yield.

But separately, hydrogen and oxygen are as yet inconvenient. It is best to replace them by unstable compounds with other elements, so that in place of hydrogen we will have hydrogen compounds, and in place of oxygen, oxygen compounds. The most suitable for combustion in oxygen are hydrocarbons. Both hydrogen and carbon, when combined with oxygen, yield volatile products. In this respect, they are suitable. When combined with oxygen, hydrogen yields more energy per unit mass of products than does carbon. Namely, hydrogen yields from 3,233 (vapour) to 3,833 (water), and carbon, 2,136 (all subsequent numbers are expressed in small calories per gram or per gram-molecule of substance). Therefore, hydrocarbons liberate upon combustion the more energy, the greater the percentage of hydrogen. Such are the saturated hydrocarbons. The most elementary one is methane (CH_4), or marsh gas. It contains the highest percentage of hydrogen (25%). But one must bear in mind that most of these compounds are

[5] According to modern findings, the boiling points are: hydrogen, −252.8°C; oxygen, −182.98°C; ozone, −112°C (Editors).

exogenous, i.e., heat is liberated in their formation. When these compounds burn in oxygen, they first have to disintegrate into H_2 and O_2, which is accompanied by the absorption of heat. Moreover, liquefied methane has a low boiling point ($-82°C$) and is therefore inconvenient. But let us compute its explosive energy. C demands O_2. In the process, 94,000 calories is liberated per gram-molecule (mole). H_4 requires O_2 with the release of 116,000 calories per 36 grams. Eighty grams liberates a total of 210,000 calories. But a preliminary decomposition of CH_4 requires 18,500 calories per 16 grams (mole). This leaves 191,500 calories for 80 grams. We get 2,394 calories per gram of product.

Among the hydrocarbons there is one which contains a smaller percentage (12.5%) of hydrogen, but is formed with the absorption of heat (endogenous compound). This is ethylene (C_2H_4). We find it to be more suitable. Indeed, C_2 requires O_4, and liberates 188,000 calories per 89 grams. H_4 requires O_2 and liberates 116,000 calories (vapour) per 36 grams. Hence, 124 grams liberates 304,000 calories. But upon decomposition, C_2H_4 releases back again the earlier absorbed 15,400 calories for the 28 grams (mole), so that in all we get 319,400 calories. This is for 124 grams. We obtain 2,576 calories per gram of product, which is slightly greater than from methane. Ethylene is readily liquefiable since its critical temperature is 10°C and the critical pressure is 52 atmospheres. Ethylene is readily obtainable from ethyl alcohol or ether when the latter are passed through clay balls heated to 300-400°C. It turns out that ethylene is more suitable than marsh gas (methane).

Let us now test benzene (C_6H_6). Being a rather dense liquid, it is most suitable for an astroplane. But it contains only 8% of hydrogen. What is the energy released per unit mass of products when it combines chemically with oxygen? Benzene is an exogenous compound. In its formation it liberates, per mole (gram-molecule, or 78 grams) a total of only 10,200 calories. But still we shall make the calculation. C_6 requires O_{12} and H_6 needs O_3. This means that 738,000 calories is liberated per 318 grams of products. Deducting the absorption of heat for decomposition of C_6H_6, we get 727,800 calories. This is for 318 grams. We find 2,289 calories per gram of product. This is somewhat less than for ethylene, but on the other hand we have a liquid of ordinary boiling temperature and of very low vapour pressure.

Acetylene (C_2H_2) of the same percentage composition is not convenient because it is a gas. And this exogenous compound liberates much more heat in its formation than benzene (about 18 times more). Which means that it absorbs more in combustion as well. Moreover, the more carbon there is in the hydrocarbon, the higher the dissociation temperature and, consequently, the temperature of explosion. Liquefied hydrogen is the best; but there are difficulties in obtaining and storing it, to say nothing of the enormous volume it occupies. The following are the results of our calculations on the heat of combustion of alcohols, ether, and turpentine:

Methyl alcohol (CH_4O) . . . . 2,123 calories
Ethyl alcohol (C_2H_6O) . . . . 2,327 calories
Ether ($C_4H_{10}O$) . . . . 2,512 calories
Turpentine ($C_{10}H_{16}$) . . . . 2,527 calories

On the right is the number of calories liberated per unit of combustion product. It is obvious that these fuels cannot be disregarded.

In our calculations we have assumed liquefied oxygen. This is extremely inconvenient. Now ozone is chemically unstable and practically inaccessible. For this reason, let us take up the oxygen compounds.

Of interest are the oxygen compounds of nitrogen. We enumerate the ones most suitable for our purposes. The endogenous gaseous compound nitrous oxide (N_2O) is unsuitable because of the large percentage of nitrogen. The same may be said of the endogenous compound nitric oxide (NO). The third compound is nitrogen peroxide (NO_2); it is a rather stable brownish liquid. Its formation (synthesis) is accompanied by a negligible liberation of heat. It is rather stable chemically (up to 500°C) and is very dense (1.49), which makes it extremely suitable. It is a strong oxidizer, but coating tanks, pipes, valves and other things with gold, platinum, iridium or other non-oxidizing substances protects machines from corrosion.

The fifth compound is nitric anhydride N_2O_5, which contains somewhat less nitrogen, but it is inconvenient due to its chemical instability.

Let us now take up NO_2. This compound is quite capable of replacing oxygen, but it is burdened with nitrogen. This reduces the exit velocity of the gaseous combustion products because it increases their mass. We have spoken of benzene. Its partial weight (mole, or gram-molecule) is 78. We have seen that this substance is satisfied with O_{15} or 240 grams. The weight of the products after combustion in pure oxygen is 318 grams. But we have O_2. Here, 105 grams of nitrogen (N) is added for O_{15}. The products will come out to 423 grams. This mass is greater by $423 : 318 = 1,331$. Owing to the increase in the mass of the combustion products, their exit speed is diminished 1.15 times, which makes 87%. For example, in place of 6,000 m/sec we have 5,220. The explosion energy per gram of products will amount to 1,721 calories.

But, one may say, what about nitroglycerin, pyroxylin and others, couldn't they offer more energy? Much less, unfortunately, as will be seen from the following table, which indicates the heat of formation (in small calories) of the given substances from the elements per gram of product. We have chosen the most energetic explosive substances:

Aluminium with ammonium nitrate 1,480
Black powder and smokeless powder . . . . 720 to 960
Nitroglycerin powder . . . . up to 1,195
Nitroglycerin 1,475
Dinitrobenzene with nitric acid 1,480
Picric acid 750
Mercury fulminate 350
Diazobenzene nitrate 1,330

These ready-made explosives cannot be employed because of the danger of a sudden explosion of the whole mass and also because of their low energy output.

Summarizing, we note that:

1. Hydrogen is not suitable because of its low density and difficulties of storage in the liquid form.

2. Liquefied methane, CH_4, and liquid oxygen yield 2,394 calories. They are inconvenient due to low boiling points.

3. Olefiant gas, or ethylene (C_2H_4) with O_2 yields 2,576 calories. This mixture is more suitable, since ethylene (C_2H_4) has a critical temperature of $+10°C$.

4. Benzene (C_6H_6) and oxygen yield 2,289 calories. The energy is less but this is compensated for by the convenience of the liquid state. Also usable are mixtures of liquid hydrocarbons with high boiling points (kerosene and others), all the more so since they are cheap (petroleum).

5. The employment of liquid oxygen represents a certain drawback due to its low temperature and storage difficulties.

6. Most suitable would be replacing oxygen with nitrogen peroxide (NO_2). This is a brown, chemically stable liquid denser than water.

7. When mixed with benzene, it yields 1,721 calories per unit product. These two liquids are the most suitable ones for an astroplane. But the parts of the machine must be protected from the oxidizing effects of NO_2. This is not so much energy (1,721 calories), but it is more than the energy of the best grade of powder

and the most terrible explosive substances (nitroglycerin). What is more, the latter are expensive and cannot be stored in large quantities.

8. Also suitable are alcohols and sulfuric ether.

The following is a table of the relationship between the heat of combustion and the corresponding speeds of the combustion products (for long pipes and in a vacuum).

Heat of combustion of one kilogram in large calories:

700	1,000	1,200	1,500	1,700	2,000

Ideal mechanical work in thousands of kilogram-metres:

300	428	513	642	727	856

Corresponding ideal speed m/sec:

2,450	2,920	3,200	3,580	3,810	4,130

Heat of combustion:

2,200	2,500	2,700	3,000	3,200	3,500

Ideal work in thousands of kilogram-metres

941	1,070	1,155	1,284	1,369	1,498

Speed, m/sec:

4,340	4,630	4,800	5,060	5,230	5,470

Thus, using ether we get 4,630 m/sec of speed.

In horizontal motion along rails or in the absence of gravity and resistance of a medium, we get the following final vehicle velocities, for different masses of explosive relative to the vehicle weight (with all contents, except fuel and oxygen):

Relative supply of explosives:

1	2	3	4	5	6	7	8	9	10

Maximum vehicle speed, m/sec, taking the exit velocity
in the ether at 4,630 m/sec:

3,200	5,094	6,400	7,465	8,314	9,026	9,646	10 194	10,685	11,126

Hence, with a fivefold supply we can become a satellite of the earth, with a tenfold supply, a satellite of the sun because the vehicle will leave the earth and settle into the orbit of our planet.

Astroplane

(1932)

The astroplane is just like an aeroplane but without the air screw. Owing to the extremely high speeds to be encountered, the wings have a hardly perceptible concavity. The explosive components, i.e., the fuel and oxygen, are separated (see drawing). They are injected into the carburettor by two piston pumps. Here they encounter a special "mixing lattice" and are exploded in various familiar ways. From the combustion chamber they stream into a conical pipe, out of which—cooled and tenuous due to expansion—they are expelled at high speeds from the rear of the vehicle. It is the recoil of these gases that produces the steady acceleration of the rocket. In the flared outer part of the pipe (nozzle) are the rudders: of direction, altitude and lateral stability. These operate in the rapid stream of exhaust gases and function in empty space, for they do not require any surrounding medium.

In the combustion chamber, the series of explosions remind one of a machine-gun, the sole difference being that in a reactive astroplane the barrel is conical, the explosion is a dummy (without bullets), and the explosive components are separate and brought together only in the combustion chamber. There is another difference too: the explosive components are injected by a special pumping engine. This may be eliminated by utilizing the recoil (reaction) as it is done in a machine-gun, which further simplifies our vehicle; then it will differ but slightly from a machine-gun.

A machine-gun does ten and more explosions per second. The number of explosions in an astroplane may be greater still because

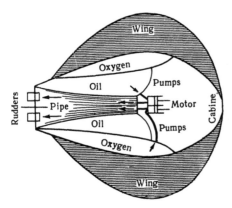

FIG. 1. *Tsiolkovsky's version of the rocket plane*

the blank explosions free the pipe (nozzle) more rapidly from the gases. Aircraft motors can produce up to 20 and more explosions per second in the working cylinders. There is even an engine with a hundred revolutions, or 50 explosions per second.

If each injection yields 100 grams of explosive, then 40 rounds per second will burn 4 kg of explosive materials. This will be quite sufficient for the flight of an astroplane weighing one ton and for constant acceleration.

But the explosion chamber and the conical pipe (nozzle) may heat up excessively if protective measures are not taken to cool them. For this reason, they are surrounded by the liquid fuel, and the latter is surrounded by liquid and freely evaporating oxygen. It is advisable to keep these liquids constantly stirred.

Another thing to remember is that the metal pipe is a good conductor of heat. Therefore its flared part, which is intensely cooled by the expanding gases, will transfer its low temperature (by means of heat conduction) to the narrow heated part of the pipe, thus reducing the temperature there. It would be more correct to say that the heat of the narrow part is transferred to the cold end of the pipe.

In machine-guns and other firearms, it is difficult to make good use of the heat of combustion because the pipe (barrel) is of necessity cylindrical and therefore very long. Now in the astroplane, the pipe is conical, highly flared, and for this reason we can make it the shorter, the greater the cone angle or the greater its flare (but not more than 30°).

If a machine-gun is feasible, then an astroplane is too. The only thing that has to be done is to borrow part of its recoil mechanism so as to dispense with a special motor.

Taking the consumption of explosives at 4 kg/sec, and the overall weight of the astroplane at one ton, we find that the supply of explosives comes out to 0.8 tons (800 kg) and is expended in 200 seconds. During this time the astroplane moving at 30° to the horizon will soon reach the upper rarefied layers of air and will acquire a velocity that will project it beyond the limits of the atmosphere.

The Astroplane and the Machines that Preceded It

(Manuscript dated 1933)

1. Improved steam turbine.
2. Powerful lightweight motor.
3. Stratoplane with such a motor.
4. Astroplane.

⁂ STEAM TURBINES. DRAWBACKS OF STEAM TURBINES

At first the turbine was simple: it had only a boiler, a nozzle and one disc with blades. Utilization of energy was low, and speed of rotation tremendous, impracticable and dangerous. Then a condenser was added, so that on one side of the blades was steam pressure, and on the other, almost a vacuum. There was an increase in the utilization of energy.

Finally, multi-disc turbines were invented with intermediate stationary discs having guide blades (diaphragms). This was a brilliant addition (Fig. 1).

We shall examine the significance of the moving and fixed discs, which have almost the same design. We leave out the details. The discs are, as it were, mounted on the work shaft, and all this is enclosed in a common cylinder. Odd discs revolve with the shaft, even ones are not attached to it but to the cylinder and are therefore stationary. (We give a simplified description.)

Imagine a longitudinal section normal to the discs. We get a number of smooth wavy curves (Fig. 2).

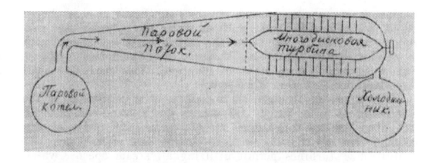

FIG. 1. *A new steam turbine. (Left to right: steam boiler, steam flow, multi-disc turbine, condenser.)*

This is not quite exact, but is sufficient for an explanation, particularly if the speed of the steam is extraordinarily high. The odd figures indicate the cross-sections of moving disc blades, even figures, the same for fixed blades. The moving blades are cross-hatched. The steam enters—through multitudes of curved channels between the blades of the first moving disc—and sets the disc in rotational motion, thereby losing a portion of its speed and performing work at the expense of the energy of its motion. The steam then enters the channels between the fixed

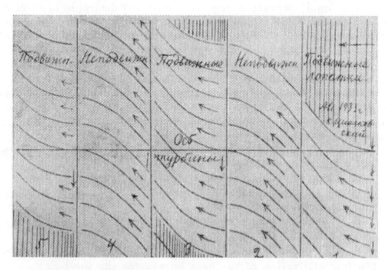

FIG. 2. *(Top, from left to right: moving, fixed, moving, fixed, moving blades; bottom, turbine axis.)*

blades of the first diaphragm, acquires rectilinear motion almost along the axis of the main shaft or along the cylinder that contains the discs. From there the steam strikes—though with a smaller speed—the moving blades of the second disc, performing work and losing some of its speed. This continues until the steam has lost most of its speed.

Having passed through all the discs, it is condensed in the condenser to form water. All this is much more complicated: the discs and the diaphragms are not quite alike and gradually change. But we dismiss familiar details and calculations.

Multi-disc turbines permit utilizing all steam speeds, which cannot be said of the one-disc type. In the one-disc turbine most of the kinetic energy is lost fruitlessly. The point is that the peripheral (maximum) speed of the blades or disc is quite definite and cannot exceed approximately 300 m/sec, no matter what material is used. Now optimum utilization of the kinetic energy of the gas requires that the blade speed be equal to at least one third of the speed of the steam. Of course, if the speed is low, say 600 m/sec, high efficiencies are possible even with the one-disc De Laval turbine. The only inconvenience lies in the dangerous speed of rotation and impracticability of applying it to electric generators and for other purposes where the speeds required are generally low. If the speed of steam is equal to 2 to 5 km/sec, then nearly all the kinetic energy is lost, since the peripheral speed of the blades cannot exceed 200-300 m/sec.

The multi-disc turbine is quite another matter. By devising blades of small curvature, we can obtain any desirable low velocity of the blades, no matter what the speed of steam or gas, and efficient utilization of heat. However, the greater the speed of the steam and the lower the desired blade speed, the larger the number of discs and diaphragms has to be. Even so I see certain drawbacks in multi-disc turbines. They are as follows.

1. The speed of compressed steam emerging from the boilers cannot exceed 500-600 m/sec. If the turbine were designed differently, it could be made to reach 2,000 m/sec. Then the kinetic energy would be 16 times greater.

2. The temperature of the steam emerging from the nozzles is much too high (300°-400°C) and exerts a deleterious effect on the discs and the cylinder.

3. When the steam condenses in the condensers, it liberates quite uselessly the energy consumed in its formation.

4. Only a small area of the discs is utilized because the steam flows out of several narrow nozzles.

We indicate ways to eliminate these defects, the chief of which is the low utilization of the heat energy, or the fuel.

※ THE DESIGN OF MY TURBINE

The turbine that I propose is of the following design (see Fig. 1, in which it is depicted schematically in longitudinal section). The steam from the boiler does not go straight to the disc blades with a low speed, but first flows through a conical pipe. It expands and cools, thus building up speed to 2,000 m/sec. In the process, it is almost completely liquefied, and in the broad part we no longer have a flow of steam but a current of droplets moving three times as fast as bullets and cannon-balls. Thus, nearly all the heat and latent heat of evaporation are converted into kinetic energy.

The stream flows onto 3/4 of the area of the first disc and then onto the others until it has lost nearly all its speed. Utilization of the fuel will be very high, and the function of the condenser will be reduced almost to zero.

Actually, there is not even any need for very high steam pressures. This greatly reduces the weight and increases the safety of steam boilers. Still, high pressures are useful because they reduce the size of the conical pipe. They are particularly useful in the absence of a condenser (in a high-pressure atmosphere).

※ THE STEAM TURBINE WITHOUT BOILER AND CONDENSER

The familiar turbine that I have described has a large specific weight, i.e., weight per horsepower: the boilers and condenser are terribly heavy! For this reason, such turbines are not suitable for dirigibles, aeroplanes, stratoplanes, automobiles—and generally where high power is coupled with low weight.

We can dispense with condensers if there is a high initial steam pressure in the boilers. The lower the steam pressure relative to the external atmospheric pressure, the more we lose in fuel utilization. This means that at high altitudes, fuel utilization will improve with increasing altitude, i.e., as the atmosphere becomes more tenuous. Hence, the advantage of devices without condensers for use in stratoplanes.

However, the boilers will remain and the whole thing will fail. Is there no way of getting rid of the boilers? (Still and all, they can be made lighter, if the external atmospheric pressure is lower.)

Fig. 3 gives the design of a powerful engine with a low specific weight. Here we store not only the fuel (petroleum) but oxygen (in the liquid form) or its oxygen compound as well. The oxygen may be impure, i.e., it may contain a considerable admixture of

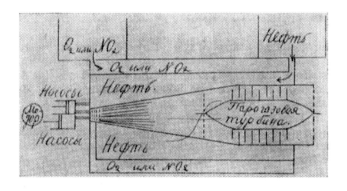

1—pumps; 2—motor; 3—O_2 or NO_2; 4—oil;
5—steam-gas turbine

FIG. 3. *Diagram of engine of small specific weight*

nitrogen. The demand for liquid oxygen is small, and that is why it is still rather expensive. But if it is employed in all kinds of lightweight motors and also with a large admixture of nitrogen, the price will fall off appreciably and it will not be any more expensive than petroleum. Petroleum and liquid oxygen are injected simultaneously, by means of pumps and an engine, into a special chamber (carburettor) located at the beginning of the conical pipe. Here the components are mixed by means of a special "lattice" and produce a steady combustion; the temperature rises to 3,000°C. Carbon dioxide is formed and also water vapour at a tremendous pressure of several thousands of atmospheres. Both expand in the pipe and are thus cooled, acquiring a higher and higher speed, which at the end of the pipe reaches 4,000 m/sec. This swift and (at the end) cold stream of gas, with the admixture of water vapour and droplets, strikes the blades of moving and fixed discs and is converted into the work of rotation.

The oxygen compound cools the petroleum, and the petroleum circulating round the conical pipe and carburettor cools the combustion chamber and prevents it from melting, burning and destruction. Moreover, the steel pipe, when heated by the carburettor, transfers its heat—by means of heat conduction—to the cold parts of the pipe that make up the continuation of the mixing chamber, and in this way is cooled further.

The motor is made heavier solely by the liquid oxygen compound. In the case of benzene (C_6H_6) and oxygen (O_2), the mass of the latter will be nearly three times that of the fuel (see "Rocket", 1927).[1]

For other hydrocarbons and a large admixture of nitrogen, this ratio may increase to 4. But on the one hand, a fuel like coal has an efficiency 3 to 4 times lower than petroleum, so that its supply will almost exceed that of petroleum together with oxygen; on the other hand, in stratospheric flights it is much simpler to store oxygen than to extract it from the tenuous atmosphere and then cool and condense it.

If the pressure in the carburettor is not very great, a continuous pumping of fuel and oxygen compound may be employed. But if it is maximum (which is an advantage in saving weight and in utilization of fuel in the dense atmosphere), then the work of pumping will be prohibitively great. It is then more convenient to employ intermittent injection of the explosive components by means of piston pumps. In this case we get a series of dummy shots. It is in the brief intervals between them that injection is effected with least energy consumption. The disc blades will be subject to varying pressure of the gas flow, and this will require making them stronger.

Of the oxygen compounds, the most suitable is nitrogen peroxide (NO_2), a brown chemically stable liquid.

The motor used to pump explosive components into the carburettor can of course borrow its work from the turbine via a special transmission. But it can also be independent, and this is more convenient. The best is an explosive motor that borrows energy from explosive components. The products are ejected into the common pipe and they enhance the reactive action.

✳ APPLICATION OF THE FOREGOING TURBINE TO THE STRATOPLANE

The design of this kind of high altitude aeroplane (stratoplane) is shown in longitudinal section (schematically) in Fig. 4.

The middle part of the body with the wings carries the motor that has been described. It sets in motion an air screw (propeller). The latter sucks in air on the right and ejects it on the left. This makes the vehicle move from left to right (see arrows outside of the hull, which indicate the direction of motion of the ship). The recoil (reaction) of the gaseous exhaust contributes to this motion. It is the greater, the less the turbine utilizes the motion of the

[1] The full title is "The Space Rocket. Experimental Preparation", Kaluga, 1927 (Editors).

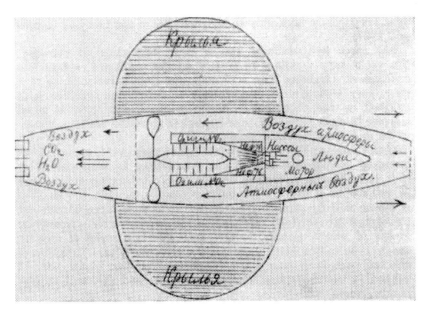

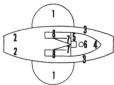

1—wings; *2*—air; *3*—atmospheric air; *4*—people; *5*—pumps; *6*—motor; *7*—oil; *8*—O_2 or NO_2

FIG. 4. *Stratoplane (longitudinal section)*

steam-gas flow. At the high speeds achieved by the stratoplane at high altitudes, the work of recoil is more important than the work of the air screw. Down below, in the dense layers of the atmosphere, the reverse is true. That is why the air screw should be employed when flying at low altitudes and at low speeds, and recoil should be resorted to at high speeds in the tenuous layers of the atmosphere.

The higher the speed of the stratoplane, the smaller should be the end openings of the hull. Otherwise, centrifugal force will destroy the air screw (see my paper "The Stratoplane", 1932).[2] On the right side of the motor, to the rear, we see a closed-off room (cabin) with an oxygen atmosphere or with ordinary air of constant density. This is the passenger compartment. It is necessary at high altitudes where the air is rarefied.

[2] The full title is "The Semi-reactive Stratoplane", see this volume, p. 256—268 (Editors).

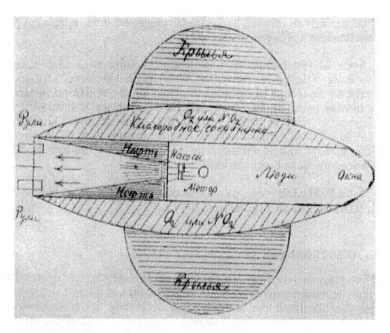

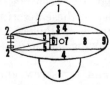

1—wings;   2—rudders;   3—oxygen compound
4—O_2 or NO_2;   5—oil;   6—pumps;   7—motor
8—people;   9—windows

FIG. 5 *Astroplane (longitudinal section)*

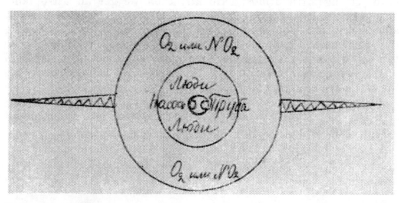

1—O_2 or NO_2;   2—people;   3—pumps;   4—pipe

FIG. 6. *Astroplane (cross-section)*

Observations can be made through several special optical instruments (periscopes).

Note 1. The last fixed disc of the turbine with blades curves the flow. The large air screw also twists the flow. This can be coutered by means of unequal inclination of two direction rudders. It is also possible to place opposite the air screw a special fixed diaphragm similar to the air screw, but with reversed curvature of the blades. It straightens the flow and this will eliminate the rotation of the stratoplane about its longitudinal axis. The diaphragm is not shown in the drawing.

Note 2. My battery-driven gas compressor is constructed along the same lines as the turbine.

✳ ASTROPLANE

The above-described semi-reactive aeroplane of considerable size can tow a purely reactive vehicle (astroplane) to the highest possible altitude. Then the astroplane, left to its own devices, will start up its purely reactive motor and hurtle out of the atmosphere. My astroplane (Fig. 5) has repeatedly been described in the press and we therefore refer the reader to these descriptions [see the magazine "Znanie—sila" (Knowledge is Power), 1932, No. 23-24]. Here I gave a simplified drawing, a longitudinal section of the vehicle.

If in Fig. 4 we eliminate the turbine and air screw and the outer casing with atmospheric air, then we get an astroplane, or a purely reactive flying machine. The drawing is clear without any description. The wings are flat. They are used prior to leaving the atmosphere and are particularly necessary for landing in the air without the need of explosion and fuel. A number of quartz windows are located in the front. The convexities along the walls are occupied with oxygen (O_2) or a compound of oxygen and nitrogen (NO_2). To the rear are three rudders: for direction, altitude, and stability. All three have special and independent drives. Fig. 6 depicts this machine in cross section.

Maximum

Rocket Speed

(From the manuscript

dated 1935)

✳ THE RELATIONSHIP BETWEEN ROCKET SPEED AND THE
MASS OF EXPLOSIVE COMPONENTS

1. We presume the most elementary of the formulae of my paper
"The Investigations" (1926), which disregard gravity and the
resistance of the medium. They give approximate values and are
applicable in the following cases:
    (a) when the action is effected in the absence of gravity and
in empty space;
    (b) when the vehicle is in horizontal motion and its shape
is elongated and very good;
    (c) when the flight takes place in the atmosphere almost hori-
zontally. The vehicle only slightly deviates from the horizon
thanks to the high speed and to the flat wings.
    We shall also apply these formulae to a vehicle moving with
a slight inclination to the horizon when in flight in the air.
    2. We have

$$v = W \ln \left(\frac{M_1 + M_2}{M_1 + M} \right),$$

where v is the velocity of the rocket, M_1 is the mass of the rocket
together with all its contents, except explosives, W (which is
constant) is the relative exhaust speed of explosives, M_2 is the
total mass, and M is the mass that has not yet burnt up, has not

yet been ejected. Naturally, v and M are variables, and ln is the natural logarithm.

3. If we put $M = 0$, i.e., the entire supply of explosives has burnt out, we get the maximum velocity of the rocket

$$v_{max} = W \ln \left(1 + \frac{M_2}{M_1}\right).$$

4. Using this formula, we compile Table 4 of the highest rocket speeds (in metres per second) as a function of the total burnt-up supply of explosives and the relative exhaust speed.

The first column gives the entire consumed mass of explosives relative to the mass of the rocket (minus explosives), the next six columns indicate the rocket speeds in m/sec for a relative exhaust velocity of 1, 2, 3, 4, 5 and 6 km/sec. Theory shows that the energy of the presently available explosive substances cannot yield combustion-product velocities exceeding 6 km/sec. Finally, the last column indicates (in %) the portion of the total explosive energy that moves the rocket. It will be seen that this percentage is very small at first, but as the relative amount of explosives is increased, it increases, reaching a maximum for a supply close to 4 (attaining nearly 65%), and then begins to fall to zero, just as it began from zero. Between a supply of 0.7 and 30 it is very decent, exceeding 40%.

The absolute velocities of the rocket reach cosmic velocities that are sufficient not only to escape from the earth but also to escape from our sun for all time and to travel among the suns of the Milky Way.

5. However, in practice, the exhaust velocity is still quite far away from 5-6 km/sec; moreover the supplies of explosives fall short of what is required to attain cosmic velocities, at least as far as overcoming the sun's gravitation and travelling among the stars of the Milky Way is concerned.

What velocities are attainable for the most modest conditions and, with such velocities, how are we to find ways of attaining cosmic speeds?

6. It is impossible to utilize 100% of the thermal energy of an explosion: the emerging products cannot cool off (by means of expansion) to absolute zero and thus convert all the heat into the kinetic motion of the gases. Also, an obstacle to the boundless expansion of gases and vapours is the external pressure of the medium (say, the atmospheric pressure), and liquefaction and solidification of the combustion products as well. The limited dimensions of the pipe are likewise a barrier to full utilization of chemical energy. All these factors will bring down the exhaust velocities below those calculated in Table 4.

TABLE 4

Rocket Speed (in m/sec)

These are speeds in the case of complete utilization of the thermal energy of chemical union for the kinetic motion of exhaust and the rocket (see 1).

Ratio of mass of exhaust to rocket mass	Relative exhaust velocity (km/sec)						Utili- zation, per cent
	1	2	3	4	5	6	
0.1	94.5	189	283.5	378	472.5	567	8.9
0.2	182.0	364	546	728	910	1,092	16.5
0.3	262	524	786	1,048	1,310	1,572	22.9
0.4	336	672	1,008	1,344	1,680	2,016	28.2
0.5	405	810	1,215	1,620	2,025	2,430	32.8
0.6	469	938	1,407	1,876	2,345	2,814	36.7
0.7	529	1,058	1,587	2,116	2,645	3,174	40.0
0.8	586	1,172	1,758	2,344	2,930	3,516	42.9
0.9	642	1,284	1,926	2,508	3,210	3,852	45.8
1.0	693	1,386	2,079	2,772	3,465	4,158	48.0
1.2	788	1,576	2,364	3,152	3,940	4,728	51.8
1.5	915	1,830	2,745	3,660	4,575	5,490	55.8
2.0	1,098	2,186	3,294	4,392	5,490	6,588	60.3
2.5	1,253	2,506	3,759	5,012	6,265	7,518	62.0
3	1,380	2,760	4,140	5,520	6,900	8,280	63.5
4	1,609	3,218	4,827	6,436	8,045	9,654	64.7
5	1,792	3,584	5,376	7,168	8,960	10,752	64.1
6	1,946	3,892	5,838	7,784	9,730	11,676	63.0
7	2,079	4,158	6,237	8,316	10,395	12,474	61.7
8	2,197	4,394	6,591	8,788	10,985	13,182	60.5
9	2,303	4,606	6,909	9,212	11,515	13,818	58.9
10	2,398	4,796	7,194	9,592	11,990	14,388	57.6
15	2,773	5,546	8,319	11,092	13,865	16,638	51.2
20	3,044	6,088	9,132	12,176	15,220	18,264	46.3
30	3,434	6,848	10,302	13,736	17,170	20,604	39.3
40	3,714	7,428	11,142	15,856	18,570	22,284	34.4
50	4,480	8,960	13,440	17,920	22,400	26,880	31.6
100	5,256	10,512	15,768	21,040	26,280	31,536	21.0
193	6,007.6	12,015.2	18,022.8	24,032	30,038	36,045.6	14.4
∞	∞	∞	∞	∞	∞	∞	0

7. The following table expresses this fact:

50%	60%	70%	80%	90%	100%
0.707	0.775	0.837	0.894	0.949	1.000

The first row indicates utilization of the heat of combustion in percentage or the magnitude of its relative transformation into kinetic energy (the motion of exhaust), the second gives the reduction in rocket speed proportional to the decrease in exhaust velocity. If the thermal or mechanical work is decreased, say, 9 times, the speed will fall off threefold. That is the basis of Table 4. To obtain the true top rocket speed that accords with the percentage of heat utilization of the explosion, multiply the numbers of Table 4 by one of the fractions of the second row.

8. Let us apply this to the compilation of a new table on the assumption of 70% utilization of heat and a relative exhaust speed of 4 km/sec. The latter, of course, depends also on the kind of explosive materials used. We find:

0.5	1	1.5	2	3	4	5	6	7	8	9	10
1,356	2,320	3,063	3,677	4,620	5,387	6,000	6,515	6,960	7,356	7,710	8,028

The first row is the relative quantity of explosives, the second, the corresponding maximum speed of the rocket. It will be seen that given a tenfold supply, the speed attained is sufficient for projecting a satellite into an orbit around the earth just outside the atmosphere.

9. Here is a more detailed table on the same topic (see p 294).

The first row gives the speed of explosive products (from 2 to 4 km/sec), the second, the percentage of heat utilization, the others, the final speed of the rocket when all explosives have burnt out; the first column gives the supply of explosives relative to the rocket weight. It is thus evident that the practical speed is hardly sufficient for the role of a close-to-earth satellite.

But we will now indicate other ways of obtaining far greater rocket velocities. They consist in sending up several identical rockets at the same time with modest speeds. With the exception of the last rocket, they expend only half of the supply of explosives taken along, the other half going to supply one another. Only the last rocket acquires the highest velocity. The other vehicles, their supplies spent, glide back to the earth.

294

TABLE 9

Speeds for Different Utilization of Heat of Combustion and Complete Consumption of Explosives

Relative supply of explosives	Speed of products = 2,000 m/sec			Speed of products = 3,000 m/sec			Speed of products = 4,000 m/sec		
	Utilization of heat (%)			Utilization of heat (%)			Utilization of heat (%)		
	50	60	70	50	60	70	50	60	70
	Final rocket speed, m/sec								
0.3	370	406	439	556	609	658	741	812	872
0.5	573	628	678	859	942	1,017	1,145	1,255	1,356
0.7	748	820	885	1,122	1,230	1,328	1,496	1,640	1,771
1	980	1,074	1,160	1,450	1,611	1,740	1,946	2,151	2,320
2	1,545	1,694	1,830	2,329	2,553	2,744	3,105	3,404	3,676
3	1,951	2,139	2,310	2,927	3,208	3,465	3,903	4,278	4,620
4	2,275	2,494	2,693	3,414	3,741	4,040	4,550	4,988	5,387
5	2,534	2,778	3,000	3,801	4,166	4,500	5,068	5,555	6,000
6	2,752	3,016	3,258	4,127	4,524	4,886	5,503	6,033	6,524
7	2,940	3,222	3,480	4,410	4,834	5,220	5,879	6,445	6,960
8	3,107	3,405	3,678	4,660	5,108	5,517	6,213	6,811	7,355
9	3,256	3,570	3,855	4,885	5,354	5,783	6,513	7,139	7,710
10	3,391	3,717	4,014	5,086	5,575	6,021	6,781	7,434	8,028

✳ ROCKET SPEED IN THE CASE OF PARTIAL BURN-OUT

10. In formula (2) we put $M = M_2 - M'$; i.e., we state that the remaining mass of explosives is equal to the total quantity minus that burnt up or jettisoned.

11. Then we get

$$v = W \cdot \ln \left(\frac{M_1 + M_2}{M_1 + M_2 - M'} \right) .$$

12. Transforming, we get

$$v = W \cdot \ln \left(\frac{1 + \dfrac{M_2}{M_1}}{1 + \dfrac{M_2}{M_1} - \dfrac{M'}{M_2} \cdot \dfrac{M_2}{M_1}} \right) .$$

13. Putting $\dfrac{M_2}{M_1} = x$ and $\dfrac{M'}{M_2} = y$, we get

$$v = W \cdot \ln \left\{ \frac{1 + x}{1 + x (1 - y)} \right\} .$$

14. Suppose that the burnt-up portion is $y = 0.5$. We then find

$$v = W \cdot \ln \left(\frac{1 + x}{1 + 0.5x} \right) .$$

From the formula it is seen that the rocket speed does not increase without bound in the case of an infinitely great supply (x) of explosives, but has a limit. Indeed, suppose $x = \infty$, then $v = W \cdot \ln 2 = W \cdot 0.693$. If, say, $W = 3,000$, then the rocket speed will be 2,079 m/sec, despite the infinite exhaust (x). It is thus evident that there is no great advantage in large supplies if only one half undergoes combustion.

15. Using this formula, we compile Table 15, which will confirm this idea once again.

From this table we will find the rocket speed (in m/sec) when only half of the entire explosive material is consumed, where x is the full supply.

198

TABLE 15

W (exhaust [velocity, m/sec)	x (supply)					
	0.1	0.3	0.5	1	2	3
1,000	46	122	182	287	405	470
2,000	93	245	365	575	810	940
3,000	139	368	547	863	1,215	1,410
4,000	186	490	729	1,150	1,620	1,880
5,000	232	613	911	1,438	2,024	2,350
6,000	279	736	1,094	1,726	2,429	2,820

W (exhaust velocity, m/sec)	x (supply)						
	4	5	6	7	8	9	10
1,000	511	539	567	573	588	598	606
2,000	1,023	1,078	1,134	1,146	1,176	1,196	1,212
3,000	1,534	1,617	1,701	1,719	1,764	1,794	1,818
4,000	2,046	2,156	2,268	2,292	2,352	2,392	2,424
5,000	2,557	2,695	2,835	2,865	2,940	2,990	3,030
6,000	3,068	3,234	3,402	3,438	3,528	3,588	3,636

It is taken that the conversion of heat into the motion of the exhaust and of the rocket is complete.

The first row gives the total relative supply of explosives, the first column, the relative exhaust velocity. Even taking it at 2,000 m/sec, we see from the table that the rocket speed reaches 1,023 m/sec for a total supply of 4 and consumption one half (2). For total supply 2 and consumption one half (1), we get a rocket speed of 1,215 m/sec if the relative exhaust velocity comes to 3,000 m/sec.

296

✳ THE SPEED ATTAINED BY ONE ROCKET THROUGH THE USE OF AUXILIARY ROCKETS

16. We shall now see what meaning there is in limiting consumption of explosives for the attainment of cosmic velocities.

17. Let there be a large number of absolutely identical rockets each with a supply of 1, and let each consume half the supply. Let the exhaust velocity of all rockets be 4,000 m/sec.

By means of a squadron of these rockets and transfusions of the explosive supplies, we will be able to attain velocities that are beyond the reach of a single rocket. To take an example, the transfer of petrol from one aeroplane to another is not only possible, but is even done occasionally in stunt flying.

18. Suppose there is one rocket in flight. From Table 4 (formula 3) the maximum velocity will be 2,772 m/sec.

19. Now let two such rockets be flying at the same time next to each other. Let both use up one half of their explosive supplies. They will then gain a speed of 1,150 m/sec (see 15).

One of the rockets transfers the unburnt half supply to the other, and itself glides back to the earth. The second, now with a full supply (1), will build up an additional speed of 2,772 m/sec, making a total of 3,922 (1,150 + 2,772) m/sec.

20. Now let there be four rockets in flight. When they have used up half their supplies, all of them, flying next to one another, receive the same speed of 1,150 m/sec. But two of them add to the supply of the other two, and then glide back to the earth. The remaining two use up one half of their supply and develop a speed of 2,300 m/sec (1,150 + 1,150). One of them then transfers its fuel to the other and lands. Now the last one consumes its full supply of fuel and gains an extra speed of 2,772 m/sec, making a total of 5,072 m/sec (1,150 + 1,150 + 2,772). The vehicle will then have to land by gliding.

21. Now we compile a table of speeds of the last rocket, depending on the total number of rockets. We assume: $W = 4,000$ and the supply $= 1$.

Number of rockets	1	2	4	8
Speed of last rocket	2,772	3,922	5,072	6,222

Number of rockets	16	32	64	128
Speed of last rocket	7,372	8,522	9,672	10,822

Number of rockets	256	512	1,024	2,048
Speed of last rocket	11,972	13,122	14,272	15,422

Number of rockets	4,096	8,192	16,384	
Speed of last rocket	16,572	17,722	18,872	

22. The first row in this table gives the number of identical rockets participating in building up the speed of the last rocket, in the second is the velocity of the last rocket (in metres per second).

23. The first cosmic velocity[1] is already attained with the aid of 32 rockets. For escape from the earth into a circumsolar orbit, one needs 256 rockets, and for escape from the planets and the sun we need 4,096 rockets.

24. The most important thing is to get out beyond the earth's atmosphere and settle securely into the orbit of an earth satellite. Subsequent increases in speed may be achieved in other ways and more easily than on the earth. Still the number of rockets is extraordinarily great.

25. But we are in a position to take a larger supply of explosives, say 4. Then, with the modest exhaust velocity of 3,000 m/sec, the rocket speed, in the case of one-half consumption, will come to 1,534 m/sec (see Table 15). Now the total speed is 4,827 m/sec (Table 4). This is sufficient to propose a new table.

Number of rockets . . .	1	2	4	8	16
Speed of last rocket . .	4,827	6,361	7,895	9,429	10,962

Number of rockets . . .	32	64	128	256	512
Speed of last rocket . .	12,497	14,031	15,565	17,099	18,633

Here, 256 rockets suffice for travelling out among the suns of the Milky Way. An earth satellite can be established with 4 rockets, and a satellite of the sun with 16 rockets.

26. The exhaust velocity may be made greater than 3 km/sec, and then a smaller number of rockets will be needed to attain cosmic velocities.

27. We can derive a general formula of the speed of the last rocket as a function of the number of rockets, the exhaust velocity (W) and the relative supply of explosives. The number of rockets we denote by 2^n. Then the speed of one rocket will be (see 3):

$$v = W \ln (1 + x),$$

where x is the total relative supply of explosives. With the number of rockets 2^n, the speed of the last one will be (see formula 14):

$$W \ln (1 + x) + n \cdot W \cdot \ln \left(\frac{1+x}{1 + 0.5x} \right) =$$
$$= W \{(n + 1) \cdot \ln (1 + x) - n \cdot \ln (1 + 0.5x)\}.$$

Orbital velocity (Translator).

28. The second term of the left-hand side has a limit, no matter how great x or the relative supply of explosives (see 14) is. It is equal to $n \cdot W \cdot 0.693$. Still it is capable of increasing without bound as n or the number of rockets 2^n increases. But the first term increases without bound as x, or the relative supply of explosives, increases. Thus, it is necessary, as far as possible, to increase both x and n.

29. If it is impossible to increase greatly the supply (x) of explosives and the relative speed of the combustion products (W), we can still change the number of rockets (2^n) and hence the speed of the last of the participating rockets.

30. Practice has demonstrated that physical communication between two aeroplanes moving with the same speed is quite possible. Fuel has been pumped from one aeroplane to another. The only thing needed is a well worked-out technique. In our undertaking the matter is much more complicated because we have to transfer two components separately: hydrocarbons (fuel) and an oxygen compound. This may be done in a variety of ways, for example:

A. By transfusion through a line connecting the two flying vehicles.

B. By transfer of tanks containing the explosive components.

C. By firing (injecting) a component into the rear part of a vehicle flying in front.

Which of these methods will turn out to be the better will be found through tests and experiments.

✳ THE PRACTICAL METHOD

31. We will have to begin with the most imperfect and feeble jet aeroplanes. At first we will learn to fly one. We will have to put the exhaust velocity very low, say, 2,000 m/sec, and the supply of explosive substances at unity. Table 4 will show us the maximum speed at 1,386 m/sec. This kind of rocket plane can fly horizontally or at an incline. If we disregard air resistance, the plane could rise to a height of 96 km at this velocity. But owing to the resistance of the medium and the necessity for having a certain reserve speed, it will not reach such an altitude but will rise only to about 50 km. From that height, it will have to glide back to land or to a water surface because no explosive components will be left.

Since the highest speed attainable by this modest rocket plane does not exceed 1 km/sec, elongation need not be very great.

32. The following table indicates the necessary elongation of the rocket plane as a function of highest attainable velocity (see my article entitled "Pressure", 1930).[2]

v	1	2	3	4	5	6	7	8
λ	4	8	12	16	20	24	28	32

v	9	10	11	12	13	14	15	16	17
λ	36	40	44	48	52	56	60	64	68

The first row indicates the speed of the vehicle (in km/sec), the second, the necessary minimum elongation, the shape being good, of course. From the table it will be seen that for the first modest rocket the elongation can be limited to 4. If the elongation is less than indicated in the table, then no matter how tenuous the ambient air, it will be compressed in front of the vehicle like a wall of steel.

33. Since a high speed, roughly 5 km/sec, is attained beyond the atmosphere, the elongation need not exceed 20 (according to the table).

34. Having learned to control a single rocket plane with elongation 4, let us construct two identical rockets with greater elongation. Here we will begin practising transfer of explosive components from one rocket plane to another. Then we will go over to a group of four rockets with still greater elongation, then to a group of eight rockets, etc. At the same time the vehicles will become more refined, for example, there will be an increase in the relative supply of explosives and the speed of the exhaust.

35. Meanwhile we propose a modest table of rocket-plane velocities versus number of rocket planes, on the assumption that the exhaust velocity is 2,000 m/sec and the supply of explosives is unity.

To this table we also add the least elongation of a group of equivalent rocket planes.

We take advantage of tables 4 and 15.

Number of rockets	1	2	4	8	16	32	64	128	256	512
v	1,386	1,961	2,536	3,111	3,686	4,271	4,846	5,421	5,996	6,571
λ	5	8	10	12	14	16	20	22	24	26
Height of ascent	95	192	320	484	680	910	1,170	1,470	1,800	2,160

[2] The full title is "Pressure on a Plane in Normal Motion in the Air", Kaluga, 1930 (Editors).

The first row indicates the number of rockets in a group, the second, the maximum velocity, the third, the elongation of each member of a group, and the fourth, the maximum altitude of ascent in kilometres upon utilization of total speed. Actually, of course, we will achieve only half of this. For a group of 8 or 16 rocket planes, we may be able to get out beyond the limits of the atmosphere where elongation is of no significance, so that it will not exceed 12-14. This means that a vehicle with largest diameter 2 m will have a length of no more than 24 to 28 m.

36. But during these tests (or before) we hope to attain exhaust velocities greater than 2 km/sec, since the extreme limit is 6 km/sec. The supply can also vary from unity to 5 and more. In that case, we will attain cosmic speeds even with small squadrons of identical and not very elongated rocket planes.

37. As the limit of our aspirations, we imagine that the exhaust velocity is 6 km/sec, the explosive supply, 10. On the basis of tables 4 and 15, we compile the following table:

Number of rockets . . .	1	2	4	8	16
v	14,388	18,024	21,660	25,296	28,932

Here there is no need to speak even of altitude or elongation. One rocket or a group will rapidly get beyond the atmosphere, without even attaining a speed of 2 km/sec, so that an elongation of 8 is quite sufficient for all rockets and for ultimate success.

38. But we cannot yet hope for such success. It is a theoretical conclusion restricted by a multitude of subsidiary conditions.

✳ THE AIM OF THE NEW METHOD

The purpose of this chapter is to indicate the methods by means of which, even when we have an extremely imperfect rocket plane, it is possible to attain cosmic speeds—with the aid of several vehicles—sufficient not only for harnessing solar energy, but also for travelling among the other suns of our Milky Way. This method consists in employing a group of rocket planes and in transferring the explosive components to the last rocket plane, which will be able to reach the ultimate cosmic velocity.

39. Earlier, for the same purpose we proposed artificial roads on the ground and rocket trains. Possibly this is all right, but at the present time it is too expensive and there are other objections as well.

40. Still less applicable are "cannons", i.e., specially devised tracks, which are still more expensive. All these trains, roadways,

and "cannons" will come into use in the distant future when the significance of interplanetary travel has grown in stature, attracting the attention of mankind at large and instilling confidence and realistic hopes. And these will bring with them expenditures and sacrifices far greater than those involved in all other human requirements.

41. The method of the first groups of low-power machines and the transfusion of explosive components are much more accessible to the frame of mind of present-day society. Even a single rocket plane will spur on experiments with two identical and imperfect vehicles.

These experiments are valuable in themselves: they will do service even one at a time. Experiments with several rocket planes will be performed simply as exciting stunts. But these stunts will unavoidably lead to the attainment of cosmic velocities.

So the basis of this success will be the construction of the first rocket plane, no matter how poor it is. The construction of several identical vehicles will advance the building up of velocity, to which there is no limit.

42. In preceding chapters[3] we attempted to justify the construction of separate rocket planes. Of course, the more refined the rocket plane, the better will be the results of experiments with groups for the same number of flying vehicles in a group.

✳ EXIT VELOCITY OF EXPLOSION PRODUCTS

43. Let us once again examine the case of a single rocket plane. Of great importance is the rate of exit of the explosion products. What does this speed depend on? In an earlier chapter entitled "Choice of Explosive Components" we gave tables of ideal maximum exhaust velocities of explosion products. They occur almost completely under the following joint conditions.

A. When the combustion products are gaseous or very volatile.

B. When there is no external pressure preventing expansion of the gaseous products.

C. When the pipe that conducts the ejection flow is extremely long.

D. When the pipe does not excessively broaden at the exit, i.e., when it does not deviate appreciably from the cylindrical shape.

[3] The author refers to chapters of his manuscript "The Principles of the Design of Gas Machines, Motors and Flying Vehicles" (1934—1935) (Editors).

E. When there is no loss of heat due to thermal conduction and radiation.

F. When the pipe diameter is so great that friction of the gases against the inner walls of the pipe may be neglected.

44. Not all these conditions may be complied with in actual practice. We shall indicate a number of deviations.

A. A vehicle of ordinarily small dimensions. The pipe is therefore short. To better utilize expansion of gases and the conversion of heat into motion, the pipe must be made conical. This reduces the recoil, for the flow will spread out sideways.

B. External pressure is eliminated only in a vacuum, when the atmosphere is left behind, or at a speed exceeding 300 to 500 m/sec, when because of rapid motion a vacuum is produced behind the blunt rear part of the rocket. The rear of the rocket is generally made narrow. But the part of it that contains the explosion pipe (flared) is unavoidably blunt. Here is where a rarefied air space may develop. (Naturally, it becomes filled with emerging products of the explosion.)

C. As a result of the limited size of the explosion pipe and a certain external pressure, the emerging gases do not have time to cool off to absolute zero and retain some energy for a certain time, depending on the degree of their expansion. Thus, not all the heat energy of combustion is converted into the motion of gas jets. Because of this incomplete utilization of heat, the exhaust velocities indicated in the tables are actually less. If, for example, in the table we see a speed of 5,000 m/sec for a specific explosive, it will prove to be less because of loss of heat.

45. The following table takes this factor into consideration.

The first row indicates the ideal speed of the products, which depends solely on the energy of the chemical union of its component parts. Here we give the speed from 2 to 4 km/sec, although it may even reach 6 km/sec. The second row indicates in percentage the utilization of the heat of combustion, which naturally depends on the temperature of the gases emerging from the end of the pipe.

The first column contains the total relative supply of explosive components: from 0.3 to 10.

The second column gives half consumption for producing speed. Finally, at the intersections we find the speeds (in metres per second) at one-half consumption of the basic explosion.

All these conditions are very moderate and quite feasible.

From the tables it may be seen that the speed of the rocket plane attains 2,029 m/sec upon consumption of only one half of the supply of explosives.

Rocket Speed Upon Expenditure of 0.5 of Supply of Explosives and with 50%, 60% and 70% Utilization of Combustion Heat

Total supply of explosives	Utilized part	Speed of explosion products (ideal)								
		2 km/sec			3 km/sec			4 km/sec		
Percentage of heat utilization . .		50	60	70	50	60	70	50	60	70
Speed of explosion products . . .		141.4	155.0	167.4	212.1	232.5	251.1	282.8	310.0	334.8
0.3	0.15	173	190	205	260	285	308	347	380	410
0.5	0.25	258	290	305	387	424	458	515	565	610
0.7	0.35	326	357	386	489	536	579	652	715	772
1	0.5	407	446	481	610	669	722	813	892	963
2	1.0	571	620	678	850	942	1,017	1,145	1,255	1,355
3	1.5	665	729	787	996	1,093	1,180	1,329	1,457	1,574
4	2.0	723	733	856	1,084	1,189	1,284	1,446	1,585	1,712
5	2.5	762	835	902	1,143	1,253	1,353	1,525	1,671	1,805
6	3.0	800	877	947	1,199	1,315	1,420	1,600	1,753	1,894
7	3.5	815	892	963	1,225	1,338	1,446	1,627	1,783	1,926
8	4.0	831	911	984	1,246	1,367	1,476	1,663	1,822	1,968
9	4.5	846	927	1,001	1,268	1,390	1,497	1,691	1,853	2,002
10	5.0	858	940	1,015	1,285	1,409	1,522	1,714	1,879	2,029

✳ ✳ ✳ ✳ ✳ ✳ ✳

The life of every prominent scientist is of considerable interest
to historians of science and also to specialists investigating the
psychology of scientific creativity. This is particularly true of
the life of such an originally thinking scientist as was Konstantin
Tsiolkovsky.

As Academician A. Ishlinsky has said, Tsiolkovsky is an
extraordinary phenomenon in the scientific-technological world
at large. Though living at about the same time as Zhukovsky
(1847-1921), Meshchersky (1859-1935), and Krylov (1863-
1945), he paid no attention, as it were, to the creations of his contemporaries and went the way of a pioneering genius.

His scientific biography is poor in external events. Konstantin
Tsiolkovsky was born on September 17 (Sept. 5, old system),
1857 in the village of Izhevskoye, Spassky Uyezd (district) of
Ryazan Gubernia (province). His father, Eduard Tsiolkovsky
(1820-1880) was a forester, teacher and government official
in succession. The family very often moved from place to place
and frequently felt the pinch of need. The care of the children
and their early education was in the hands of the mother, Maria
Yumasheva (1830-1870).

Up to the age of ten, Tsiolkovsky did not differ in any particular way from his playmates; he liked games, went skating in
winter, sent up kites, climbed fences, and dreamt of becoming
strong and agile. He liked to read and dipped into everything
he could get his hands on.

20—67

Then in 1867-1868, an event occurred that exerted a tremendous influence on his future life. At the age of ten, Tsiolkovsky was taken seriously ill, and as a result of complications almost completely lost his hearing. Deafness prevented him from continuing his studies at the gymnasium, and the source of external impressions was greatly narrowed.

The years following his illness and loss of hearing (1868-1871) were very trying. Later he recalled: "This three-year interval through my lack of consciousness—was the saddest and darkest time of my life. I try to reconstruct it in my memory, but there is at present nothing that I can recall. There is simply nothing to mark that time. All that I can remember is skating, sleighing...."[1]

Gradually, however, Tsiolkovsky got over the moral shock and, as he put it, "there were flashes of serious mental understanding". By the age of 14-16, his clear-cut interest in inventions came to the fore: he would be found devising paper dirigibles and self-moving carriages and locomotives driven by spiral springs; he made models of steam engines and pumps, he constructed a tiny lathe and all kinds of windmills, a self-propelled carriage with an air vane and an automobile propelled by the reactive force of steam. "But," Tsiolkovsky recalled, "these were all playthings that I made by myself, they had nothing to do with the reading of scientific and technical books."[2]

It is about this time that Tsiolkovsky began to interest himself in theoretical knowledge. At 14 he was reading from his father's library and undertook a systematic study of the natural sciences. He goes on to recollect that "there were very few books, and I had no teachers at all, so I had to create and devise more than absorb and imbibe from others. There were no hints, no aid from anywhere; there was a great deal that I couldn't understand in these books and I had to figure out everything by myself. In a word, then, the creative element, the element of self-development and originality, was predominant."[3]

When Tsiolkovsky's father noticed his inventive talent, he sent him to Moscow in 1873 to continue his self-education. In Moscow, Tsiolkovsky lived very modestly and was frequently needy. He spent almost all his time in educating himself and in conducting scientific experiments. Studying all by himself, he covered the full course of mathematics and physics of school and a considerable part of the university course.

---

[1] Tsiolkovsky, "From My Life", Archives, USSR Academy of Sciences.
[2] Ibid.
[3] Tsiolkovsky, "Autobiography", Archives, USSR Academy of Sciences

These were the years when Tsiolkovsky began to take a particular interest in a variety of scientific and technical problems. Some of the problems that engaged him were, for example:

1. Is there not some way in which to utilize the energy of motion of the earth?
2. What shape of surface does a liquid in a vessel rotating on its axis take?
3. Is it possible to send round the equator a train in which, because of centrifugal force, there would be no gravity?
4. Is it possible to construct gas-tight metal balloons that would float about in the air eternally?
5. Cannot the high-pressure exhaust steam of steam engines be utilized?
6. Is it not possible to apply centrifugal force to lifting vehicles beyond the atmosphere out into celestial space?

In 1876 Tsiolkovsky returned to his home town from Moscow and began giving private lessons. In his spare time he devised all kinds of tools and machines. He was so intensively drawn to this work that he even rented a room for his workshop. As he wrote in later years, "My whole life consisted of meditation, calculations, practical undertakings and experiments. I have always carried along my own workshop. If it was destroyed, say in a fire or flood, I would always set it up again."[4]

In 1879 Tsiolkovsky took examinations as an extern for the title of school teacher and in 1880 began to teach arithmetic and geometry at the Borovsk Uyezd School, Kaluga Gubernia. At the same time he began a series of scientific studies, devoting nearly all his spare time to this work.

Until just recently, Tsiolkovsky's biographers considered his first scientific paper to be "The Theory of Gases" written in 1881. However, a careful study of his own remarks about his works shows that as early as 1880 he wrote a paper entitled "The Graphical Depiction of Sensations". The manuscript of this work was lost, but from a summary written by Tsiolkovsky it is clear that in this paper he considered such problems as the mathematical evaluation of human sensations.[5]

Tsiolkovsky's study of the kinetic theory of gases in the paper that was just mentioned is extremely interesting in the sense that without any knowledge of the investigations of Clausius, Boltzmann, Van der Waals and other scientists, Tsiolkovsky arrived at the same conclusions quite independently. The results

---

[4] Tsiolkovsky, "Autobiographical Sketches", Archives, USSR Academy of Sciences.
[5] Archives, USSR Academy of Sciences.

that he obtained were not new to science, and were not quite exact. The Russian Physico-Chemical Society, to which Tsiolkovsky had sent his manuscript, did not consider it possible to have it published; it did however note the great capabilities and industry of the author and it expressed its readiness to help him in subsequent investigations.

In 1882-1883, Tsiolkovsky wrote a paper entitled "On the Theoretical Mechanics of the Living Organism", which, as Academician A. I. Oparin says, is basically concerned with solving the problem of how the force of gravity affects the build and dimensions of living beings and their movements on the earth's surface and in the air. Again, this paper was not published but it earned a favourable response of the noted physiologist I. M. Sechenov, who pointed out that Tsiolkovsky's paper demonstrates a definite talent. On the basis of submitted papers, Tsiolkovsky was elected member of the Russian Physico-chemical Society.

It was about this time that Tsiolkovsky completed his manuscripts "The Duration of Radiation by the Sun" (which was published later under a somewhat different title) and "Absolute and Relative Phenomena", which, in the words of the author, was not finished but was conceived on a very broad scale. Here is what Tsiolkovsky wrote, "Absolute phenomena are more or less known. But relative, apparent, phenomena that occur in a body which is not moving in a straight line or uniformly are quite different from absolute phenomena and are of extreme interest. To the uninitiated, they are unbelievable, magical. I have in view this composition which no one has seen, for to this day I have retained full respect for it and do not see any delusions in it."[6]

The range of Tsiolkovsky's scientific interests was tremendous indeed. He was attracted by the most diverse problems of natural science and technology, from astronomy and celestial mechanics, generation of power and astrobiology to physics and geochemistry. He also busied himself with philosophy and linguistics. But he was particularly devoted to the study of aviation, aeronautics and interplanetary travel. It is to these three problems that Tsiolkovsky devoted his principal works.

Tsiolkovsky became interested in aeronautics at a very early age, between 15 and 16. He was then already enthused with the idea of constructing a metal balloon and was engaged in solving the problem of "what size a balloon should be to

---

[6] Tsiolkovsky, "Autobiographical Sketches", Archives, USSR Academy of Sciences.

carry people aloft if made of a metal shell of a definite thickness."[7]

In 1885 Tsiolkovsky began a systematic study of the designs of lighter-than-air flying machines. In his manuscript "The Theory and Experiment of a Horizontally Elongated Balloon" (1886), he substantiates theoretically the design of an all-metal dirigible. In the spring of 1887 he reported his results to a meeting of the department of physical sciences of the Society of Lovers of Natural Science. Professor A. G. Stoletov, who chaired the meeting, sent the manuscript to Prof. N. Ye. Zhukovsky for a review.

In the years that followed, Tsiolkovsky continued to improve his design. One of the peculiarities was the use of a corrugated metal casing and also the possibility of varying the volume of the aerostat in flight and of heating the gas inside the balloon by utilizing the heat of the combustion products. The necessity of varying the volume of a dirigible in flight stemmed from a desire to maintain a constant lifting force for various temperatures of the surrounding air and at different altitudes; heating the gas made it possible to regulate the lifting force during ascent and descent without loss of gas or ballast.

In 1890 Tsiolkovsky sent his study of an all-metal dirigible and a small paper model to Dmitri Mendeleyev, who proposed a discussion of Tsiolkovsky's design at a meeting of the VIIth Aeronautical Department of the Russian Technical Society. Tsiolkovsky extended the theory of the all-metal dirigible in his paper "A Controllable Metal Balloon", (1892). However, despite the fact that these ideas were approved by a number of scientists, Tsiolkovsky did not receive any aid and he had to give up plans for the construction of a dirigible.

Tsiolkovsky devoted considerable attention to problems of aerodynamics and aviation. In 1890 he completed a manuscript entitled "On the Problem of Flying by Means of Wings", in which he investigated the magnitudes of forces acting on a flat plate when in motion in the air. Here, Tsiolkovsky made the first attempt to give a quantitative estimate of the effect of elongation of the plate on the value of the aerodynamic forces.

This study was favourably received by Zhukovsky, who pointed out that the novel methods of investigation, the reasoning and clever experiments of the author are not devoid of interest and that, in any case, they characterize him as a talented investigator.

---

[7] Tsiolkovsky's autobiography in his paper "The Elements of an Airship and Its Construction", 2nd edition, Kaluga, 1904, p. IV.

In 1891 a piece of this manuscript was published in the transactions of the department of physical sciences of the Society of Lovers of Natural Science under the title: "The Pressure Exerted on a Plane Moving Uniformly in a Liquid". This was Tsiolkovsky's first published work.

In 1892 Tsiolkovsky returned to Kaluga and continued teaching without interrupting his scientific research. In 1895 the journal "Nauka i zhizn" (Science and Life) published his paper "The Aeroplane or Bird-like (Aviation) Flying Machine". Here, Tsiolkovsky proposed the design of an aircraft with a metal framework that was very much like modern vehicles: a monoplane with a streamline fuselage, cantilever wing of thick profile and with rounded leading edge, and wheel undercarriage. An analysis was also given of this design both from the viewpoint of aerodynamics and structural strength.

This paper likewise posed in clear-cut fashion the problem of employing internal-combustion engines in aviation and the use, in aeroplanes, of twin air screws revolving in opposite directions. The idea was also suggested here of using gyroscopes in flying machines as an elementary mechanical pilot.

The important point in this case is that as early as the end of last century, Tsiolkovsky had a clear conception of the future trends of aircraft development and proposed transferring some of the functions of flight control from man to an automatic device. The first thing he proposed (in 1893) was the design of an automatic device for stabilization of the horizontal position of the longitudinal axis of a balloon.[8] The system of stabilization that Tsiolkovsky worked out was based on the electrical contact principle. The working medium here was mercury in a double-sweep tube of a communicating vessel. When the longitudinal axis of the balloon dipped, the level of the mercury went down, breaking the circuit and actuating a special pump that restored the normal attitude of the balloon.

Later (1894) Tsiolkovsky came to the conclusion that his device could not be employed for stabilization of flight of heavier-than-air flying machines. He wrote as follows: "It seems to me that for horizontal-position control of an aeroplane we should use a small rapidly rotating disc (driven by a low-power electric motor) mounted on axes in such a manner that its plane could always retain a single position despite rotation and inclination of the vehicle. When the disc (gyroscope) is kept in rapid rotation, its plane will be stationary relative to the vehicle until the latter changes its own direction, but if the vehicle

[8] Tsiolkovsky, "A Controllable Metal Balloon", Kaluga, 1893, p. 46.

alters its direction, the relative position of the rotating disc will change too. Quite naturally, such a change can serve to close or break an electric circuit that actuates an electromagnet and a rudder, which will force the deviating vehicle back into its horizontal position."[9]

It is interesting to note that the idea of employing rapidly rotating discs for stabilizing flying machines came to Tsiolkovsky as early as 1883. In his unpublished manuscript "Free Space" he wrote: «Imagine that inside the travelling sphere there are two rapidly rotating discs whose axes or planes are mutually perpendicular (or only inclined). Then the irregular (non-central) actions of the forces on the sphere, in the material of which the axes and discs are rotating, will impart, approximately, only parallel motion, and not rotational motion, to both the sphere and the axles. Thus, by medns of a special pair of discs we attain stability of the sphere that is the greater, the faster the discs rotate.»[10]

It is quite evident that already in this manuscript Tsiolkovsky clearly realized the principle of applying a gyroscope device for stabilization of flying machines.

Subsequently, he advanced that idea and suggested the above-described approach, which may be considered the beginning of electro-automatics.

Working on the designs of a dirigible and an aeroplane, Tsiolkovsky found it necessary to obtain precise information about air resistance. After a series of experiments in natural conditions, he arrived at the idea of testing models in an artificial current of air. In 1897 in Kaluga he constructed a wind tunnel with a free current of air in which he tested bodies of different shapes. This was the first wind tunnel in Russia used for investigations into problems of aviation. The results of his experiments and the conclusions that he drew therefrom were given by Tsiolkovsky in a paper entitled "Air Pressure on Surfaces Introduced into an Artificial Air Flow" (1898), which was published in the journal "Vestnik opytnoi fiziki i elementarnoi matematiki" (Herald of Experimental Physics and Elementary Mathematics).

In September 1899 Tsiolkovsky submitted a request to the Academy of Sciences to consider the results of his first experiments on air resistance and to allot funds for their continuation. At the meeting of the physico-mathematical department of the Academy, Academician M. A. Rykachev gave a very favourable review of Tsiolkovsky's experiments, pointing out that they

---

[9] Tsiolkovsky, "The Aeroplane or Bird-like (Aviation) Flying Machine", "Nauka i zhizn" (Science and Life), 1894, No. 46.
[10] Tsiolkovsky, "Free Space". This volume,p. 39.

"deserve the full attention of the Academy both as to the idea and to the diversity of the experiments."[11]

On the basis of Rykachev's report, the Academy of Sciences allocated funds for further experimentation on air resistance, enabling Tsiolkovsky to expand considerably his program of investigation. In May, 1900, Tsiolkovsky began the construction of a new wind tunnel of much larger size than the first (the cross-sectional area of the tunnel was increased fourfold). The new wind tunnel was completed by the end of the year and Tsiolkovsky was able to begin experiments; a year from then he submitted a report to the Academy on the first part of his experimentation.

Tsiolkovsky figured that the "Report to the Academy of Sciences on Experiments Dealing with Air Resistance" would come out in the Academy publications; however, despite the fact that his report contained a number of important conclusions, the work did not appear in print until after the October Revolution of 1917. Tsiolkovsky was able to publish in the journal "Nauchnoye obozreniye"—Science Review (in 1902) only a small article entitled "Air Resistance and Aeronautics", in which he gave the basic conclusions from experiments on air resistance carried out in 1900-1901.

Salient among all Tsiolkovsky's works are his studies in the field of rocket dynamics and astronautics. The idea of the possibility of conquering the limitless expanses of outer space came to Tsiolkovsky very early, during his first visit to Moscow in 1873-1876. At that time he proposed developing cosmic velocities by utilizing the effects of centrifugal force. As he wrote in later years, "I was excited, even staggered, to such an extent that I could not sleep all night; I wandered about Moscow and kept thinking of the great consequences of my discovery. But already by morning I was convinced that my invention was false. My disappointment was just as intense as my enchantment had been. That night left an imprint that has lasted my whole life; 30 years later I still sometimes dream that I am rising to the stars in my machine and I experience the same delight as I did that unforgettable night."[12]

In 1878-1879 Tsiolkovsky began compiling "astronomical drawings"; at the same time he devised an instrument for studying the effect of the acceleration of gravity on a living organism; and four years later, he first came to the idea of utilizing the

[11] From the minutes of a meeting of the physico-mathematical department of the Academy of Sciences, 6 October 1899, Archives, USSR Academy of Sciences.

[12] Tsiolkovsky, "The Elements of an Airship and Its Construction", Kaluga, 1904, p. VI.

$$16... \frac{v}{v_1} = -\ln at\left\{1 + \frac{M_2}{M_1}\right\}$$

$$20... v_1 = 5700 \text{ мтр.}$$

$$\frac{v^2}{2g} = \frac{5}{2g}\left[...\right]$$

Для Табл. 22

$$28... t = \frac{v}{p}, \quad 29... \frac{p}{g}$$

$\frac{M_2}{M_1}$	$\frac{v}{v_1}$	v
1	0,693	3920
2	1,098	6260
3	1,386	7880
4	1,609	9170
5	1,792	10.100
6	1,946	11.100
7	2,079	

$$31... t = \frac{v_2}{p - g}, \quad 32... \frac{r}{g} \quad p - g, \quad 33... \frac{p-1}{g}$$

$$34... v = v_2\left\{\frac{p}{p-g}\right\}$$

$$35... v_2 = -v_1\left\{1 - \frac{g}{p}\right\} L\left(1 + \frac{M_2}{M_1}\right)$$

$$\frac{M_2}{M_1} = e^{\frac{v_2}{v_1}\left(1 - \frac{g}{p}\right)} - 1$$

$$\frac{M_2}{M_1} = e^{\frac{v_2 \cdot h}{v_1(p-g)}} - 1$$

$$44... p_1 = p - g$$

$$45... h = \frac{p-g}{2}t^2$$

$$46... h = \frac{v_2}{2(p-g)}, \quad 47... h = \frac{v^2}{2p}\left(1 - \frac{g}{p}\right)$$

$$51... T = t - \frac{g}{p}, \quad T = \frac{v}{2g} ... 48$$

TSIOLKOVSKY'S FAMOUS FORMULA OF ROCKET MOTION (THE PHOTO DEPICTS A MANUSCRIPT PAGE DATED 1897)

reactive principle for propulsion in outer space. In his earlier mentioned manuscript "Free Space", which was completed in 1883, he wrote: "Suppose we have a barrel filled with a highly compressed gas. If we open one of its minute stopcocks, the gas will stream out of the barrel in a continuous jet, and the elasticity of the gas (it is this elasticity that pushes the gaseous particles into space) will likewise continually repel the barrel. The result will be a continual change in the motion of the barrel."[13] In the same paper, Tsiolkovsky came to the conclusion that motion in free space is impossible without loss of matter.

Generally, the manuscript "Free Space" is of considerable interest to investigators of the scientific legacy of Tsiolkovsky, for in this work which was not published during his lifetime we encounter, in embryo, many ideas that were expressed by him in general form but were developed in his later works. It has already been mentioned that in this manuscript Tsiolkovsky came to the conclusion that the only possible mode of propulsion in airless space is the method based on the reaction of particles of matter ejected from a body; he also proposed an elementary gyroscopic device for stabilization of flying machines.

In this work he gave a simple diagram of a spaceship and examined problems both of the conditions of growth and reproduction of plants and living beings, their shapes and dimensions in interstellar space.

Tsiolkovsky's ideas of interplanetary flight were further developed in his science-fiction writings "On the Moon" (1893), and "Dreams of the Earth and the Sky and the Effects of Universal Gravitation" (1895). Science fiction occupied a prominent place in his thinking. He wrote: "At first we inevitably have an idea, fantasy, fairy tale, and then come scientific calculations; finally execution crowns the thought. My work has to do with the middle phase of creativity. More than anyone else I am aware of the chasm that separates an idea from its accomplishment, for during my whole life I not only did many calculations but also worked with my hands. But there must be an idea: execution must be preceded by an idea, precise calculation by fantasy."[14]

Tsiolkovsky's most interesting science-fiction production is his "Dreams of the Earth and the Sky..." in which, among other things, he first expressed the idea of setting up an artificial satellite of the earth. He wrote that "an imaginary satellite of the earth,

[13] "Free Space". See this volume, p. 27.
[14] Tsiolkovsky, "Investigation of World Spaces by Reactive Vehicles", Vestnik Vozdukhoplavaniya (Herald of Aeronautics), 1911, No. 19, pp. 16-17. See this volume, p. 84.

something like the moon, but arbitrarily close to our planet, just outside its atmosphere—which means about 300 versts from the earth's surface—will represent an example of a medium of very small mass and free from gravity;"[15] and he posed the problem of how "to impart to a terrestrial body a velocity sufficient for generating centrifugal force that would eliminate the earth's gravity when this velocity approaches 8 versts per second."[16]

Starting from 1896 Tsiolkovsky began profound theoretical investigations into the possibility of solving the problem of interplanetary travel by means of rockets. He did so in his customary way of first greatly simplifying the conditions of the problem. He began by studying rocket flight in a medium where the gravitational forces and air resistance are practically inoperative.

Rockets were of course well known long before Tsiolkovsky. They had been employed in firework displays and for signalling, for illuminating localities and as a weapon of war. Many scientists and inventors had been engaged in improving them, but no one proposed utilizing rockets as a means of interplanetary flight.

Yet prior to Tsiolkovsky many inventors had meditated on the problem of flight in outer space; they had advanced such devices as a gigantic sling, a circular rail track, superlong-range artillery, and others, but not a single one of the authors of these numerous projects proposed using rocket-propelled flying machines for this purpose.[17]

Tsiolkovsky's achievement consists in the fact that he united these two technical trends, gave a rigorously scientific substantiation of the possibility of applying the reactive principle to flights in outer space and established the theory of rocket motion.

A study of the manuscripts and notes of Tsiolkovsky found in the Archives of the USSR Academy of Sciences shows that as early as 1897 he had derived his now famous formula which establishes an analytical relationship between the rocket speed at any instant of time, the speed of gas exit from the nozzle of

---

[15] Tsiolkovsky, "Dreams of the Earth and the Sky and the Effects of Universal Gravitation", Moscow, 1895, pp. 49-50.

[16] Ibid, p. 50.

[17] It is worth pointing out that the use of rockets for flights to the moon is encountered in two science-fiction books: Cyrano de Bergerac's "Another World or the States and Empires of the Moon" (1647-1650), and Jules Verne's "From a Cannon to the Moon" (1874). However, in the former case the proposal is of quite a fantastic nature, while Jules Verne employs rockets only for changing the trajectory of flight of the spaceship.

the engine, the mass of the rocket and the mass of consumed explosives.

In deriving this formula, Tsiolkovsky proceeded from the assumption of constant relative speed of exit of gas particles. This hypothesis of Tsiolkovsky is today still extensively in use in rocket dynamics.

According to Tsiolkovsky's formula, the flight speed of a rocket (disregarding gravitational forces and air resistance) is

$$v = v_1 \ln \left(\frac{M_1 + M_2}{M_1 + M} \right),$$

where v is the rocket speed at any instant of time,
       v_1 is the relative speed of exit of gas particles,
       M_1 is the mass of the rocket minus explosives,
       M_2 is the total mass of explosives at start of motion,
       M is the variable mass of explosives that has not been exploded up to a given instant of time.

The maximum speed will, at $M = 0$, be

$$v_{max} = v_1 \ln \left(1 + \frac{M_2}{M_1} \right).$$

It will readily be seen that the rate of motion in empty space is theoretically unlimited and depends solely on the exhaust velocity of gas particles and the ratio of the mass of explosives (propellants) to the mass of the rocket.

This conclusion of Tsiolkovsky was of great significance in the subsequent development of rocket technology, for it pointed to the possibility of attaining cosmic velocities and indicated the directions of theoretical investigations in this field. According to Tsiolkovsky's formula, increased rocket velocities would stem from boosting the exhaust velocities of gas particles and from increasing the relative (but not absolute) supply of propellant.

This formula yields the ideal rocket velocity when we disregard losses due to gravitational forces and resistance of the medium. Tsiolkovsky subsequently made the problem more complicated by introducing the attraction of the earth and air resistance and then performed the calculations for cases close to actual ones.

Introducing the force of gravity, Tsiolkovsky obtained

$$v_{max} = v_1 \left(\frac{p - g}{p} \right) \ln \left(1 + \frac{M_2}{M_1} \right),$$

where p is the absolute acceleration of the rocket,
      g is the acceleration of the earth's gravity.

In 1903 Tsiolkovsky published his classical work entitled "Investigation of World Spaces by Reactive Vehicles", in which for the first time he scientifically substantiated the possibility of accomplishing space flights by means of rockets and gave the principal formulas for computing trajectories. In this same paper he devoted considerable attention to the problem of propellants for a space rocket. Up to the end of the 19th century, only solid-fuel rockets found application (powder rockets). Tsiolkovsky, however, demonstrated that for long-range rocket flights the most effective engine would be one powered by a liquid propellant, and he gave the basic operating scheme of such an engine.

It is hard to overestimate the significance of "Investigation of World Spaces by Reactive Vehicles". Tsiolkovsky's great service lies in the fact that he contributed much to the new division of mechanics, the mechanics of bodies of variable mass; he created the theory of rocket flight with allowance made for varying mass of the rocket in flight and substantiated in rigorous scientific fashion the possibility of attaining cosmic velocities.

However, in the first decade of the twentieth century, Tsiolkovsky's "Investigation of World Spaces by Reactive Vehicles" went unnoticed both in Russia and in other countries. It was published a second time (in a considerably expanded version) in 1911-1912 in the journal "Vestnik Vozdukhoplavaniya" (Herald of Aeronautics). In this article, he investigated in detail the resistance of the atmosphere and came to the conclusion that the work required to overcome the resistance of the air amounts to only a very small portion of the work needed to overcome the force of gravity. It was here that Tsiolkovsky first suggested utilizing the energy of disintegration of atoms for space flight. He wrote: "It is believed that as radium disintegrates continually into more elementary matter it liberates particles of different masses moving with amazing, inconceivable velocities close to that of light.... And so if it were possible to accelerate the disintegration of radium or other radioactive bodies, and probably all bodies are of this kind, then its employment might yield—all other conditions being equal—a velocity of the reactive vehicle such that to reach the closest sun (star) would be possible in 10 to 40 years."[18]

At the same time he advanced the idea of building electro-jet engines, pointing out that "it may be that with the aid of

[18] Tsiolkovsky, "Investigation of World Spaces by Reactive Vehicles", "Vestnik Vozdukhoplavaniya" (Herald of Aeronautics), 1912, No. 9, pp. 7-8. This volume, p. 123.

electricity it will be possible, in time, to develop tremendous velocities for particles ejected from a reactive vehicle."[19]

In this same paper, Tsiolkovsky expressed his views on the future development of mankind, on man's expansion throughout the limitless space of the universe, on conquering the enormous reserves of world energy. Here is how he put it: "Vehicles in revolution about the earth and with all the accessories for the existence of intelligent beings may serve as a basis for the further expansion of humanity. People inhabiting the vicinity round the earth in the form of a multitude of rings like those of Saturn... would increase 100- to 1,000-fold the reserves of solar energy that are allotted to them on the surface of the earth. Even so, man may not be satisfied, and from this conquered base he may extend his hands to capture the rest of the solar energy, which is two thousand million times greater than what the earth gets."[20] He wrote also: "In all likelihood, the better part of humanity will never perish but will move from sun to sun as each one dies out in succession. Many decillion years hence we may be living near a sun which today has not yet even flared up but exists only in the embryo, in the form of nebulous matter designed for eternity and for high purposes."[21]

It is noteworthy that Tsiolkovsky did not confine the problems confronting mankind to reaching and exploiting the planets and other celestial bodies. Furthermore, he pointed out that there is not even any need to stay on the heavy planets, except for studying them. He visualized the conquest of world spaces in the form of establishing artificial settlements in interplanetary and, later, in interstellar space.

In 1914, Tsiolkovsky published a booklet supplementing the works of 1903 and 1911/12, in which he formulated his theorems of reactive motion. It was here that he suggested the use of ozone as an oxidizer. In later years, Tsiolkovsky several times returned to his "Investigation of World Spaces by Reactive Vehicles", developing and adding to the ideas.

Tsiolkovsky did not confine himself to an elaboration of the theoretical problems of reactive flight, he gave a series of practical suggestions on problems of design and construction of rocket components. Between 1903 and 1917 he advanced a number of designs of rocket-propelled spaceships. He also considered rocket control in a vacuum, the cooling of the walls of the combustion chamber by one of the propellants, the use of refractory elements, and other problems.

[19] Ibid., p. 8. This volume, p. 123.
[20] Ibid., No. 7, p. 6. This volume, p. 111.
[21] Ibid., No. 9, pp. 10-11. This volume, p. 127.

During the years preceding the first world war, Tsiolkovsky continued his studies in aeronautics in addition to his work devoted to reactive flight. Between 1910 and 1914 he published a number of booklets on all-metal dirigibles. In May, 1914, Tsiolkovsky took part in the Third All-Russian Aeronautics Congress that was held in St. Petersburg. Here he delivered a paper on his dirigible design and demonstrated a number of models. His invention was patented in Germany, England, France, Italy, Belgium, but in pre-revolutionary Russia his all-metal dirigible was never actually built.

Tsiolkovsky's investigations also touched on a number of other spheres of natural science and technology. In 1914 he published "The Second Law of Thermodynamics", in which he objected to the boundless extension of the range of applicability of Clausius' famous entropy postulate: "Heat cannot pass spontaneously from a body of lower temperature", and was doubtful of Clausius' assertion that "the entropy of the universe tends towards a maximum".

This paper was directed against the comparatively wide-spread view of the constant devaluation of energy and of the supposedly inevitable heat death of the universe. The proponents of this theory proceeded from this postulate and, by elevating it to the rank of a universal law of nature, asserted that the time will come when the sun will die out, the world will come to an end, and all living things will disappear. Tsiolkovsky claimed that this would not take place if we did not recognize the Clausius postulate as a law and if we regarded it only as an "observation frequently repeated, apparently obvious, but one that would seem to be violated in the words of those same scientists".[22]

Considering in this paper the gravitational reversibility of energy, Tsiolkovsky wrote: "...a seed of hope is maturing in my soul concerning the reversibility of the process of heat dissipation. If this is so, then a future opens up to mankind that is independent of solar energy."[23]

An examination of the scientific legacy of Tsiolkovsky shows that he began to think over the problems of reversibility of phenomena towards the end of last century.[24] In 1905 he completed the manuscript of "The Second Law of Thermodynamics", which he succeeded in publishing only in 1914. In later years, Tsiolkovsky came back to the reversibility of phenomena a number of times and wrote a series of articles on it.

[22] Tsiolkovsky, "The Second Law of Thermodynamics", Kaluga, 1914, p. 6.
[23] Ibid., p. 23.
[24] Archives, USSR Academy of Sciences.

After the publication of "The Second Law of Thermodynamics", Tsiolkovsky approached the Society for Advancing the Experimental Sciences and Their Practical Applications through Kh. S. Ledentsov with a request for funds to conduct the above-described experiments, This was in September 1916. However, the findings of a commission of experts of the Society were negative and the aid was refused.

The years of the first world war were one of the most trying periods of Tsiolkovsky's life both financially and morally. His family was always in need and experienced deprivations. The meager opportunities for publishing his works—and to him that was of extraordinary importance, for only in that way could he hope to pass on his ideas to future generations—became even more limited. It is indicative that during the last two years of the war (1916-1917) he succeeded in publishing only one of his works; it went by the picturesque title of "Grief and Genius".

Prior to the Revolution the conditions for his creative work were extremely bad. Tsiolkovsky's ideas, which were far in advance of his time, were not recognized by representatives of the official science. He constantly encountered indifference and disbelief, many considered him a visionary and were sceptical of the self-taught scientist with no diploma. Without any material or moral support, Tsiolkovsky was left almost entirely to himself. With bitterness he wrote: "It is hard to work by oneself many hours and under unfavourable conditions and not experience any gratification or support at all."[25]

However, he found support in his faith in the success of his undertaking, to which he had devoted his entire life. He fought against the view taken by many that his works were unfounded fantasy doomed to failure. "There was a time—and very recently," he wrote, as if challenging those who did not believe in the feasibility of his concepts, "when the idea of the possibility of learning the composition of celestial bodies was considered senseless even by prominent scientists and thinkers. That time has now passed. The idea of the possibility of a closer, direct, study of the universe will today, I believe, appear still wilder. To step out onto the soil of asteroids, to lift with your hand a stone on the moon, to set up moving stations in ethereal space, and establish living rings round the earth, the moon, the sun, to observe Mars from a distance of several tens of versts, to land on its satellites and even on the surface of Mars—what could be more extravagant! However, it is only with the advent of reactive vehicles that

[25] Tsiolkovsky, "Investigation of World Spaces by Reactive Vehicles" (Supplement to parts I & II of this paper), Kaluga, 1914, p. 7. This volume, p. 128.

a new and great era in astronomy will begin, the epoch of a careful study of the sky. "[26].

Tsiolkovsky's conditions of life and work changed radically after the Great October Socialist Revolution. In 1918 Tsiolkovsky was elected member of the Socialist (later, Communist) Academy; and in November 1921 he was given a personal pension by order of the Council of People's Commissariats of the Russian Federation.[27] For the first time in many years, Tsiolkovsky was able to devote all his time to scientific work.

The recognition and high estimate of his works caused a new influx of creative strength. Of a total of over 500 papers, only 130 were written in the course of 60 years prior to the Revolution and of these only 50 were published.

In his autobiography he wrote: "With the support of the Soviet Government and with an ensured pension I could work freely and though hardly noticed before I was now exciting interest in my studies. "[28]

Tsiolkovsky's ideas began to be put into practice. The Soviet Government recognized the necessity of accomplishing his design of an all-metal dirigible. A number of organizations began a series of experimental studies according to the proposals of Tsiolkovsky, who continued to develop the theory of a metallic balloon, critically examined the existing systems of dirigibles, and gave consultations and advice.

During this period, Tsiolkovsky continued his investigations into interplanetary travel. In 1920 he published his science-fiction story "Beyond the Earth" as a separate book, which he had actually begun as early as 1896. Here, Tsiolkovsky set forth in popular form the program of future space conquests by man; he described the conditions of flight and life in a spaceship, on artificial satellites of the earth, on the moon and on asteroids. The book was fiction and the style engaging, but all the calculations and explanations of the author were based on rigorously scientific foundations and, as a rule, were the result of his own investigations.

In this book he clearly stated that the problem of conquering outer space requires the combined efforts of scientists of all countries, the establishment of an international team of scientists, engineers and inventors with all the necessary conditions for fruitful work.

[26] Tsiolkovsky, "Investigation of World Spaces by Reactive Vehicles", "Vestnik Vozdukhoplavaniya" (Herald of Aeronautics) 1912, No. 9, p. 8. This volume, p. 123—124.
[27] Archives, USSR Academy of Sciences.
[28] Tsiolkovsky, "From My Life", Archives, USSR Academy of Sciences.

Among the papers written by Tsiolkovsky at the start of the 1920s, of particular interest are his unpublished notes entitled "The Spread of Man in Space"[29], which for a long time remained outside the field of view of students of Tsiolkovsky's work. These notes cannot be regarded as a finished work but rather as rough sketches, which nevertheless are significant in that they apparently represent the first attempt of the scientist after the war of 1914-1918 to return to a scientific elaboration of problems associated with the possibility of reaching outer space by means of reactive vehicles.

At the very beginning of the manuscript (the entry is dated 21 September 1921) Tsiolkovsky enumerates the possible methods of developing cosmic velocities. He points out that for this purpose the following may be utilized:

"1. The expulsion of ordinary matter: gases, solids and liquids (reactive vehicles).

2. Electric current.... The ejection of negative electricity or positive electricity.

3. The pressure of light rays...

4. The radiation of matter, for example, of radium..."[30].

Somewhat later (11 October 1921), Tsiolkovsky returned to this problem and to the question that he posed to himself: "For what purpose are engines designed?" His reply was:

"1. The direct pressure of light is for world motions, for leaving the sun or approaching it, for restoring velocities.

2. Motors are for propulsion in a gaseous medium and for developing speed or a first impulse..."[31].

It is readily seen here that Tsiolkovsky touches on the problem of possible applications of various types of engines and points out that reactive engines operating on chemical fuel are needed to overcome the gravitational potential and the resistance of the medium; and after the spaceship has surmounted the potential of the earth's gravitation and is in a dynamically balanced state, it is advisable to resort to low-thrust engines.

Half a month later (27 October 1921) Tsiolkovsky made the following entry: "Begin to write a complete theory of the rocket."[32] Apparently, this entry is connected with the plan of the article "Rocket"[33] dated 23 October, in which he intended to consider

[29] Tsiolkovsky, "The Spread of Man in Space. Fighting Gravitational Forces. Victory Over the Earth's Gravity. Victory Over Universal Gravitation". Archives, USSR Academy of Sciences.
[30] Ibid.
[31] Ibid.
[32] Ibid.
[33] Archives, USSR Academy of Sciences.

a number of problems of jet propulsion in a vacuum and within the limits of the atmosphere. To this period also belong the following manuscripts and published papers: "The Space Rocket" (1923), "The Reactive Vehicle" (1924), "The Rocket in Outer Space" (1924), "The Spaceship" (1924), "Investigation of World Spaces by Reactive Vehicles" (1926) and others.

Towards the middle of the 1920s, Tsiolkovsky, in his desire to reduce the quantity of propellant necessary for space flight, suggested the possibility of returning to the earth without expenditure of fuel, by utilizing the resistance of the atmosphere. [It is noteworthy that this problem was also studied by F. A. Tsander and Yu. V. Kondratyuk of the USSR, and by W. Hohmann of Germany. The proposal was first made in print (1924) by Tsander in his article "Voyages to Other Planets".]

It is about this time that Tsiolkovsky began working on the problem of a transport facility on an air cushion, which is a fundamentally new and promising type of ground transport.

Until recently, Tsiolkovsky's biographers had believed that his interest in the problem of air-cushion transport began in 1926 when he was working on the manuscript "The Friction of Gases"[34] and that it was first expressed in his paper entitled "Resistance of the Air and High-Speed Trains", which was published in 1927.

However, studies of the manuscript legacy of Tsiolkovsky have shown that this principle was clearly grasped already in 1921 in his paper "The Spread of Man in Outer Space". In the section entitled "Rapid Translational Motion on the Earth"[35] he lists as one of the possible modes of propulsion "sliding on a liquid or gas", i.e., when a ground (or water-surface) vehicle is propelled by sliding it on an elastic air cushion generated by powerful engines. Tsiolkovsky pointed out that "with polished planes, the layer of gas between them would be very small. This would be something in the nature of flight."[36]

Later, the idea of air-cushion transport was further developed in Tsiolkovsky's works: "The High-Speed Train"[37] and "The General Conditions of Transport".[38]

In the mid-twenties Tsiolkovsky began work on the theory of flight of jet aircraft. From his manuscripts found in the Archives of the USSR Academy of Sciences, it will be seen that already in 1924-1925 he carried out a number of calculations relating

[34] Archives, USSR Academy of Sciences.
[3] Ibid.
[36] Ibid.
[37] Tsiolkovsky, "Resistance of the Air and High-speed Trains", Kaluga, 1927. This volume. p. 164—186.
[38] Archives, USSR Academy of Sciences. See also K. E. Tsiolkovsky, Collected Works, Vol. 4, Moscow, 1964, pp. 348-351.

to jet aircraft. In 1926 he completed a paper entitled "The Rocket Aeroplane (a new aircraft of high altitudes and velocities)", which served as the basis for his published work "The New Aeroplane". The theory of jet aircraft was further developed in the following works (both published and in manuscript form): "A New Aeroplane" (1929), "Reactive Aeroplane" (1930), "The Increasing Accelerated Motion of a Rocket Plane" (1930), "The Semi-Reactive Stratoplane" (1932), and others.

After examining types of aircraft suitable for different speeds and altitudes, Tsiolkovsky came to the absolutely correct conclusion that as altitudes and speeds of flight increase, piston engines will have to give way to jet engines. His are words of prophecy: "The era of air-screw aeroplanes will be followed by the era of jet aeroplanes or aeroplanes of the stratosphere."[39] The significance of these words becomes particularly clear if we recall that they were spoken long before the construction of the first jet aircraft, during the heyday of piston-driven aviation.

Reviewing the various types of aircraft engines, Tsiolkovsky noted that for aircraft flying at altitudes that do not exceed 3-4 km, with speeds of 500 km/sec, the most suitable are piston engines. For higher altitudes and speeds, he recommended first turbo-propeller and then turbo-compressor engines and, finally (for still higher altitudes and greater velocities), liquid-fuel jet (reactive) engines.

In the 1920s, Tsiolkovsky's ideas about conquering outer space began to take root in the USSR. In 1924, a Jet Propulsion Department was set up in the Scientific Military Society of the Academy of the Air Fleet, its aim being to unite all persons working on this problem in the USSR. That same year, a Society was set up in Moscow for the study of interplanetary travel (it had 150 members). In 1927 the first World's Exhibition was organized in Moscow displaying designs of interplanetary vehicles and mechanisms. Prominently displayed was the work of Tsiolkovsky and other Soviet scientists and also that of scientists from other countries active in this field.

At the end of the 1920s and the beginning of the 1930s, Tsiolkovsky devoted most of his time to solving two problems in the field of interplanetary travel: attaining cosmic velocities and finding optimal rocket propellants.

The theoretical problem of reaching cosmic velocities was resolved by Tsiolkovsky as far back as the end of last century. but the engineering solution of the problem involved considerable

---

[39] Tsiolkovsky, "Reactive Aeroplane", Kaluga, 1930, p. 19. This volume. p. 247

difficulties. One of the most complex problems was the design of the rocket that had to carry a supply of propellants sufficient for developing cosmic velocities. Calculations showed that the quantity of propellants was many times greater than the weight of the empty rocket (rocket minus propellant). To construct a rocket of this kind was beyond the engineering capabilities of the times. Ways had to be found for carrying such quantities of propellants or for reducing the necessary amount.

Working on this problem, Tsiolkovsky, already in 1926, arrived at the conclusion that a rocket can attain cosmic speeds only if it gains a relatively high initial velocity without expenditure of its own supply of propellant. After analyzing various possible methods of imparting such a preliminary speed to the rocket, Tsiolkovsky concluded that "the simplest and cheapest approach in this case is the rocket, reactive, principle". He therefore proposed a two-stage rocket for attaining cosmic speeds, the first stage of which —the "ground rocket" in Tsiolkovsky's terminology —was to move along the ground and in the dense layers of the atmosphere.

Tsiolkovsky also calculated the amount of propellant, the mass of the vehicle, the velocities and other parameters of each stage.

Tsiolkovsky further developed the theory of multi-stage rockets in his paper "Space Rocket Trains" (1929). It is noteworthy that the idea of multi-stage rockets is several centuries old. They were first mentioned in the 16th and 17th centuries. In the 20th century, the multi-stage rocket principle was advocated by A. Bing (Belgium, 1911), R. Goddard (USA, 1914), Yu. Kondratyuk (Russia, 1917), H. Oberth (Germany, 1923).

However, Tsiolkovsky's contribution lies in the fact that he did not confine himself to enunciating the operating principle of multi-stage rockets, but gave a detailed mathematical theory and rigorous scientific proof of the possibility of generating cosmic velocities by means of rocket engines with chemical propellants.

By introducing a number of simplifications —he regarded all rocket stages as identical and he disregarded the gravitational forces of the earth and air resistance —Tsiolkovsky obtained the following formula for determining the additional velocity of any stage of a composite rocket:

$$v_i = W \ln \left(1 + \frac{1}{(1+Z)(n-i+1)-1} \right),$$

where v_i is the additional speed of the ith stage,

W is the exhaust velocity of the combustion products,

Z is Tsiolkovsky's number, which here characterizes the ratio of the mass of each stage to the mass of propellant in the given stage,

n is the total number of stages in the rocket,

i is the serial number of the stage for which the calculation is being made.

The speed of the first stage, or, to use Tsiolkovsky's terminology, of the first rocket train, was determined by the above formula, the velocity of the ith stage was equal to the sum of the additional velocities of the first i trains and, finally, the maximum velocity attained by means of multi-stage rockets was given by the sum of the additional velocities of all stages:

$$v = v_1 + v_2 + v_3 + \ldots + v_n.$$

As the ideas of space flight spread and received general acceptance, Tsiolkovsky more and more often reverted to the meaning of this remarkable achievement, to the advantages that man would be able to extract from conquering outer space.

He wrote about this in "Investigations of World Spaces by Reactive Vehicles" (1926), in "The Future of the Earth and Man" (1927), "The Aims of Astronautics" (1929), and elsewhere.

In his opinion, the chief purpose of space flights should consist in the spread of man throughout the expanses of outer space, the establishment of extended settlements—at first around the earth and later far out in the vast reaches of the universe; and this, Tsiolkovsky pointed out, would in turn lead to the organization of life and industry on utterly new bases, radically different from those on the earth.

By the end of the 1920s, Tsiolkovsky's writings on rocket technology and interplanetary travel were already widely recognized in the Soviet Union and abroad. His works were then under study in many countries and his theorems and formulas were being used. Tsiolkovsky deservedly became the dean of the new science of rocket dynamics and astronautics.

In this respect, Tsiolkovsky's correspondence, at present in the Archives of the USSR Academy of Sciences, is of considerable interest. An analysis of this correspondence shows that Tsiolkovsky played a great role in the development of rocket technology in this country not only as the creator of the basic theory of rocket flight and a tireless popularizer of interplanetary travel and jet flight, but also as a figure whose personality alone contributed to locating and spiritually uniting all persons in the Soviet Union interested in this branch of knowledge.

The small house in Kaluga became the centre, as it were, of invisible ties linking the founder of the theory of astronautics and rocket technology with numerous workers and organizations throughout the country engaged in these problems. It was not by accident that when State or social organizations — either the Section of Jet Propulsion, or the Society for the Study of Interplanetary Travel, or groups studying jet propulsion, or the Scientific Research Institute of Reactive Motion —took up problems of rocket technology or astronautics, the heads of all these institutions would invariably approach Tsiolkovsky for advice or aid and would strive to maintain regular contact with him.

Nearly every person who in those years played some part in the development of rocket technology in the USSR was in correspondence with Tsiolkovsky or connected with him in one way or another. Among his correspondents were F. A. Tsander, Yu. V. Kondratyuk, I. T. Kleimenov, G. E. Langemak, N. A. Rynin, Ya. I. Perelman, and many other scientists, engineers and popularizers of the ideas of rocket technology and interplanetary travel.

Tsiolkovsky's correspondence was not confined to the Soviet Union. Letters came from England, Austria, France, the United States and Sweden and, particularly, from Germany. The noted German scientist and investigator of jet propulsion in outer space, Prof. H. Oberth wrote to Tsiolkovsky in 1929: "You have kindled a fire, and we shall not let it die out, but will bend every effort to make the greatest dream of mankind come true."[40]

The attitude of the German scientists to Tsiolkovsky was expressed with still greater clarity in a message of greetings sent by the German "Society for Space Travel" (Verein für Raumschiffahrt) on the occasion of Tsiolkovsky's 75th birthday. It read: "Highly Esteemed Mr. Tsiolkovsky, the Society for Space Travel has from the day of its inception always considered you to be one of its spiritual leaders and has never missed an opportunity to point out, both orally and in written form, your great services and your unquestionable Russian priority in the scientific elaboration of our great idea."[41]

It must be noted that Tsiolkovsky never engaged in problems of the military application of rockets. All his intentions were aimed at the peaceful utilization and expansion of our knowledge

[40] Translated from the German. Herman Oberth's original letter to K. Tsiolkovsky is kept in the Archives of the USSR Academy of Sciences.
[41] Translated from the German. The text of the original is given in the book "Konstantin Eduardovich Tsiolkovsky, 1857-1932". Moscow and Leningrad, 1932, p. 55, which is a scientific anniversary edition commemorating his 75th birthday and the 40th anniversary of the publication of his first works on dirigibles.

of the laws of nature. He recognized only one kind of war—the war against ignorance and the imperfections of nature and man.

In his work "Investigation of World Spaces by Reactive Vehicles" (1926) he wrote: "It is necessary to fight against the pressure of gases, the killing rays of the sun, the imperfection of the nature of man and plants. It is unavoidable that we must struggle for comfort, knowledge and the perfection of human beings, and so on."[42]

During the last years of his life, Tsiolkovsky continued to devote all his attention to scientific work, despite his advanced age. In 1932 he wrote "Reaching the Stratosphere" in which he summarized, as it were, his many years of research into problems of rocket energetics and formulated the properties of explosives to be used in rocket engines. He wrote:

"The explosive components for this machine must possess the following properties.

1. They must release maximum work per unit mass in combustion.

2. When they combine, they must produce gases or volatile liquids which, upon heating, yield vapours.

3. In combustion they must develop as low a temperature as possible, i.e., have a low temperature of dissociation so as not to spoil the barrel (nozzle).

4. They must occupy a small volume, i.e., have as high a density as possible.

5. They must be liquid and mix readily. It is complicated to employ them in the form of powder.

6. They may be gaseous but have a high critical temperature and a low critical pressure so as to be convenient for use in the liquid form. Generally, liquefied gases are not advantageous due to their low temperature, for they absorb heat in raising their temperature. Therefore, their use entails losses due to evaporation and there is the danger of explosion. Also unsuitable are expensive products that are chemically unstable or difficult to obtain."[43]

In this paper, Tsiolkovsky had already formulated the principal thermodynamic and performance properties of propellants for rocket engines. Soviet scientists continued working on the problem of rocket propellants and made great advances in this sphere reaching the foremost position in world science.

In 1934-35, Tsiolkovsky proposed yet another method of generating cosmic velocities; it went by the name "rocket squadron". In this method, the rockets were connected in parallel and

[42] Tsiolkovsky, "Investigation of World Spaces by Reactive Vehicles", Kaluga, 1926, p. 88.
[43] Tsiolkovsky, "Reaching the Stratosphere", 1932 (this volume, p. 273).

operated in unison, but they did not use up all the propellant (only one half). Then the remaining propellant of one part of the rockets was transferred to the half-empty tanks of the other rockets, which then continued on their way with a full supply of fuel. The empty rockets were detached from the squadron and returned to the earth. The process of transferring propellants continued until there was only one rocket left; this one attained the desired cosmic velocity.

It must be pointed out that Tsiolkovsky gave a very sober appraisal of his works in the field of interplanetary travel, stressing their theoretical significance, yet noting at the same time that a great deal had to be done in order to realize the ideas he advanced.

As early as 1903, in his article "Investigation of World Spaces by Reactive Vehicles" he wrote:

"This study of mine does not by far examine all aspects of the matter and does not at all resolve it from the practical viewpoint (relative to its feasibility); but in the far distant nebulous future one perceives such intriguing and significant promises as hardly anyone today dreams of."[44]

And in the twenties he wrote: "The value of my studies consists mainly in the conclusions that stem therefrom. I have hardly done anything in the engineering aspect. It requires a long series of experiments, construction and developed techniques. This practical aspect is what will yield the engineering solution to the problem."[45]

In another paper written during this period, Tsiolkovsky states: "I think to play the part of initiator. Mathematicians who know more and are more powerful will perhaps finish the solution of the problems I have posed. Experienced and knowledgeable technicians will help them to design and construct the spaceship itself."[46]

These words were fated very soon to come to fruition. In the 1930s, Tsiolkovsky's ideas concerning jet propulsion were put into practice in the USSR. As early as 1929, the Leningrad Laboratory of Gas Dynamics (GDL) began theoretical and experimental studies in the field of electric and liquid-fuel rocket engines. In 1931, in Moscow and Leningrad, groups for the study of jet propulsion (GIRD) were set up that played an important part in the development of rocket technology in the Soviet Union. It was these two organizations, whose members included some of the

---

[44] See this volume, p. 55.
[45] Tsiolkovsky, "Space Rocket Studies", Archives, USSR Academy of Sciences.
[46] See this volume, p. 163.

most prominent Soviet specialists in rocket technology, and also the Scientific Research Institute of Reactive Motion (RNII), which was established in 1933 on the basis of these two institutions, that laid the foundations of Soviet rocketry.

Tsiolkovsky kept in close touch with the work of these groups and with the Institute; he corresponded with many of the scientists that had worked in the GDL, GIRD, and RNII, and met them personally.

Almost immediately after the establishment of the Institute of Reactive Motion, the leading scientists wrote to Tsiolkovsky stating that with the founding of this Institute a base had been established for stupendous development along the strictly scientific lines of the ideas advocated by Tsiolkovsky and they stressed the necessity of close cooperation with him as the person who worked out the theoretical principles of jet propulsion.

Tsiolkovsky responded by elaborating a program of studies of the RNII[47], which included in a specific sequence the problems that, in his opinion, should be investigated first. These are the points of the program:

1. Choice of fuel and oxygen compound. 2. Choice of materials for: a) pumps, b) pipelines, c) combustion chamber, d) conical pipe, e) tanks, f) frame. 3. Experimental verification. 4. Stationary machine for explosions. 5. Determination of recoil. 6. Consumption of components of the explosive mixture. 7. Automobiles. 8. Sleighs. 9. Hydroplanes. 10. Control of direction rudder. 11. Rudders of lateral stability (bicycle). 12. Testing of an altitude rudder on a vehicle with one axle and two wheels. 13. Testing of all rudders on a gig (two-wheeled carriage). 14. Application to gliders (rocket planes). 15. Test flights and refinements. 16. Flights higher than 5 kilometres with a closed chamber. 17. Same without chamber but in a protective suit. 18. Purification of the air in the chamber by means of plants. Choice of plants.

Tsiolkovsky continued to be in contact with the RNII. In 1935 the Technical Council of the Institute passed a resolution to elect Tsiolkovsky honorary member of the Institute. It was also decided to call the ratio of the weight of the rocket to the remaining weight Tsiolkovsky's number. The team of scientists of the Institute were particularly gratified to hear of Tsiolkovsky's consent to contribute to the "Trudy RNII" (Transactions of RNII). This response of the Institute workers was quite natural, for, as the heads of that institution wrote to Tsiolkovsky, "Most of those who are today actively working on rockets first learned

[47] Archives, USSR Academy of Sciences.

the elements of jet propulsion from your remarkable books, studied those volumes and were inspired by your enthusiasm and faith in the ultimate success of this undertaking."[48] When we consider the scientific legacy of Tsiolkovsky, we are struck by the range of his interests. A simple enumeration of the titles of some of his writings demonstrates with full clarity the versatility of his investigations and the widely separated problems that engaged his attention.

Indeed, during the last fifteen years of his life he wrote such diversified works as "The Conditions of Life in the Universe", "A Common Alphabet for the Human Race", "The Mechanism of Higher Animals and Their Senses", "Development of Hot Deserts", "The Future of the Earth and Man", "Monatomic Hydrogen", "Auto-trailer on Tracks", "The Reversibility of Phenomena", "Solar Energy and Its Applications", "The Elasticity of Solids". And the list could be extended considerably.

At first glance it seems strange that one person should be interested in such divergent problems as the hypothesis of recurring stellar phenomena and the theory of autogenesis, studies of technical progress and of the similarity and deviations of organisms, elaboration of problems of transport and studies of the invisible particles of matter.

However, a careful study of his researches will show that they are all directed at resolving the fundamental problem that Tsiolkovsky posed: perfection of the human race, the complete victory of man over the forces of nature, the conquest by man of outer space and the establishment of new conditions for human life as the highest form of its development.

Tsiolkovsky was a great humanist who devoted his entire life to the service of mankind; he strove to enrich human life and make it easier and more interesting.

Tsiolkovsky evaluated his work and activities in the following words: "The prime motive of my life is to do something useful for people, not to live my life purposelessly, but to advance humanity even the slightest bit. That is why I have interested myself in things that did not give me bread or strength. But I hope that my studies will, perhaps soon but perhaps in the distant future, yield society mountains of grain and limitless power."[49]

Tsiolkovsky had boundless faith in the potentialities of human reason and believed that there was no limit to the perfection of human life. Refuting the predictions of certain scientists about

[48] Correspondence of Tsiolkovsky and RNII, Archives, USSR Academy of Sciences.
[49] Tsiolkovsky, "First Model of an All-metal Aero-vehicle Made of Corrugated Iron", Kaluga, 1913, p. 1.

the inevitable end of all living things on the earth due to the cooling off and extinction of the sun, Tsiolkovsky wrote: "If today we are able to believe somewhat in the infinitude of mankind, what will it be like several thousand years from now when our knowledge and reason will have increased? "Thus, there is no end to life, to reason and to perfection of mankind. Its progress is eternal...

"Advance boldly, great and small workers of the human race, and you may be assured that not a single bit of your labours will vanish without a trace but will bring to you great fruit in infinity."[50]

To the end of his days, Tsiolkovsky remained a tireless investigator and a passionate fighter for scientific and technical progress. Konstantin Tsiolkovsky died on September 19, 1935. Shortly before his death he bequeathed his scientific works to the Communist Party of the Soviet Union and to the Soviet Government. He wrote, "I bequeath all my works on aviation, rocket flight and interplanetary communications to the Bolshevik party and the Soviet State, the true leaders of cultural progress. I am confident that they will successfully complete my work."[51] These words are of a special significance today as we witness the triumph of Soviet space science, when the ideas of Tsiolkovsky are being translated into the launchings of artificial earth satellites and space rockets, when the first practical steps into space have been taken and we are witnessing the realization of Tsiolkovsky's prophetic words: "Mankind will not remain on the earth forever, but in the pursuit of light and space will at first timidly penetrate beyond the limits of the atmosphere, and then will conquer all the space around the sun."[52]

[50] Tsiolkovsky, "Investigation of World Spaces by Reactive Vehicles", "Vestnik Vozdukhoplavaniya" (Herald of Aeronautics), 1912, No. 9, p. 11. See this volume, p. 127.
[51] Tsiolkovsky's letter to the Central Committee of the All-Union Communist Party, "Pravda", 17 September 1935.
[52] From a letter of Tsiolkovsky to B. Vorobyov dated 12 August 1911 (Archives, USSR Academy of Sciences).

Appendix

Conversion Table

1 verst = 1.067 km = 0.6630 mi.
1 sagene = 2.134 m = 7.0 ft.
1 arshin = 71.12 cm = 28 in.
1 pood = 16.38 kg = 36.38 lb.
1 desiatina = 1.093 ha = 2.70 acre

INDEX *

* The index includes all the titles of Tsiolkovsky's works cited in this book (Translator).

333

CPSIA information can be obtained
at www.ICGtesting.com
Printed in the USA
LVHW040859191218
600892LV00001B/42/P